MONUMENTS ILLUSTRATING NEW COMEDY

by

T. B. L. WEBSTER

University of London

INSTITUTE OF CLASSICAL STUDIES

Bulletin Supplement No.11

1961

Published by
Institute of Classical Studies
31-34 Gordon Square London WC1

Distributed by
International University Booksellers Ltd
39 Store Street London WC1

PREFACE

As for 'Monuments Illustrating Old and Middle Comedy' I have many acknowledgments to make to those who have helped me in producing this list. First, to the Institute for Advanced Study at Princeton, because membership there gave me the chance of three months in which to work on my lists in ideal surroundings. Secondly, to the Central Research Fund of London University, which gave me a grant towards travel in Greece in 1958 and for buying photographs. I owe a great deal to discussions with Professor Homer Thompson, Mrs. D.B. Thompson, Mr. R. A. Higgins, Dr. Gisela Krien, Miss Lucy Talcott, Mr. D. M. Bailey, but I am entirely responsible for any errors that my lists contain. I must also mention particularly Madame S. Mollard-Besques, Miss Virginia Grace, Miss Hetty Goldman, Professor B. Ashmole, Dr. Lore Frei (née Asche), Dr. N. Degrassi, Dr. H. Riadh, Mr. N. Coldstream, M. François Salviat, who have given me information about dramatic monuments in many different places and have sent me photographs. Acknowledgments for photographs and permission to reproduce them are due to Agora excavations, Athens; American School of Classical Studies, Athens; Alexandria Museum; Fratelli Alinari; British Museum, London; Cleveland Art Museum; Msgr. E. Coleiro; French School at Athens; Miss Hetty Goldman; Oxford University Press; Princeton University Art Museum; Museo Archeologico, Verona. Miss Clairève Grandjouan sent me the numbers from her catalogue of Roman Terracottas in the Agora and they are included with the Inventory numbers. The Princeton University Press sent me a microfilm of the proofs of the second edition of Miss M. Bieber's *History of the Greek Theater* and I have been able to include references to her figures in the Concordance and in the Roman Section. Miss Mary Cosh checked many of my references and has made my lists presentable by her beautiful Varityping.

T.B.L.W.
January 1st 1961

LIST OF CONTENTS

LIST OF PLATES

I   a) Thebes, from Halai (BT 1)   Photo: Miss Hetty Goldman
         b) Agora T 213 (AT 2)   Agora Excavations
         c) Agora P 22191 (AV 15)   Agora Excavations
         d) Agora P 18666 (AV 16)   Agora Excavations
         e) Agora P 17085 (AV 23)   Agora Excavations
         f) Alexandria 24129 (ET 2)   Alexandria Museum
         g) Alexandria 24130 (ET 3)   Alexandria Museum

II   a) Mykonos Museum (AV 25)   French School at Athens
         b),c) Cleveland Museum of Art (GV 1)   Cleveland Museum

III   a) Verona, Museo Archeologico (AS 8)   Verona Museum
         b) Athens (AS 4)   German Archaeological
                                                    Institute
         c) Malta, Roman Villa Museum (JS 1)   Monsignor Coleiro

IV   a) British Museum 906 (IL 28)   British Museum
         b) British Museum 1231 (XL 3)   British Museum
         c) British Museum 898 (IL 29)   British Museum
         d) British Museum 905 (IL 33)   British Museum
         e) British Museum 986 (IL 37)   British Museum

V   a) Agora T 3635 (AT 31)   Agora Excavations
         b) Agora T 478 (AT 32)   Agora Excavations
         c) Agora T 2404 (AT 37)   Agora Excavations
         d) British Museum E 70 (IT 81)   British Museum

VI   a) Princeton University Art Museum
                         40.435 (ZM 4)   Princeton Art Museum
         b) Rome, Lateran Museum (IM 9)   Alinari
         c) Ince Blundell Hall 232 (IS 50)   B. Ashmole

INTRODUCTION

The number of monuments illustrating New Comedy and included in this
Catalogue is rather over fourteen hundred.   The list does not pretend
to be complete and the most that can be claimed for it is that it includes
most of the kinds of objects on which actors and masks are represented,
most of the types of actors and masks which have survived, much of the
material that has been published and a good deal of material which is
listed here for the first time.   It is hoped that it will serve as a
guide which is so organized that it will be fairly easy to discover what
masks and costumes were current at any particular time or in any particular place and to make additions without excessive confusion as new
material turns up.

The number of objects is so large that it seemed convenient to divide
the list into Hellenistic and Roman, and the line between them is drawn
at the end of the first century B.C. because it seemed unreal to separate,
e.g. terracottas of the first century B.C. at Myrina from their predecessors
of the late second century.   The large number of undated monuments and
the difficulty of drawing lines between periods which would be valid for
all places precluded any further chronological subdivision.   Within the
two main headings, Hellenistic and Roman, the subdivisions are topographical
and are marked by the first letter of the two-letter prefix (A = Athens,
B = Boeotia, etc.).   Doubtful proveniences have always been indicated
either in the Catalogue entry itself or in the notes which precede each
section.   The dates which are given immediately after the provenience
in the first line of the Catalogue entry are firm dates, based either on

1

excavation or on style where style can be regarded as giving a firm
date: thus vases, lamps, and inscribed monuments can often be given
a firm date even when the excavational context of the object itself
is unknown. Conjectural dates, based on the style of the object itself
and its likeness to other dated objects, are added in the notes. Each
section of the Catalogue is preceded by a brief discussion of the general
characteristics of the section and the most interesting objects in it.
The whole is introduced by a short history of masks and costumes based
on the dated monuments.

Everyone who has worked on dramatic monuments knows that it is sometimes difficult to decide whether a given object is ancient or modern,
dramatic or not dramatic, tragic or comic, satyric or comic, male or
female. In the majority of instances it is clear that the object is
or is not a comic slave, old man, young man, or woman, but a list like
this which aims at being as complete as possible gives an interpretation
to many objects which others have classified or will classify otherwise.
The difficult boundaries are between tragic and comic young men and women
where they have an *onkos*, between papposilenoi and satyrs on the one hand
and comic old men and slaves on the other, and between comic young men
with smooth brows and long hair and comic young women. Some of these
difficulties are discussed in the history section; others in the notes
to individual monuments.

Forgeries have been excluded as far as possible, but some made-up
terracottas which appear in all the books have been left in the list
with a cautionary note; even so other forged terracottas probably remain
undetected. Against these may be set the considerable number with
certain proveniences and the many others which are stylistically close
to them.

The distinction between dramatic and non-dramatic is not always easy
to draw: even the obvious criterion, open-mouth and shut mouth, is not
infallible. For instance the hetaira mask on the altar tombstone from

Breccia (IS 2) has its mouth shut but is otherwise indistinguishable from many other certain hetaira masks; on the other hand many caricatures, which should not be regarded as dramatic, have mouths like comic masks. Some doubtful cases whnch appear in the books have been included in the lists with a note that they should be regarded as non-dramatic, but they have been excluded from the index of masks. Logically perhaps Munich Inv.6949-6951 (Bieber, *D.*, no.159-161, *H.T.*[1], figs.245, 251, 283) should have been added to these but they have no connection with drama. Among caricatures, which have been discussed most usefully by Dr. W. Binsfeld in *Grylloi* (Cologne, 1956), may be reckoned all masks with hooked noses or enlarged ears; some of these certainly have something to do with the mime.

Some of the masks with shut mouths may be the masks of pantomimi; the masks of pantomimi have recently been studied by Dr M. Kokolakis (*Pantomimus and the treatise* περὶ ὀρχήσεως, Athens, 1959, 36f.). To his examples may perhaps be added Alexandria 9620 (Breccia, *Terracotte*, 1, 64, no.352), Paris, Cabinet des Medailles (Babelon no.980), Vienna (Von Sacken, pl.32, no.4). The masks are either girls or smooth-browed young men of the class where distinction between tragedy and comedy is difficult. Some of the masks included in the list should probably be reckoned rather as masks of pantomimi, particularly FB 1, XB 1, YT 13, NT 26, all of which belong to the class of beautiful young men or young gods, and ET 64, a girl in a Phrygian cap.

Nevertheless when all subtractions have been made a large number of firmly dated monuments with known provenience remains to form a foundation for a history of comic masks and costumes from the late fourth century B.C. to the late fourth century A.D. Dated monuments occur in many different places but the following are the larger groups: terracottas and pottery from the Athenian Agora (particularly in the third century B.C.); mosaics and terracottas from Delos (2nd century B.C. to early first); terracottas from Myrina (late second and 1st century B.C.);

terracottas from Priene (second century B.C.); Early Hellenistic Tarentine terracottas and Gnathia vases; dated terracottas from Etruscan sites; mosaics, paintings, and terracottas from Campanian sites (Late Hellenistic to 79 A.D.); Roman lamps (a dated series lasting from Late Hellenistic to Late Roman times); the late terracottas from the Athenian Agora (early third century A.D.), which with contemporary mosaics from Antioch, and contemporary mosaics and terracottas from Italy foreshadow the masks and costumes of the Terence miniatures.

HISTORY OF MASKS AND COSTUMES

On the basis of this material an attempt can be made to sketch the
history of masks and costumes. The foundation must be the objects
which are firmly dated by excavation or by stylistic or other criteria
which are extrinsic to the object itself: the large number of terracotta, bronze, and other statuettes which can only be dated by the style
of the object itself can only be used as a check on the sequence obtained
from well dated objects. From the second century B.C. and still more
obviously in the Roman period artists can in some cases be shown tc be
following an artistic tradition which derives from earlier theatre
practice and may therefore be out of touch with the contemporary theatre.
For the Roman period a further question must be raised, whether it is
possible to distinguish Greek from Roman comedy. The Hellenistic and
Roman periods are for convenience treated separately, although it is
impossible to draw any hard and fast line between Late Hellenistic and
Early Roman.

A. HELLENISTIC PERIOD

1. SLAVES

The material is fuller for slaves than for old men, young men, and
women; they are therefore treated first. In Middle Comedy (cf. *Bulletin
Supplement*, no.9, p.9) six masks were used for slaves:
B, with a good head of hair, running straight across the forehead and
descending over the ears nearly to shoulder level and a deep trumpet mouth
of which the bottom edge is rounded;

5

C (much less common), with hair coming up to a peak in front, upward flying eyebrows, and a longish pointed beard;

K, with a good head of hair striated and coming to a low peak in front, sometimes (at any rate) with one eyebrow raised and the other level, and a wide striated beard descending to a point;

N, with untidy hair sometimes long and wavy, sometimes with a marked peak, upward flying eyebrows and a wide beard coming to a small point;

P, bald with a very short spade beard;

PP, bald except for a tuft of hair in the middle of the forehead.

Pollux' mask list (IV, 143 f.) seems to be based on an Alexandrian scholar of the third century B.C. and his seven types of slave mask have been convincingly identified.   It is clear that B is the ancestor of Pollux' Leading Slave (no.22), that K and N together belong to the ancestry of Pollux' wavy-haired leading slave (no.27), and that P and PP are the ancestors of Pollux' two cooks, the Maison and the Tettix (nos.25 and 26).   The list is a very useful guide to third century usage and in the Catalogue I have noted or myself made identifications with the Pollux list.   We do not however know whether Pollux' list derives from Alexandrian or Attic practice, and his descriptions provide less than we require or demand more than we know.   He tells us about colour, which we only know from painting and mosaics and very occasionally from terracottas.   He tells us about hair (except for the *pappos*, no.21), distinguishing no.22 as having a *speira* or roll of hair, nos.23 and 24 as having receding hair (*anaphalantias*), nos.25 and 26 as bald, and no.27 as having wavy hair.   In practice it is not easy to distinguish either between hair in a *speira* and wavy hair, or between hair (*speira* or wavy) with a peak and receding hair which may be represented by a peak from which the hair recedes (e.g. the Middle Comedy mask C).   He does not tell us of any slave with uneven brows like Middle Comedy mask K.   More serious is his complete neglect of beards because slave beards can be easily seen and have well marked types.   In what follows the classification is first into slaves with good heads of hair and bald slaves and

then within these classes by types of trumpet beard.   (Masks encircled
with wreaths are noted in the Catalogue;   they are not a separate class;
in most cases it is clear whether they are bald or not.)

Details of date are given in the Catalogue;   here a summary classification into early and late 3rd century B.C., early and late 2nd century
century B.C., early and late 1st century B.C. will suffice.

Early 3rd century B.C.

Mainland: AT 5, AV 4, 5, 7;   BT 1-2, CJ 1, XT 1
Egypt   ET 2, EV 1
Sicily and Italy: TJ 1, 2;   TT 1, 2;   TV 1;   IV 1

Three masks can be distinguished.   The *first* has a mass of hair and
a trumpet beard coming to a point: AT 5, XT 1, CJ 1, TJ 1 (with wreath),
2.   It is probably the New Comedy successor of K and N, and may be
identified because of the mass of hair with Pollux' wavy-haired slave,
no.27.   It will be convenient to refer to it as mask K to show its
ancestry.   The hair is peaked in AT 5, but not in XT 1, TJ 1 and 2.
The *second* mask has a good head of hair and a deep trumpet with a rounded
bottom edge: AV 4, EV 1, ET 2, TJ 1, TT 2, TV 1.   On TT 2 the *speira*
is peaked;   on TV 1 the top corners of the trumpet are nearly right angles.
This is the successor of Middle Comedy mask B (the letter of which it
will keep) and may be identified with the Pollux no.22.   The *third* mask
is bald, often wreathed, and has a deep trumpet with a rounded bottom :
AV 5 (wreathed), 7, BT 2 (wreathed), TT 1 (wreathed), IV 1 (wreathed).
In AV 5 the top of the trumpet is curved so that the whole trumpet makes
an *oval*;   in TT 1 the top of the trumpet is horizontal so that the trumpet
becomes *semicircular*.   ST 2 has a semicircular trumpet with the top
twisted.   Bald masks may keep the Middle Comedy letter P.   (The slave
in BT 1 is too unclear to classify.)   The Middle Comedy PP (Tettix) is
represented by AT 17 which is stylistically dated at the turn of the
fourth to third century B.C.

Late 3rd century B.C.

Mainland:	AT 6, 7; AV 6, 11, 13, 14, 15, 20
Asia Minor:	ZL 2, ZV 2
Egypt:	EL 4-7, EV 3
Sicily and Italy:	IT 24, 51, IV 3

AT 6-7 have no heads.   The rest can be divided between masks B
and P.   *Mask K* does not appear;   some of the Attic mask B (AV 6, 15)
would naturally be interpreted as wavy-haired and it is possible that
in Attica now the wavy-haired slave could have the rounded instead of
the pointed trumpet beard.   *Mask B*. AV 6, 11, 13, 15, 20:   6 has the
oval trumpet, the rest the deep rounded trumpet.   ZV 2 also has a deep
round trumpet.   EL 4:   peaked *speira* with shock of hair over ears,
oval trumpet.   EV 3 shows for the first time a *wide twisted* trumpet.
IV 3 has the deep rounded trumpet.   *Mask P*. AV 14 has a semicircular
trumpet, but the top edge is curved downwards instead of being straight
and this is on the way towards the *wide twisted* trumpet of IT 24, 51
(wreathed):   ZL 2 has a normal *semicircular* trumpet;   it is wreathed
and it is not certain that it is bald.

Early 2nd century B.C.

Mainland:	AJ 1, AV 10, 21-24, 31-2
Islands:	DM 1
Asia Minor:	ZT 14, 22-3
Sicily and Italy:	IT 1, 3; IV 2

Mask B. The *oval* trumpet is seen on AJ 1, AV 21, 22, but AV 24
has a *semicircular* trumpet.   The *speira* is peaked on AV 21, 24, IV 2.
The *semicircular twisted* trumpet occurs on AV 31, 32, DM 1, ZT 22, 23,
IT 1, 3 (wreathed), IV 2.   The trumpets of AV 31 and ZT 23 have wavy
hair round the edge.   AV 31 and 32 have wavy hair.   DM 1 certainly
and ZT 22 probably have a peaked *speira* and IT 1 peaked hair.   ZT 14
has a *wide twisted* trumpet.

Mask K. On DM 1 the wavy-haired slave has the old pointed shape of trumpet so that here the contrast between the neat leading slave (B) and the unkempt wavy-haired slave is clear. (Unfortunately the hair of ZT 23 is broken off but its trumpet has wavy hair round the edge: it is tempting to suppose that it is the wavy-haired slave with the new type of mouth, like AV 31 and 32, and contrasts with the neat leading slave ZT 22; both decorated the same room in Priene.)

Mask P. AJ 1 has the *oval* trumpet; AV 10 the *wide twisted* trumpet (wreathed); AV 23 the *deep twisted* trumpet.

Late 2nd century B.C.

Mainland:	AT 23, AV 34
Islands:	DT 6, KL 1
Asia Minor:	MT 2, ZL 1, ZS 2
Africa:	EL 9, 13
Italy:	NB 2-3, NV 1

Mask B. AT 23 with peaked *speira* has the *oval* trumpet. AV 34 has peaked hair under a wreath and *wide twisted* trumpet. DT 6 is extremely like AT 23. KL 1 has a peaked *speira* and *wide twisted* trumpet. ZL 1 (the lamps from Knidos) may cover a considerable range of time and cover the change from a deep rounded trumpet to a wide rounded trumpet; in Attica the range is 150-75 B.C., and Howland suggests that they may have been in use elsewhere in the first half of the second century although this cannot be proved. NB 2 is extremely carefully modelled with peaked *speira* and *semicircular twisted* trumpet. NB 3 and NV 1 both have a *wide twisted* trumpet and peaked *speira*. (For MT see below.)

Mask K. MT 2, ZL 1, EL 9, 13. The last two are wreathed. The masks with pointed trumpets on the Knidos lamps (ZL 1) should be distinguished from the masks with rounded trumpets. MT 2 has wild hair ending in curls over the ears and a deep trumpet of flowing hair.

9

MT 2 takes with it a group closely associated in style: one slave
with very similar hair has a *semicircular* trumpet with hair inside,
MT 27 (with white hair); others have a *semicircular* smooth trumpet;
two are wreathed and it is difficult to see the hair, MT 32, 39; one
is certainly bald, MT 30; but one has wild hair, MT 29. One has a
wide twisted trumpet and is wreathed, MT 28. Presumably MT 30 is the
bald-headed Maison (Mask P), MT 27 the *pappos* (Pollux no.21), and MT 2
the wavy-haired leading slave (Pollux no.27). But outside these there
are two types: MT 32 and 39 with smooth *semicircular* trumpet, and MT 28
with *wide twisted* trumpet. It would be natural to regard MT 32 and 39
as the leading slave (Pollux no.22) and MT 28 as a further type. Robert
identifies MT 28 as the 'curly-haired' slave, no.24, but the very curious
head MT 13, which actually has receding curly hair, might be preferred.

Mask P. (For Myrina see above.)

Mask PP. ZS 2 is a fine Tettix mask with *semicircular* striated
trumpet.

Early 1st century B.C.

Mainland:	AT 20, AV 35
Islands':	DT 8, 9, 10, 11 12, 14, 15, DL 1-4 (of these 8-12 may be still second century)
Asia Minor:	ZL 6
Egypt:	EL 14, 15
Italy:	IC 1, IL 1-2, IV 5-6
The West:	JM 2

Mask B. AT 20, AV 35 both have the *wide twisted* trumpet and straight
hair; AV 35 is wreathed. In Delos DT 8, 10, 15 have straight hair;
their trumpets are all variations of the smooth round kind, the *oval*
trumpet; they could be regarded as descendants of the neat slave on DM 1.
DT 11 and DL 2 both have peaked hair: DT 11 (with which the undated DT 19
may be compared) has a wig of roughly striated hair and *wide twisted*

trumpet;   DL 2 has very neat striations and a *semicircular* trumpet; they are probably the local first century versions of the wavy-haired leading slave and the leading slave (cf. below on DT 9).   EL 14 is wreathed, with a shock of hair over the ears, and a *semicircular* trumpet.   IL 1 and 2 are essentially like DL 2 but the hair is left smooth and the face is fatter.

Mask K. DT 9 has wavy hair; DT 22, a very similar mask, which is not dated, wears the military *causia*.   (The lamp lid DL 1 has curiously slanted eyes and might perhaps be a satyr mask.)   A slave mask probably with wavy hair is held by the Muse of Comedy on the Roman coin, IC 1; this may be inspired by an earlier original, statue or painting.

Mask P. DT 12, 14, EL 15, ZL 6, JM 2 all represent the same bald slave mask with a shock of hair over the ears and *semicircular twisted* trumpet.   DL 4 has a *wide twisted* trumpet and a wreath (it is not certain that he is bald).

Late 1st century B.C.

Mainland: AS 3, 4
Asia Minor: MT 4-7, ZL 5
Africa: EL 20-24
Italy: TT 3, IT 46-9
Unknown: UL 3-4

Mask B: The Attic marble masks (AS 3, 4) have hair with no peak and *wide twisted* trumpet.   MT 5 has a carefully striated peaked speira and a *semicircular twisted* trumpet.   EL 23 has two masks, one wreathed with a *semicircular twisted* trumpet.   EL 24 and UL 3-4 (which may also be Egyptian) have peaked striated speira and a new version of the *semicircular twisted* trumpet with a narrow flat striated edge.   IT 46-8 have the *wide twisted* trumpet, whereas the earlier IT 58 still has the *semicircular* trumpet.

Mask K. EL 20 and TT 3 are both freakish and possibly copies of earlier works.   11

Mask P. MT 4 and 6, which come from the same tomb as MT 5, both
have *semicircular twisted* trumpet and MT 6 is wreathed.   ZL 5 has a
wide trumpet.

Certain points seem to emerge from this survey.   No new treatment
of hair appears and all the varieties survive through the whole period.
On the other hand the treatment of the slave beard shows considerable
variation.   It is possible that the oval trumpet and the semicircular
trumpet are merely different careless stylizations of the semicircular
twisted trumpet.   The main variations are therefore four and may be
briefly named deep, semicircular, wide, and pointed.

The deep trumpet and the pointed trumpet are a legacy from Middle
Comedy.   The deep trumpet is common in the third century but the only
second century dated example is on the Knidos lamps and they may be very
early in the second century.   After that (and the mask twice repeated
on AJ 6 may put the date back into the third century) the standard
trumpet for the leading slave is semicircular.   Of the undated terracottas with the deep trumpet XT 3 and UT 72 seem from their proportions
to belong with the earliest Myrina groups, i.e. early second or even
third century.   The bald slave with a deep trumpet, TT 8, should also
be early.   In some examples which may be much later the depth of the
trumpet is due to its use as an orifice, e.g. YV 3, IT 49.

The pointed trumpet of the wavy-haired slave lasts into the second
century for the Delos mosaic and the Knidos lamps.   Before the middle
of the second century the semicircular trumpet for the wavy-haired slave
is well attested for Athens (AV 32) and Priene (ZT 23 contrasted with
the leading slave with semicircular trumpet ZT 22) and on stylistic
grounds a Myrina terracotta should also belong here (MT 26).   If AV 6
and 15 are rightly interpreted as wavy-haired slaves, we can say that
the change was introduced in Attica in the late third to early second
century, and this is supported by a mask on AJ 6.   This raises the
question whether pointed trumpets later than the early 2nd century

derive from earlier originals: this is likely for IC 1 and possible
for DT 9 and EL 20. The very fine late 2nd century Myrina terracottas
(MT 2 etc.) may be the work of a small number of artists who copied
earlier wall-paintings and therefore evidence for third century rather
than late second century theatre practice (for details cf. introduction
to MT Catalogue).

The undated ZT 29 and 46 are very like MT 2 and may well be works
of the same group of craftsmen. Most of the other undated examples
are Early Hellenistic on style : KT 3 and 4 and UT 50 are particularly
good. ET 27 and UT 63 may be late but an earlier example of the same
general type is provided for ET 27 by the Tarentine slave with an amphora,
TT 8. It is interesting that we apparently have only two examples of
the pointed beard surviving for the bald slave from the Middle Comedy
period, XT 9 and ET 23. AV 32 has been mentioned as Attic evidence for
the change in the wavy-haired slave from the pointed beard to the semicircular trumpet: three very similar undated masks, NT 15, TT 12, UT 74,
have a very similar trumpet but the bottom edges slope to a rounded point.
They may be described as transitional.

On the evidence it looks as if the semicircular trumpet in its various
forms was first introduced for bald slaves and was given to them in the
third century in Attica (Halai probably also reflects Attic practice,
BT 2), South Italy, and Sicily. Probably before the end of the third
century and certainly early in the second century it was used for leading
slaves (as also for wavy-haired slaves) in Attica, Asia Minor, Egypt,
and Italy. BT 8, EV 15, and NT 7 are undated but from style seem to be
Early Hellenistic. The final development of the semicircular trumpet,
which certainly belongs to the Roman period, is the semicircular trumpet
with a flat striated edge. A foreshadowing of this trumpet can be seen
on a small terracotta with wavy wig hair from Corinth, CT 2, and another
from Vulci, IT 19.

The wide trumpet emphasizes still more the grinning complacency of the slave.   The two Italian examples (one from Rome and one from Clusium) seem to be still third century and are both bald slaves. AV 10 of the early 2nd century is probably the next example: it is not certain that it is Attic and not quite certain that it is bald as it has a large wreath.   The next dated example of a bald mask with a wide trumpet is ZL 5 in the late first century.   Other dated bald slaves of the late second (including the Pergamon Tettix) and the early first century still have the semicircular trumpet.   The undated masks IT 22, ST 8, ST 27 probably belong to the second century and do something to fill the gap.

Two masks dated late third to early second century, ZT 14 and EV 3, show the wide trumpet on other masks: ZT 14 is certainly a wavy-haired leading slave.   ET 35 is a very fine example which should be Early Hellenistic.   In the later second century the wide trumpet is so used in Attica, Cyprus, and Campania, and in the first century in Delos and Attica.   Possibly the wide trumpet now becomes normal for the wavy-haired slave and contrasts with the semicircular trumpet of the leading slave (DT 11, 19 and DL 2).   The Delos slave has parallels in two statuettes of unknown origin which must be contemporary, UT 42 and 62. The gravestone of the actor Alexandros (AS 4) is a clear indication of late 1st century Athenian practice.

Little need be said about costume.   The decent chiton reaching nearly to the knee is universal for slaves.   But it may be possible to draw a distinction between the fat slaves with a girdle above and below their bellies, particularly clear in the second century Myrina series and earlier, and the more attenuated late Hellenistic slaves whose chitons are not double girt.

2. OLD MEN

Old men can be treated briefly.   Few types are involved and they do not change.   In Middle Comedy young men were still usually bearded and the distinction between old and young in the monuments was not easy to draw.   Now young men are always clean-shaven, and at the other end the very old men (masks G and E) have vanished.   The regular masks are Pollux no.3 (leading old man with a wreath of hair about his head, hook-nosed, flat faced, right eyebrow raised), no.4 (wavy-haired old man with a wreath of hair round his head, long full beard, brows not raised, sluggish in expression), no.7 (the Lykomedeian, curly-haired, long-bearded, one brow raised, shows that he is a busybody), no.8 (the *pornoboskos - leno* or procurer - is otherwise like the Lyko-medeian but has grinning lips and has receding hair or is bald). Costume is always long chiton and long himation.

Nos.3 and 4 are probably descendants of the Middle Comedy masks M and L, but the 'wreath of hair', set off from the hair behind it, distin-guishes them from their predecessors.   Nos.7 and 8 continue with less change Masks C and CA of Middle Comedy.   Other Middle Comedy masks survive particularly in the earliest period.   AV 1 (early 3rd cent.), BT 9 and UJ 1 (both early on style), have the mask with pointed beard and a good head of hair, mask A.   AT 1 (early 3rd century) and YT 8 (probably Early Hellenistic) have the rather uncommon variant AA, which has much more luxuriant hair (possibly the mask of Knemon in Menander's *Dyskolos*).   These are probably both included in Pollux, no.6, the wedge-bearded mask.   CT 3 and 4 (both Early Hellenistic in style) have a bald mask with a scrubby beard, which may be Pollux no.9, the second Hermonian, noted in Middle Comedy as mask F.   (TT 19 is unique and perhaps not dramatic.)

The following are dated examples of Old Men's masks:

No.3.   Leading Old Man.   Early 3rd century: XT 1, ET 1

Late 3rd century: AL 1, AV 12, 16, 17

Early 2nd century: AJ 1, AV 11, DM 1

Late 2nd century: ZL 1

Late 1st century: UL 1

The type seems to have been fixed very early. Both XT 1 and ET 1 may be before the end of the fourth century. On Megarian bowls (AV 16 etc.) the hair waves out from a slight central peak with even brows and a large squarish beard. The Attic gold necklace (AJ 1) has flat striated hair, raised brows, and the beard stylized in corkscrew locks. The mask on the contemporary Delos mosaic (DM 1) is very like this but is one of the very few which shows the brows differentiated as raised and smooth (so also XT 1). The late lamp (UL 1) shows the mouth itself enlarged so that it looks like a slave trumpet with the corkscrew locks beneath it.

No.4. Wavy-haired Old Man.   Early 2nd century: AV 15, 19, 29, DM 1
                                              Late 2nd century: ZS 3

The clear distinction between the two old men where they are paired (DM 1) is that the wavy-haired old man has more hair, a longer face, and a less regular longer beard. His narrower eyes explain Pollux' 'sluggish in expression'. ZS 3 is a very fine example with luxuriant hair and a very large beard. In spite of Pollux and the Delos mosaic the uneven brows are not a necessary distinguishing mark between the two old men: many leading old men do not have uneven brows, slaves may have uneven brows, and one wavy-haired old man (TT 18) has uneven brows. Good examples of the two masks, nos.3 and 4, in their normal form are FT 1 and UT 5; AV 29 is a freak as the long beard comes to a point at the bottom.

No.7. Lykomedeian Old Man, 'busybody'.   3rd century: AT 2
                                                       1st century: JM 2

The curly hair and beard are clear; neither of these (nor any of the undated examples) has the uneven brows described by Pollux.

No.8. *Pornoboskos.*   Late 3rd century: AT 3 (?), ZA 1
                             Early 2nd century: AV 26-8, DM 1, ZT 20
                             Late 2nd century: MT 8-10, ZS 3, ZV 1
                             1st century: CL 1

Pollux' description presumably means that the procurer has curly hair round his ears and a long beard as well as grinning lips.   The baldness and the beard are clear;   the mouth is wide and the upper lip is either straight or turns up slightly.   He often wears a wreath, which is sometimes very elaborate, and is draped in an enormous and elaborate cloak (MT 8-10).   The wreathed head alone is very easily confused with a papposilenos head and only a clear marking of the ears shows which the artist intended (ZV 1).   It is possible that a variant, fierce and unsmiling, should also be recognized: AT 19, ZS 3, UT 2.

3. YOUNG MEN

Young men in New Comedy are clean-shaven.   The masks surviving from Middle Comedy are O with smooth brows and wavy hair, Z a mask with raised brows, Q the fat parasite, QA the normal parasite (both the last with receding hair).   Pollux' list gives no.10 *panchrestos* (admirable), athletic, with a few wrinkles on the forehead, a wreath of hair, raised brows;   no.11 *melas* (dark), younger, smooth brows, studious;   no.12 *oulos* (curly-haired), fair and young, raised brows, one furrow on the forehead;   no.13 *hapalos* (delicate) with hair like no.10, nurtured in the shade;   no.14 *agroikos* (rustic) with broad lips, snub nose, and a wreath of hair;   no.15, the first *episeistos* (wavy-haired), soldier and braggart;   no.16 the second *episeistos*, more delicate;   no.17 *kolax* (flatterer) and no.18 the parasite, hook-nosed;   the parasite has more broken ears, and is more cheerful, whereas the eyebrows of the flatterer are more maliciously raised;   no.19 the *eikonikos* has grey in his hair;   no.20 the Sicilian is a third parasite.   If the last four are set aside as specialists the normal young men are distinguished first by hairdressing, i) wreath of hair, nos.10, 11, 13, 14, ii) curly hair, no.12, iii) wavy hair, nos.15 and 16.   Within these groups there is a distinction of eyebrows - raised: no.10, 15 (and 12), smooth: no.11, 13, 16. No.14 alone has a snub nose.   The dated monuments are as follows:

Early 3rd century: AT 11;   BT 1, 3;   XT 1;   ZV 3;   TJ 1;   GV 1;
                     NT 1

Late 3rd century: AT 4;   IT 2

Early 2nd century: AJ 1, AV 15, 25, 30;   DM 1;   ZT 21

Late 2nd century: AT 18, DT 3, 4, 5;   MT 1, 15, 17-20;   ZS 2;
                     ZV 3;   NB 1

Early 1st century: ZT 27

Late 1st century: AT 25;   MT 3;   FB 1

Of the early monuments BT 1, which probably echoes an Attic type
of the late fourth century, is invaluable evidence that young men wore
the knee-length chiton at the beginning of New Comedy;   the face however
is not enough worked to show more than a large nose surmounted possibly
by a wreath rather than by wavy hair.

XT 1 and NT 1 show two rather different varieties of a mask with
raised eyebrows which should be Pollux no.10;   the admirable youth.
On XT 1 the hair, which comes down slightly below the ears, is done in
striations going back off the forehead;   on NT 1 the hair is done in
a smooth, slightly peaked *speira*.   Neither stylization could be described
as 'wavy' or 'curly' and a head on AJ 6 (which Zahn dates convincingly
to the late third century) comes between them with a striated peaked
speira.   These stylizations of the 'wreath of hair' make it possible to
identify not only other examples of the 'athletic' no.10 but also of the
'studious' no.11, the 'delicate' no.13, and the 'rustic' no.14.   (Some
of the more interesting undated masks are added after the dated masks in
each section.)

	Like XT 1	*Like NT 1*	*Like AJ 6*
No.10.	AJ 1, IT 37, UT 10, 16, 20,(27)	YT 11, MT 20, 21	AT 18, AV 30, ST 18, TT 7, UT 8
No.11.	DM 1	TJ 1, ST 1, UT 28	ST 20, UT 9, BT 13
No.13	(AJ 1), (DT 3), (MT 1),(ZT 2), (ZV 3),(ST 19,21), (TT 6),(IT 42)	AS 3, AV 15, AT 25, BT 11, MT 22, ST 13	ZT 27, IT 41, UT 18, UT 23
No.14	AV 25,AJ 6(?), ST 24	AT 11 (?)	ET 15, BT 18

18

The main distinction here is between the group like XT 1, where the hair runs flat on to the forehead, and the other two groups, where the front ridge of the hair is emphasized. The same distinction can be seen in the masks of old men and slaves. The evidence is not sufficient to say that the type with emphasized front ridge (Pollux' 'wreath of hair' or *speira* in the case of slaves) is later than the type with no ridge. But it is true that in Middle Comedy only slave masks show this emphasized front ridge (neither O nor Z nor the old man's mask M shows it) and that portraits on coins show something like it for the first time in the third century (e.g. Antiochos I and II, Philip V); it may therefore be the later stylization.

Some of these masks are wreathed: no.10: UT 16, 20, 27; no.13: DT 3; MT 1, 22; ZT 2; ZV 3; TT 6; IT 42. The wreathed heads of youths are as difficult to diagnose as the wreathed heads of slaves, where the form of the beard sometimes helps. Wavy hair or wreath of hair or curly hair may be obscured by the ornamental binding, which is often large and hangs down over the ears. It will therefore be convenient to set down the youths with wavy hair too before discussing the wreathed masks.

No.15.   DT 5, MT 17, NB 1.   Add undated AT 12, XT 10, BT 5; BT 10; DT 17; ZT 4, 43; ET 17; TT 20; NT 4; UT 12

No.16.   (BT 3), (GV 1), DM 1, DT 4, (ZS 2), MT 3, FB 1.   Add undated BT 4, BT 12, KT 2, YT 9, MT 24, ZT 5, EL 28, ET 11, ST 25, TJ 3, TJ 4, TT 23, (NT 13)

Of these the wreathed masks are no.15: NB 1, AT 12, XT 10, BT 5, BT 10, TT 20, and no.16: GV 1, BT 12; YT 9; ZT 5; EL 28; NT 13. About the masks with raised brows there is no doubt: no.10 UT 16 and 20 (probably UT 27 also belongs here as the locks below the wreath seem to be short and formally brushed back), and no.15 all the examples quoted. The difficulty is to distinguish the two types of 'delicate' mask, nos. 13 and 16. Here the best clue is offered by YT 9 and EL 28 in both of which wavy hair can clearly be seen descending below the wreath, showing that they are no. 16: in both the eyes are largeish and round, quite different from the narrow sharp-lidded eyes of DT 3, MT 1, MT 22, ZV 3, ZT 2; as none of these show hair descending below the wreath and in MT 22 the wreath is combined with a smooth *speira*, which fixes it as no. 13, the eyes may be used as a criterion to divide the wreathed masks with smooth brows between nos. 16 and 13, and masks with the larger round eyes from which the hair has been broken off have been grouped as no. 16 (ST 25 is unwreathed and its wavy hair survives). If no. 10 with wreath of hair corresponds to no. 15 with wavy hair, no. 16 corresponds to no. 11 the 'studious' youth rather than to no. 13 the 'delicate' youth (no. 16 is *more* delicate than no. 15 and not delicate in its own right like no. 13). The two, nos. 11 and 16, appear on DM 1 each in association with the corresponding old man's mask, nos. 3 and 4.

Some of the wavy-haired masks are extremely alike although they come from different places and have different dates. Of no. 15, AT 12, BT 5, XT 10, NB 1 (BT 12 is softer) all give the soldier as he appears at the feast. DT 5 unwreathed is much more solemn, but he is no. 15, because he is clearly the counterpart of DT 4 with smooth brows and DT 4 is fixed as no. 16 by its likeness to DM 1 and to the compact group YT 9, EL 28, BT 3, BT 4, ST 25.

DT 17 has often been regarded as tragic because of its contorted brows and great mass of wavy hair above the forehead, which recalls the tragic *onkos*; there is apparently no doubt that the head belongs to the body or that the figure wore a short chiton and sandals, both of which are impossible for tragedy. The stylization of the hair is not unique but recurs in a less extreme form on MT 17, ET 17, NT 4, UT 12. None of these need be earlier than the late 2nd century B.C., and this pseudo-onkos must be regarded as a new stylization of the wavy-haired mask. Of the younger masks (no. 16), KT 2 with long wavy hair welling up from the forehead could well be regarded as a stage between the shorter and more naturalistic wavy hair of ST 25 and the wreathed pseudo-onkos of MT 24, if this last should not be excepted and taken as a young Dionysos mask (cf. below on NS 28).

The most elusive of the normal young men are nos. 12 and 19. Two examples of no. 19 have been identified, MT 20 and ET 21, but they may rather be more haggard examples of no. 10. The same distinction between solemn and cheerful was observed in the wavy-haired youths, and among the instances of no. 10 AJ 1, IT 37, UT 10, 16, 20 very obviously emphasize the worried lover at the expense of the athletic young man.

No. 12 is the curly-haired young man, fair and young, with raised brows, and one furrow on the forehead. Pollux' description is itself difficult, because 'fair and young' conflicts with raised brows and the furrow on the forehead, which are both characteristic of the oldest youth, no. 10. The curly youth may in fact be rare if in many comedies two households distinguished by 'wreath of hair' and 'wavy hair' were sufficient. And when the youth of a third 'curly' household was needed he may have been either older or younger. A possible identification for the older is EV 14, which has short corkscrew locks descending over the forehead and raised brows, and for the younger the very pretty mask from Selymbria with similar hair and smooth brows, XT 21.

The three hangers-on, the Flatterer (no. 17), the Parasite (no. 18), and the Sicilian parasite (no. 20) have been convincingly identified. They all wear short chitons like soldiers. AT 4 is a very fine early example of the flatterer; it is much the same date as the example of no. 10 on AJ 1. Similar pairs of flatterer and admirable youth are given by IT 10 with 37 and UT 17 with 16. Two Myrina statuettes with very similar bodies are distinguished by their heads as flatterer MT 18 and parasite MT 19. The Sicilian parasite has been found in NT 6.

4. WOMEN

Pollux' list starts with three old women: no. 28, the dry or wolfish old woman with long face, many fine wrinkles, squint; no. 29, the fat

21

old woman with wrinkles in a fat face and a fillet round her hair: no.30, the little housekeeper, snub-nosed with two teeth in each jaw. They follow the masks in Middle Comedy labelled RR, Y and U respectively. There are not many examples. The early group of Attic terracottas contains two: AT 15 with its long nose is probably no.28, AT 14 which is almost if not completely bald is probably no.29. AV 25 of the early second century includes a fine example of no.30. NT 11 is an interesting example of the fat woman no.29 because she holds a skull in front of her; if, as is probable, the fat woman is a procuress, this is an admonition to live the life of pleasure while it is possible.

Pollux then lists young women (not consistently because nos.36, 37 are certainly old). No.31, the garrulous, has hair round her head with the locks smoothed down (the phraseology is extremely difficult here), straight brows, white skin, no.32 the curly-haired has different hair. It is assumed that these are the masks for young wives. No.31 is the Middle Comedy mask TT. Only one example of each has been identified in the Hellenistic material, NT 12 and IT 26.

No.33, the maiden, has her smoothed hair parted, straight black brows, and yellowish white skin. In Middle Comedy two masks were distinguished, SS with long hair and S with short hair. Both types continue: CT 1 is a very fine early example of an actor carrying the mask of a maiden with long hair, IT 1 has long straggly hair and this type recurs later on Roman mosaics and paintings; AV 12 and TJ 1 are good early examples of the maiden with short hair.

No.34, the first false-maiden, who has whiter skin and her hair bound about her forehead, is the Middle Comedy mask W. AJ 6 and AV 13 are early examples; BT 7 is interesting as the mask is carried by the Muse of Comedy. This is an almost certain identification and easy to recognize.

No.35, the second false-maiden, is distinguished from no.34 by unparted hair. This mask has been plausibly identified with the successors of Middle Comedy mask V, which is easily recognizable by its bunch of hair

over the forehead sometimes held by a clasp.   The same form appears
in the early third century on GV 1 and 2 and ST 15.   Perhaps the head
on AJ 6 with a tiny bow over the forehead may be associated with it
but it may rather be a young hetaira.

   Pollux inserts next two older women, no.36, the grey-haired garrulous
'she shows her appearance by her name and signifies a hetaira who has
given up her profession;   the concubine (no.37) is like her but has
hair round her head'.   These sentences are confusing: if no.36, as
the first clause implies, is only distinguished from no.31 by the colour
of her hair, why has she not also 'hair round her head' like no.31?
And if she is, as her name suggests, an elderly wife, how can she be a
'hetaira'?   This description must rather belong to no.37;   probably
it should therefore simply be switched with 'but she has hair round
her head', which then merely picks up the similarity with no.31.   Very
few masks need be considered: AT 16, XT 1, ET 57, GV 3, IT 29, of which
AT 16, XT 1, GV 3 are not later than the early third century.   All
these are old women with considerable hair round their foreheads and
continue the tradition of Middle Comedy mask R.   AT 16 and IT 29 have
their hair tied up in a scarf such as is commonly seen on hetaira masks
(cf. below on no.41);   this mask may be classified as no.37 and XT 1,
ET 57, and GV 3 as no.36.

   Pollux then continues with hetairai: no.38, full-grown hetaira redder
than no.34 with hair round her ears, no.39, the little youthful hetaira,
who is the least made up and has a fillet round her head, no.40, the
golden hetaira with much gold on her hair, no.41 the scarfed hetaira
with a coloured scarf round her hair, no.42 Little Torch because her
hair is twisted into a tail, no.43 the shorn maidservant who wears only
a white chiton, no.44 the little servant with smoothed hair and parted
locks, who is snub-nosed and serves hetairai, wearing a scarlet chiton.
These criteria mentioned by Pollux are not mutually exclusive, and it
is unclear whether wearing a chiton only is the mark of a servant even

if the wearer has a straight nose and a scarf round her hair (MT 45),
whether a hetaira is to be classed as Little Torch when she also wears
a scarf (UT 94 etc.), or whether a young girl is to be classed as a
full-grown hetaira when she has locks over her ears (DT 2). However
the following classification may come somewhere near his intentions.

No. 38 the full-grown hetaira: Middle Comedy type X. One mask on
AJ 1 with fat face and an elaborate wreath should qualify, probably also
GV 4, which is not very young, perhaps also ZT 13, ET 5. UT 91, DT 27.

No. 39 the youthful hetaira: Pollux' type with a fillet can be seen
in AT 9, DT 27, ZT 28, IT 60, and UT 92. AV 25 has the fillet tied in
a bow at the top. Another type of very young hetaira wears a wreath,
sometimes an ivy wreath: AJ 1, AJ 6, XT 5, ZM 1. DT 2 is also very
young and has a clasp on the top of her head. Yet another type is the
young hetaira with melon hair, Middle Comedy type XD; MT 49, FB 2, ST 11,
GV 5 (with wreath), PT 4, NT 1, IT 28 (with wreath), IT 30, 31, IV 7,
UT 80, UT 87 (with wreath). Melon hair came in about 320 B.C. and
probably did not last beyond the middle of the third century (the style
seen on the masks still appears on the coins of Arsinoe II but not on
the coins of Berenice II). All of our melon hair masks (including the
first pseudokore and the Lampadion with melon hair, IT 59 and ZT 38)
look Early Hellenistic in style and the only one with a first century
date is IV 7, an Italian Megarian bowl, which may very well preserve a
traditional mask (like many Italian gems). Probably then the mask with
melon hair is the earlier version of no. 39.

No. 40 cannot be identified. No. 41 may be confined to masks with a
scarf but without the tail of back hair: it is Middle Comedy XA. It
is very common. AJ 6 has a fat example which looks older than the
rest; ST 17 has a wreath. MT 45 and 46, although dressed only in a
chiton, probably belong here. No. 42, Middle Comedy XC, has variants
with a fillet (BT 6, ZT 6), a scarf (DT 25, UT 93, 94), and a wreath
(ZT 13, UT 83). No. 43 cannot be identified. No. 44 may be seen in
some masks with parted hair, snub noses and little adornment (XT 20, ZT 24,
TT 13).

24

B. ROMAN PERIOD

Study of the Roman period has two distinct aims, to add to our knowledge of the Hellenistic period from Roman copies and to give some conception of production in the Roman period itself. Examination of the Hellenistic period has given some clues to the dating of the originals of Roman copies: slaves with deep or pointed trumpets are likely to derive from originals of the third century or earlier, slaves with semicircular trumpets from the second century, bald slaves with wide trumpets may be Early Hellenistic but other slaves with wide trumpets are Late Hellenistic: finally the semicircular trumpet with a narrow striated flat edge does not appear much before the end of the first century B.C. The marked roll of hair in the masks of old men and young men probably does not belong to the earliest period of New Comedy but is established early in the third century, the pseudo-onkos of the young wavy-haired mask is not introduced until the late second century. Among the women melon hair is a sign of early date since it does not seem to last long into the third century.

The following survey includes only such monuments which add new knowledge of Hellenistic or Roman comedy; the rest are noted as traditional or modern in the introductions to the separate sections of the Catalogue, where also the cross connections between different groups and individual pieces are suggested. A few late Hellenistic monuments are included in this section because to put them in the Hellenistic section would have destroyed their obvious context, e.g. the Hellenistic mosaics in Pompeiian houses, the Campana reliefs, the earliest Arretine pottery, or the monument of the Julii. Monuments of unknown date are only included when they are relevant to dated monuments. As before the order of treatment is Slaves, Old Men, Young Men, Women.

1. SLAVES

Interesting monuments:

Late Hellenistic: NM 4; IM 3; IT 65; IV 8; JS 3; UJ 25

1st century A.D.:   AL 3, AS 8;   ZL 7;   ZT 56, 57;   EG 5;   NP 6 = 46, 13,
                      23, 27, 38, 45;   NS 17, 25;   IL 8, 11, 12, 14, 28;
                      IS 4, 14, 21, 37;   IT 71

2nd century A.D.:   AT 27;   CL 4;   XL 3;   ZS 6;   ZT 60;   IM 6;   IS 22, 25,
                      46, 47, 53

3rd century A.D. (and later):   AL 4;   AT 31, 32, 36, 37, 39, 44;   ZM 4,
                      5, 6;   ZS 5;   EV 16, 17;   FM 3, 4;   IL 50, 51;   IM 8, 9;
                      IP 2;   IS 31, 48, 50;   IT 80, 81;   US 1

Unknown date: AS 9, 11, 13;   ZS 7;   NS 31;   IS 30;   UB 10;   UJ 11, 24,
                      44;   UT 107, 108, 109, 110, 111, 112, 113

   Some of these can be separated out at once as copies of earlier originals.
In them the slave masks are particularly useful when they date other masks.

Late Hellenistic: IM 3 goes back to a third century original of a slave
discovering a child.   IV 8 is in the tradition of the Megarian bowls.

First century A.D.:   Early Hellenistic originals must be supposed for
NP 38, IS 4, IS 14.   Originals of the 2nd century B.C. must be supposed
for NP 27, NS 17 (where the slave mask is reminiscent of Attic braziers),
IL 14 (a curious survival of the wavy-haired slave with semicircular
trumpet), IS 27.   Late Hellenistic originals must be supposed for ZT 56,
57 (Tarsus), NP 6 = 46, 13 (the soldier slave and the leading slave),
NP 45, IL 13 (probably best explained as the Late Hellenistic leading
slave with the wide trumpet), IT 71.

Second century A.D.:   IS 25 and AS 11 (and other large marble masks like
them) are probably best explained as derived from Early Hellenistic leading
slaves.   The Pentelic marble of AS 11 suggests that the original also
was Attic.

Third century A.D. and later: ZM 4 presupposes a Late Hellenistic original.
So also do the slave masks of EV 16 and 17, but they are additions to the
Early Hellenistic composition which is copied by the Augustan ET 65.

   IT 65 and JS 3 may indicate Roman practice in the first century B.C.
JS 3 is the funeral monument of the Julii and the masks may therefore

have some relations to the masks worn at the funeral plays.   IT 65
(which is known in several replicas) is so like the tragic relief on
the funeral monument of Numitorius that it may also have been used for
funeral monuments and therefore represent a scene whnch could occur in
funeral plays.   The slave masks on both have the wide trumpet and flowing
hair of the wavy-haired slave known from Greek monuments of the first
century B.C.   The seated slave of IT 65 should be compared with NP 45
and IS 30.

At the end of the first century B.C. a new form of the semicircular
trumpet with narrow flat striated edge was noted on three lamps, one
certainly and the other two probably from Egypt.   From the first century
A.D. it becomes common first for the leading slave (22) and later for
the wavy-haired slave (27).   An early Imperial glass plaque from Egypt
(EG 5) combines it with two rolls of hair on the forehead and a different
stylization of the same treatment of the hair is seen on Roman lamps
(IL 28 etc.).   AL 3 has the new trumpet with peaked hair; it was compared
by Brueckner with the undated AS 9 which he suggested came from the Council
House of the Artists of Dionysos.   If so, it is evidence for contemporary
Athenian practice, as is certainly the mid-first century A.D. grave relief
of Bathyllus, AS 8.   The same mask in Italy is given by IL 8.

These are all leading slave masks (22).   Three wavy-haired slave
masks (27) of the first century A.D. differ considerably from each other.
NS 25 from Pompeii may be the earliest; it differs from the late Hellenistic IT 65 in having a much fatter face.   IL 11 has much more hair
and the hair is elaborately arranged in a double row of locks over the
forehead.   These both have the wide twisted trumpet; ZL 7, which may
be the latest, has the new semicircular trumpet with the flat striated
edge.

IS 21 is unique.   The petal formation of the eyes precludes a date
before the first century A.D.   The hair is peaked and unlike any other

slave mask grows in little spirals all over the top of the head.   This
stylization must represent curly hair: otherwise it is used for the
Lykomedeian old man and for the Kolax.   Presumably this is the curly-
haired slave (no.24).

In the second century XL 3 probably derives from a late Hellenistic
original.   AT 27, CL 4, IM 6, IS 47 show the same type of leading slave
as in the preceding century.   IS 22 shows the wavy-haired leading slave
with the semicircular trumpet with flattened edge like ZL 7, but the
hair rises from the forehead in flames to form a sort of onkos (cf. IS 46
and the undated NS 31).   ZT 60 from Tarsus with the same stylization
may also still belong to the second century.   IS 53 is curious: the
slave on the right has the new form of trumpet but the hair is naturalistic
wavy hair.

The flame hair is very common in third century wavy-haired slaves:
AL 4, AT 31 (seated, wearing the new quilted tights, cf. for these quilted
tights the headless AT 36, 44 and IL 50, IT 80, 81), AT 39, IM 9, IS 31,
UT 109, 110 etc.   AS 13 shows the same mask with the actor's mouth
showing through.   The large Agora mask AT 32 is the corresponding leading
slave (22), the striations of the trumpet are carefully framed, and the
hair is combed back from the forehead instead of rising in flames.   This
mask is also worn by the slave of AT 37 (the hair of the corresponding
IT 81 has a stylization more like the earlier peaked wig) and IL 50,
perhaps also IT 80;   the hair seems to be treated much less formally on
the corner mask of the very curious and interesting sarcophagus IS 50;
perhaps the masks of IS 48 are also slave masks although the trumpet
has no sign of striations and is very narrow (this may be a continuation
of the tendency already seen in IL 28).

The wavy-haired slave head AT 39 is of the right size to fit the body,
AT 36, which has already been noted for its quilted sleeves.   The clothing
is a long chiton and a small himation over the left shoulder.   The long
chiton is now possible for a slave (but not obligatory as the contemporary

AT 31, 44 show).   AT 36 is very similar to the standing slave of
IT 80, who wears long chiton and small cloak; it is very difficult
to be certain about IT 81 and AT 37 but probably the bunching just
above the feet represents a long chiton.   The slave of IL 50 wears
a shorter chiton but still it comes down far below the knee.   All
these are early third century.   The Menander mosaic from Antioch,
ZM 4, has the same date: there Comedy, holding what seems to be a
slave mask in her left hand and a stick in her right hand, wears a
long chiton and a small cloak over her left shoulder.   She seems to
be Comedy dressed as a slave (on the Archelaos relief, ES 1, Comedy
is dressed as a comic hetaira and Tragedy is dressed as a tragic
heroine).The figures in long chitons on either side of the door of
IS 50 wear masks according to Ashmole but they do not look like any
known comic masks.   FM 4, of the fourth century in Sousse, also has
a slave in a long chiton.   UT 108, a slave in a wavy-haired mask
with striated low onkos, appears to wear a long chiton: there is no
reason to date him earlier than the third century.   We have therefore
no evidence before the third century for the introduction of the long
chiton for slaves.   The mosaicist of Antioch evidently thought thus
of the slave in Greek comedy and AT 36 would naturally be interpreted
as a slave of Greek comedy.   But AT 37 (the Agora mould which may be
the model for the moulds from Ostia and Paestum, IT 81), is inscribed
PYLADES COMEDIA (Pylades was presumably, like the Bathyllus of
AS 8, an actor who had a well-known pantomimus name) which suggests
Latin comedy, and the many slaves with long chitons in the Terence
miniatures, IP 2, point the same way.   But there is no reason why
the change in slave dress should not have taken place at the same
time in Greek and Roman comedy.   They seem to have run parallel in
the third century A.D. as on our evidence they did in the first
century B.C. (AS 4, IT 65, JS 3).

2. OLD MEN

Interesting monuments:

Late Hellenistic: NM 4;   IT 65;   JS 3

1st century A.D.:   AS 8;   NM 3;   NP 27, 39, 47;   NS 9, 17, 25, 26, 28;
                      NT 30, 33;   IL 6, 10;   IS 10, 14;   UJ 2

2nd century A.D.:   XL 3;   ZM 3;   IS 53;   JS 1

3rd century A.D.:   AT 38, 52;   IP 2;   IS 31, 50
  (and later)

Unknown dates: AS 6;   EB 3;   UJ 27

It is more difficult to get a clear picture of the old men in the
Roman period.   The two commonest old men (nos. 3 and 4) often have
shorter beards than earlier.   Sometimes however this seems to be due
to the needs of composition, masks set in a garland (NM 4 etc.) or with
other masks in a relief (IS 14 from a third century original, NS 17
from a second century original).   Of the copies, where composition
does not apply, NP 47 from an early Hellenistic original has a long
beard and NS 28 is very like it;   NP 27 from a second century original
has a longish beard, but NM 3 has a shortish beard.   Probably therefore
short beards are possible but not universal from the second century B.C.

This would give a top date for the wavy-haired old man's mask in the
Menander relief (AS 6, IS 10).   The two versions probably represent an
earlier and a later copy of an original made not earlier than the second
century B.C.   But the original itself derives from an Early Hellenistic
statue of Menander holding the mask of a youth which has a different
echo in ET 65, EV 16, 17.

The late Hellenistic Roman reliefs, IT 65, JS 3, both give the wavy-
haired old man (4) a long beard;   on IT 65 the leading old man (3) has
a shorter beard.   In the first century A.D. both the old men on the
Naples Comedy relief, NS 25, have short beards and the mouth is stylized
almost like a slave trumpet.   The trumpet is seen also in the very fine
head NS 9, which is interpreted as a wavy-haired old man although it has

30

a short corkscrew beard.   This stylization had come in late in the
first century B.C.:   on UL 1 the corkscrew beard hangs below the slave
mouth.   In the Roman period it cen be seen in IL 10, perhaps IS 53
(the curiously naturalistic head on the extreme left which looks like
a satyr but has a human ear), XL 3, UJ 2 and 27.

A further development of this stylization is to treat the beard so
that it appears to be inside the trumpet instead of hanging below the
trumpet.   Thus in the Roman period when the slave trumpet has a narrow
flattened striated edge round a smooth interior, old men may have a
deepish rounded trumpet with curly hair inside it which is not unlike
the semicircular trumpet of wavy-haired slaves of the second century
B.C., e.g. ZT 23.   The reason for accepting this type of mask as an
old man's mask rather than a copy of an earlier slave mask is its occur-
rence in the second century A.D. on JS 1, the relief commemorating *P.
Aelios Hermolaos Komodos*:   his mask is presumably contemporary and a
contemporary slave mask would have the trumpet with a narrow flat striated
edge.   This variant with straight striations inside the trumpet and hair
combed back from the forehead recurs on IS 53 (second from the left).
In the first century NT 33 has similar hair but a short curly beard
hanging below the trumpet.   It is probably mask 7, the Lykomedeian, and
AT 52 is a third century copy of this mask from an Early Hellenistic
original.   The wavy-haired old man (4) can be seen in this form in NS 26,
NT 30, IL 6 (and the other lamps noted in the introduction to that section
of the Catalogue).

IS 50 has a mask with a very wide quite short curly beard under a wide
trumpet.   This shows that the short-bearded old man persists into the
third century but there are also a few late examples of a wavy-haired old
man with a pointed beard and this mask is also found in the Terence
miniatures IP 2.   Of these old men with pointed beards AT 38 and IS 31
are certainly third century;   the very curious bronze EB 3 is dated by
Neugebauer 'post Julio-Claudian':   if the criss-cross stockings have any
relation to the quilted stockings of AT 31 etc. he may also be third
century.   UB 17 should perhaps also be considered in this context.

31

3. YOUNG MEN

Interesting monuments:

Late Hellenistic: NM 2, 4; JS 3

1st century A.D.: XB 1; YT 13; EG 2; ET 65; NB 9; NJ 2; NP 6 = 46,
         11, 12, 16, 23, 30, 34; NS 11, 17, 25, 28; NT 27;
         IL 33; IS 4, 6, 10, 14; IT 68

2nd century A.D.: CL 4; XL 3; ZT 61; NT 26; IM 7; IS 47, 53

3rd century A.D.: XM 1; ZM 3; ZS 5, 6; EV 16, 17; FM 4; IL 42, 43,
   (and later)   50; IM 9; IP 2; IT 80; US 1

Unknown date: AS 6; ZS 24; IS 42

Many of these masks and figures are traditional either as being copies
of or derived from earlier originals or because traditional masks survived
in use; the latter can be shown to be probable when a traditional mask of
a youth is coupled with a modern slave mask. A third century original
can be assumed for the Dioskourides mosaic: the two young men on the
mosaic have different masks from the corresponding figures from Myrina:
the castagnet player is a *hapalos* (13) on the mosaic but a *kolax* (17) at
Myrina, MT 15; the drummer is a *panchrestos* (10) on the mosaic but a
hapalos (13) at Myrina, MT 1.

Enough can be seen of the mask held by the Muse on ET 65, EV 16, 17 to
show that it could be the same as the mask (11) held by Menander on AS 6
and IS 10; therefore a third century statue of Menander with a youth's
mask may have been the ancestor of both ET 65 and AS 6; AS 6 being of
Pentelic marble presupposes an immediate Attic original of the 2nd century
B.C.

Of these masks the *panchrestos* (10) is seen again in NP 6=46, which is
a copy of a Late Hellenistic original, and in NT 28, also probably a copy;
possibly also on CL 4 of the second century A.D., which shows that mask
10 survives to that date as the other masks are modern. Masks 11 and
13 (which, as we have seen, are difficult to distinguish) also survive
with little change: IS 14 is a copy of a third century original with
nos.13 and 17 (no.17 occurs again on IS 4, also derived from a third

32

century original);   NP 34 shows no. 11 in a copy of a third century
original, NS 11 no. 13 in a copy of a 2nd century original.   JS 3
gives no. 11 in the 1st century B.C.;   in the second century A.D. IS 53
associates it with a modern old man's mask and ZT 61 with a modern slave
mask;   in the third century A.D. ZM 3 associates no. 13 with a modern
slave mask.   XM 1, the very interesting mosaic of Menander's *Achaeans*,
is modern both in details, such as the stylization of the city gate and
the house-door, and in the very large mouths of the two young men.   IS 42,
probably late second century A.D., may well be a contemporary bust of an
actor taking the part of the *kolax* (no. 17), like the late actor taking the
part of a slave from the Agora (AS 13).

The elder wavy-haired mask (no. 15) was given a pseudo-onkos in the
late second century B.C.;   therefore NP 30 without onkos may go back to
an Early Hellenistic original.   The curly-haired boy (no. 12) and the
younger wavy-haired boy (no. 16) also have an onkos on Roman monuments and
it is not easy to distinguish them: but perhaps corkscrew locks belong
to no. 12 and straggly or wavy locks to no. 16.   Then the boy on the Naples
comedy relief, NS 25, is presumably a late appearance of no. 16 without
onkos.   The onkos masks may perhaps be divided as follows:

No. 12:   1st century A.D.:   EG 2 (very like IS 47), NB 9, IL 33 (cf.
                             NT 40);

          2nd century A.D.:   IM 7, IS 47;

          3rd century A.D.:   ZS 4

No. 16:   1st century A.D.:   NP 11;

          3rd century A.D.:   IM 9

The very interesting third century representations of actors can be
divided between masks 15 and 16.

No. 15:   FM 4;   IL 42, 43
No. 16:   IS 59;   IT 80

One of the Late Hellenistic Myrina masks, MT 24, was interpreted as
possibly a young Dionysos.   The type (e.g. NS 28), an onkos mask with

large onkos with either wavy hair or corkscrew curls, has an elaborate wreath and smooth brows; the reason for suggesting that it may be Dionysos is that it is found in association with both tragic and comic masks (see introduction to Catalogue, on NS 16).

4. WOMEN

Interesting monuments:

Late Hellenistic: NM 1, 2, 4; JS 3; UJ 25

1st century A.D.: EG 6; NP 6=46, 11, 25, 38, 45, 48; NS 13, 15, 20; NT 28; IS 2, 10; IV 15

2nd century A.D.: CL 4; ZT 62; IM 6, 7; IS 40

3rd century A.D.: AT 37; XM 1; ZM 3, 4, 5; EL 33; FM 3; IL 43; (and later) IM 9; IP 2; IS 50; IT 80, 81

Unknown date: AS 6; ET 64; UJ 51

Many of the women's masks also are traditional whether as copies or survivals. Third century originals may be supposed for NM 1 and 2 (masks 29, 35, 39), NP 38 (mask 38), 48 (mask 33), UJ 51 (mask 38); a second century original for NP 25 (masks 29, 39) and a first century original for NP 45 (mask 39). Among these two new versions of the 'full grown hetaira' (no.38) are interesting: UJ 51 has a fat-faced woman with melon hair and an elaborate wreath, which should derive from the earliest period of New Comedy; on NP 38 the woman sending her slave to market has her hair done in a roll round her head; this is seen again on UJ 25. NP 45 has the little hetaira with an ivy wreath: there are many examples on gems, e.g. UJ 53.

The terracotta statue NT 28 (a short-haired kore as on the Late Hellenistic JS 3) is probably a copy like its male counterpart NT 27. The Arretine fragment, IV 15, is traditional and the kore mask recalls the Early Corinthian Hellenistic terracotta, CT 1. Many of the Campanian marble masks are probably copies, e.g. NS 13, 15, 20 with masks 43, 42, 39 respectively. The masks on the round altar tombstones (IS 2, 6, 7) are traditional, but may carry an allusion to funeral performances, although the mouths are closed.

From the first century A.D. two different masks show the hair piled very high like an onkos: EG 6 with mask 39 (with ivy wreath) and NP 11 with mask 33 (cf. UJ 50). The same treatment of the kore mask appears in the second century A.D. on IM 7 and in the third century A.D. associated with a modern slave mask on FM 3 and in the scenes on IL 43, AT 37, IT 81. But the kore masks on ZM 4 and IS 50 have no onkos, which suggests that the two forms continued side by side. Similarly on the lamp in the Terme IL 50 the mask with ivy wreath (39) has no pile of hair, and the form of little hetaira mask with a fillet tied in a bow above the forehead and no high hair-dressing is found associated with modern slave masks in the second century A.D. and later, IM 6, ZT 62.

A new form of hairdressing which is first seen in the second century is braided hair. The long-haired mask with braided hair on the Corinthian lamp CL 4 is probably a kore (33) and a similar mask appears later on ZM 5. The marble bust in the Vatican, IS 40, was interpreted by Robert and has been generally accepted as the golden hetaira (40) but the face is very young and it may rather be a modern version of the scarfed hetaira (41) with braided hair. The mask with braided hair on the Lateran mosaic (IM 9) is certainly a hetaira and possibly the full-grown hetaira (38).

SUMMARY

It may be useful to append a brief summary of the chief changes:

Early Hellenistic.　　All men wear decent chitons.　Leading slave masks have deep rounded trumpet (no.22) or pointed trumpet (no.27). Bald slave masks may have semicircular trumpet.　Old men occasionally still appear with Middle Comedy masks, but all young men are clean shaven.　The marked roll of hair for the leading old man (no.3) and some of the young men (nos.10, 11, 13, 14) is perhaps not introduced until the third century.　Hetaira masks with melon hair do not last long into the third century.

Second century B.C.　　The standard mask for the leading slave (no.22) and the wavy-haired leading slave (no.27) now has the semicircular trumpet.　The bald slave now often has the wide twisted trumpet and this is sometimes given to the wavy-haired slave particularly in the second half of the century.　Before the end of the century wavy-haired young men may have their hair in a kind of pseudo-onkos.

First century B.C.　　The wide twisted trumpet is now commonly used for wavy-haired slaves and bald slaves.　The semicircular trumpet with a narrow flat striated edge is first seen on Egyptian lamps, probably before the end of the century.　Old men's beards are shorter than before and on IT 65, which should represent a contemporary Roman performance, the leading old man (no.3) has a shorter beard than the wavy-haired old man (no.4).　AS 4 is an Attic actor's monument; JS 3 may reproduce the masks worn at a Roman funeral performance.

First century A.D.　　The semicircular trumpet with flat striated edge is now universal for leading slaves (no.22) and is introduced before the end of the century for wavy-haired slaves (cf. on ZL 7). Old men's mouths are often stylized as trumpets with the beard hanging below (no.3) or sometimes inside the trumpet (no.4).　The pseudo-onkos is now sometimes given to the curly-haired youth (no.12), the delicate wavy-haired youth (no.16), the *kore* (no.33), and the young hetaira (no.39).

36

AS 8 is a monument set up by the actor Bathyllus; AS 9 and IS 21 may be evidence for performance in the first century A.D. (AS 9 may come from the council house of the Artists of Dionysos; IS 21 is the bust of a presumably Roman actor.)

Second century A.D. Flame hair is introduced for wavy-haired slaves. The Lycomedeian old man may have his beard inside a trumpet mouth. A new fashion for *kore* and hetaira masks is braided hair.

JS 1 is the monument of an actor and IS 42 (probably of this date) represents an actor.

Third century A.D. Quilted tights are introduced; they show on the arms of slaves, young men and young women and on the legs of slaves and young men. Slaves may now wear a long chiton with a small mantle like a scarf. The wavy-haired old man (no.4) sometimes has a pointed beard now. The mouths of young men are sometimes stylized like trumpets.

AS 13 is probably an actor of this date; AT 37 shows Pylades in a Roman comedy; IS 59 shows an actor in a Roman funeral performance.

SYNOPSIS

List of Prefixes: 1:   Local   A = Attica

                                                                                       B = Boeotia

C = Corinth

D = Delos

E = Egypt

F = Africa

G = Gnathia

I = Northern & Central Italy

J = The West

K = Cyprus

M = Myrina

N = Campania

P = Paestum

S = Sicily and Lipari

T = Southern Italy

U = Unknown

X = Mainland Greece

Y = Islands

Z = Asia Minor

2:   Use or Material   A = Amphora Handle

B = Bronze

C = Coins

G = Glass

J = Precious stones, silver,
     gold, jewellery

L = Lamps

M = Mosaics

P = Painting

38

S = Stone sculpture or relief
T = Terracotta
V = Pottery

HELLENISTIC

42

LIST OF MASKS

OLD MEN

3. Leading old man
4. Wavy-haired old man (*episeistos*)
7. Lykomedeian
8. Procurer (*pornoboskos, leno*)

YOUNG MEN

10. Admirable youth (*panchrestos*)
11. Dark youth (*melas*)
12. Curly-haired youth (*oulos*)
13. Delicate youth (*hapalos*)
14. Rustic (*agroikos*)
15. First youth with wavy hair (*episeistos*)
16. Second youth with wavy hair (*episeistos*)
17. Flatterer (*kolax*)
18. Parasite
19. *Eikonikos*
20. Sicilian

SLAVES

21. Old slave (*pappos*)
22. Leading slave
23. Long-haired slave (*katotrichias*)
24. Curly-haired slave (*oulos*)
25. Bald slave (*maison*)
26. Slave with wisp of hair (*tettix*)
27. Wavy-haired leading slave (*episeistos*)

OLD WOMEN

28. Wolfish
29. Fat
30. Little housekeeper

YOUNG WOMEN

31. Garrulous
32. Curly-haired (*oule*)

33. Maiden *(kore)*
34. First false maiden *(pseudokore)*
35. Second false maiden *(pseudokore)*
36. Brindled *(spartopolios)*
37. Concubine *(pallake)*
38. Full-grown hetaira
39. Little youthful hetaira
40. Golden hetaira
41. Scarfed hetaira *(diamitros)*
42. Little Torch *(lampadion)*
43. Shorn maidservant
44. Little maidservant

ABBREVIATIONS

(Excepting journal titles and other obvious abbreviations)

A.G.   A. Furtwängler, die Antiken Gemmen

Amelung   W. Amelung, die Skulpturen des Vatikanischen Museums, I and II (III by G. Lippold)

Ashmole   B. Ashmole, Ancient Marbles at Ince Blundell Hall

B.D. *or* Bieber D.   M. Bieber, Denkmäler zum Theaterwesen

B.H.T. *or* Bieber H.T.   M. Bieber, History of the Greek and Roman Theater, [1]1939, [2]1961

Breitenstein. N. Breitenstein, Catalogue of the Terracottas in the Danish National Museum

Broneer   O. Broneer, Corinth, IV,2: Terracotta Lamps

Burr   D. Burr, Terracottas from Myrina in Boston, Boston 1934

CV   Corpus Vasorum Antiquorum

Curtius   L. Curtius, Die Wandmalerei Pompejis

Graindor   P. Graindor, Terres Cuites de l'Egypte Greco-Romaine

G.T.P.   T. B. L. Webster, Greek Theatre Production

Helbig   W. Helbig, Führer durch die Sammlungen Klass. Altertümer in Rom

Kekulé   R. Kekulé, die Antiken Terrakotten, II. Die Terrakotten von Sizilien

K.i.B.   F. Winter, Kunstgeschichte in Bildern

Larisa   K. Schefold and J. Boehlau, Larisa am Hermos, III, die Kleinfunde

Laumonier   H. Laumonier, Catalogue des terres cuites du Musée Archéologique de Madrid

Levi   A. Levi, Le Terrecotte figurate nel Mus. Naz. di Napoli

L.G.S.   A. W. Lawrence, Later Greek Sculpture

Lippold   G. Lippold, Gemmen und Kameen des Altertums und der Neuzeit

Martha   J. Martha, Catalogue des figurines en terre cuite du Musée de la Société Archéologique d'Athènes

M.u.Z.   A. Rumpf, Malerei und Zeichnung, Handbuch der Archaeologie, IV

Myrina   E. Pottier and S. Reinach, La Necropole de Myrina

Naukratis   W. M. Flinders-Petrie, Naukratis

P.C.F.   A. W. Pickard-Cambridge, Dramatic Festivals of Athens

Perdrizet   P. Perdrizet, Terres cuites de la Collection Fouquet

Pernice	E. Pernice, die Hellenistische Kunst Pompejis, IV, V, VI
Pfuhl	E. Pfuhl, Malerei und Zeichnung der Griechen
Priene	Th. Wiegand and H. Schrader, Priene
'Princeton'	F. F. Jones, The Theater in Ancient Art, 1952
Robert	C. Robert, die Masken der neueren attischen Komödie
Rohden	H. von Rohden, die antiken Terrakotten, I, die Terrakotten von Pompeji
Rohden-Winnefeld	H. Von Rohden and H. Winnefeld, die antiken Terrakotten, IV, Architekt. röm. Tonreliefs der Kaiserzeit.
R.P.	S. Reinach, Répertoire des peintures grecques et romaines
R.R.	S. Reinach, Répertoire des reliefs grecques et romaines
R.S.	S. Reinach, Répertoire de la statuaire grecque et romaine
Sambon	Collection Jules Sambon
Sieglin	J. Vogt, Expedition Sieglin
Simon	A. K. H. Simon, Comicae Tabellae, Emsdetten 1938
TK	F. Winter, Die antiken Terrakotten, III, Die Typen der figürlichen Terrakotten, part ii
W.A.M.	T. B. L. Webster, Greek dramatic monuments from the Athenian Agora and Pnyx, *Hesperia* 29 (1960), 254 ff.

CATALOGUE OF MONUMENTS

I : HELLENISTIC

ATHENS

Jewellery

AJ 1-6   There is no proof that these come from Athens, but both style and
         subject matter (and for some find-spot in South Russia) suggest
         Athens.   The style of the masks suggests that they come early in
         the New Comedy series.   The short-winged Eros on AJ 1 and AJ 2
         preclude a date much before the end of the fourth century (cf.
         JHS 71 (1951) 228).   AJ 1 must be earlier than 150 B.C. and may
         be much earlier.   AJ 6 is compared by Zahn to other jewellery
         which is dated by coins to the late third century.

AJ 1   Gold masks from necklaces   Hamburg, 1917,   Palaiokastron,   Late 3rd
                                        195   Thessaly   or early
                                                                              2nd cent.B.C.

       Masks 3,10,13,22,25,27,39,41: Old man's mask with flat striated speira
       and corkscrew beard, pl.8c;   youth with peaked striated flat hair, pl.8e;
       youth with wreath, 8d,f;   hetaira with wreath, pl.8b; 9,5 and 6;   wimpled
       hetaira, pl.9,7;   hetaira with fat face and wreath, pl.8h.   Slaves'
       masks all have oval trumpets: pl.8a, with peaked striated hair, 8g with
       peaked wavy hair and wavy hair inside trumpet;   pl.9, 8 and 9 with
       striated hair without peak and striated edge to trumpet;   9, 10 similar
       trumpet but bald head.

       Ref. Simon 188 n.8;   Küthmann-Kusel, *AM* 50 (1925), 174/5, pl.8 (necklace),
              9 (masks probably from necklace)(dates grave 150 B.C.);   G.T.P.,
              no.C 4.

       Note Pl.9,12 has baby Eros carrying Maison (25) mask.

AJ 2   Gold masks from necklace   Leningrad   S. Russia
       a) Maison (25), beard curly inside trumpet;   b) Slave (22), with striated
       beard;   c) Youth (10);   d) Slave (22) carried by Eros with short wings
       Ref. Simon 188 n.8;   Reinach, *Antiqu. Bosph. Cimm.*, pl.VII,6, XXXII, 2

AJ 3   Gold mask   Leningrad   S. Russia

        Mask 7 (or more likely 3)

        Ref: Simon 194 n.67; *Ant.Bosph.* pl.32, 8.

        Note Found with AJ 2

AJ 4   Gold masks   Leningrad   S. Russia

        a) Mask 4;   b) Mask 29 or 37

        Ref. Simon 192 n.14; *Ant.Bosph.* pl.32, 3 and 4

AJ 5   Gold mask   Leningrad   S. Russia

        Mask 14

        Ref. Simon 185 n.104; *Ant.Bosph.* pl.32, 6

        Note Found with AJ 2

AJ 6   Gold band   Berlin   Abdera

        Masks 3,4,10,14,22,27,34,35,39,41.
        a) Slave with peaked smooth speira, semicircular trumpet;   b) Girl with
        small bow on forehead;   c) Slave with wavy speira and wavy semicircular
        trumpet;   d) Youth with striated peaked speira, arched brows, hooked
        nose;   e) as b);   f) Mask 34 with fattish face;   g) Old man with smooth
        straight hair and fullish beard;   h) as b);   i) as c);   j) Youth with
        curly hair, arched brows, small nose;   k) perhaps mask 4;   l) fat-faced
        41;   m) Hetaira with ivy wreath;   n,o) as a).

        Ref. Simon 183 n.47;   184 n.79;   197 n.70.
               Zahn, *AD*, IV, 1929, 76/80, pl.42,2 figs.8,9,11,

        Note Dates late 3rd cent. B.C.

L amps

AL 1   Terracotta lamp   Athens, Agora L 4633   Agora, P-R 6-12   3rd cent.B.C.
                                                       construction filling
        Masks of old man (3) set round fill hole, beards inwards.

        Ref. Howland, *Athenian Agora*, IV, *Greek Lamps*, Type 46 D, no.607.

        Note Howland compares AV 16 below;   find place dates before 150 B.C.,
               but Howland dates by type 250/200 B.C.   For the mask cf. AV 16,
               ZL 1.

Sculpture

AS 1-5 1 and 2 are marble masks from Athens.   Only the upper part of 1 is
        preserved and it may be a satyr rather than a slave.   The realistic
        style with large rimmed eyes and unbored pupils suggests an early
        Hellenistic date.   3 is included here with some hesitation;   the
        inspiration is probably Attic, although the palm tree suggests Delos,
        Egypt, or Asia Minor as the imagined scene, and parallels have been
        rightly seen with a bronze relief of Ptolemaic inspiration in Delos
        (Bieber, *Hell.Sc.*, fig.650) and with the Archelaus relief (ES 1).

4 is the grave stone of an Attic actor. 5 is a Roman copy of an Attic original of the Early Hellenistic period: the mask has a curiously stylized beard as occasionally found on Middle Comedy terracottas.

AS 1   Marble mask from frieze   Athens, Small   Athens
Akropolis Museum
H. 0,30; 0,20 m.   2297,2301

Mask 27; wavy hair, raised brows

Ref. Walter, *Beschreibung*, nos. 418,419.

Note Only the upper part is preserved. Walter takes as comic but they may rather be satyrs.

AS 2   Marble mask   Athens N.M. 54   Athens, Stoa of Attalos

Mask of slave (27) : wild hair, uneven brows, rimmed eyes. Only upper part preserved.

Ref. Bieber, *HT*, fig. 265; *D* pl. 105/3, no. 168.

Note Find spot may indicate top date; style makes a date later than the 1st cent. B.C. unlikely.

AS 3   Marble relief   British Museum 2190
Louvre 1606
Ephesos
Kephisia (from Patras)

Dionysus visits comic poet: Masks: Profile ?13, ?33; Three-quarter 22, 27. The youth has a smooth speira. Both slaves have wide, smooth trumpet.

Ref. Picard, *AJA* 38 (1934), 137f.; Hauser, *Neuattischen Reliefs*, 37; Schreiber, *Hellenistischen Reliefbilder*, pl. xxxvii-viii; Keil, *Ö.Jh.* 24, 1929, *Beiblatt* 37f. (part found in Antonine baths at Ephesos); Bieber, *Hell.Sc.*, 154, fig. 655-7; Beyen, *Wanddekoration*, fig. 69.

Note Picard notes palm tree and suggests Alexandrian inspiration comparing Delos relief and Archelaos relief. His date 250/200 is too early; perhaps 1st cent. B.C.

AS 4   Grave column (Hymettan   Athens   Athens   ?1 B.C. to A.D.
marble)

Relief mask of comic slave with swinging eyebrows (27); wide, twisted, smooth trumpet, roughly striated hair. Inscr. Ἀλέξανδρος Κύρου Σφήττιος.

Ref. Conze, *Att.Grabreliefs*, IV, no. 1806, pl. 386; Robinson, *A.J.P.* 1910, 378, no. 3, early Roman; I.G. III, 2028, 1 A.D.

AS 5   Marble Muse Thalia   Vatican, Sala   Rome
holding mask   delle Musi 503

Mask (4)

Ref. Winter *KiB* 362/5; Lawrence, *LGS*, 17, 107; Bieber, *Hell.Sc.*, 23, fig. 44.

Note Probably copy of Attic original of late fourth or early third cent. B.C.

Terracottas: Early Hellenistic

AT 1-9   Terracottas from the Agora, mostly from well dated Early Hellenistic
deposits.   These run from the end of the 4th century to about the
middle of the second century.   With their contemporary pottery (West
Slope ware and Megarian bowls) they establish Attic practice in the
early Hellenistic period.   Two of this group, 1 and 5, show the
survival of Middle Comedy style in the pointed beard as distinct from
the full beard of New Comedy old men and the shorter trumpet beard of
many New Comedy slaves.   The *Kolax* head 4, with its big rimmed eyes,
anticipates not only a Myrina *kolax* (MT 18) but also a group of terracottas probably of Italian origin (IT 10, etc.).   The early slave
mask 5 may be compared with UT 31, 50, 52 (of which the origin is
unknown).   The third century running slave 6 anticipates a later
running slave from Myrina.

Old Men

AT 1   Terracotta mask   Athens, Agora T2273   Agora, Altar   Early 3rd
                                                          Well, B 20:7   Cent.B.C.
H. 0,032 m.

Wreathed head with pointed beard: slightly rimmed eyes.

Ref. D. B. Thompson, *Hesperia* 28 (1959), 140, pl.29, no.27;   *W.A.M.*, **no.**C 3

Note Perhaps survival of Middle Comedy type, AA.

AT 2   Terracotta mask   Athens, Agora T 213   Agora Well   3rd B.C.
                                                          G 14:2   context
H. 0,049 m.

Head of Lycomedian (7):   outlined eyes, depressed pupils, very careful
hair.

Ref. *W.A.M.*, no.C 4

AT 3   Terracotta mask   Athens, Agora T 2537   Agora, Koukla   3rd/2nd Cent. B.C.
                                                          factory fill, C 20:2
H. 0,026 m.

Bald, wreathed head with knotted brows (8 rather than 25).

Ref. Young, *Hesperia* 20 (1951), 249, 268;   *W.A.M.*, no.C 6

Young Men

AT 4   Terracotta head   Athens, Agora T 211   Agora, Well   3rd/2nd cent.B.C.
                                                          G 14:2
H. 0,037 m.

Mask of *kolax* (17) rather than parasite (18).   Very well modelled.   Light
pink clay.   Rimmed eyes, receding curly hair.

Ref. *W.A.M.*, no.C 7.

Note For head cf. MT 18.

Slaves

AT 5   Terracotta mask   Athens, Agora T 942   Agora, well to W.   End of 4th
                                                            of Tholos, G 11:4   cent. B.C.

H. 0,061 m.

Slave (27): massive hair, raised brows, wide striated trumpet with point
below.

Ref. H. A. Thompson, *Hesperia*, Supplt. IV (1940), p.100 (Shaft E);
        *W.A.M.*no.C 2

AT 6   Terracotta figure   Athens, Agora T 2509   Agora, Komos   Late 3rd
                                                            Cistern, M 21:1   cent. B.C.

H. 0,095 m.

Actor in fringed cloak, left hand pierced, right arm raised.

Ref. H. A. Thompson, *Hesperia*, 17 (1948), 160, pl.42/2; *W.A.M.*, no.C 1

AT 7   Fragmentary mould   Athens, Agora T 2523   Agora, Komos   Late 3rd
                                                            Cistern   cent. B.C.

Arm in fringed cloak.

Ref. *W.A.M.*, n.110

Women

AT 8   Terracotta mask   Athens, Agora T 1019   Agora B 10   2nd/1st cent.B.C.

H. 0,062 m.

First pseudokore (34)

Ref. *W.A.M.* no.C 5

AT 9   Terracotta mask   Athens, Agora T 584   Agora F: 14   Hellenistic
                                                                                context

H. 0,054 m.

Fragment of girl's mask.   Bright red clay.   Fillet in hair and earrings
(perhaps 39).

Ref. *W.A.M.*, no.C 8

AT 10   Terracotta mask   Athens, Agora T 3498   Agora, surface find

H. 0,035 m.

Lower half of mask of young woman(perhaps 39).

Ref. *W.A.M.*, no.C 9

AT 11-17   Terracottas which for various reasons seem to be Attic and provide a
           further range of Attic masks of Early Hellenistic date.   AT 11 comes
           from Vari in Attica and the pottery found with it suggests a date before
           150 B.C.   It apparently comes from a vessel and should perhaps have been
           classed AV.   AT 12-17 are alike in style, very finely modelled and rea-
           listic, reproducing the contours of the living face rather than the mask
           (cf. Tragedy, AT 9-10).   A date at the turn of the fourth to third century

B.C. is suggested by comparison with a dated Papposilenos head from the Agora (cf. on AT 14). The clay of AT 12 is said to be Attic. South Russian provenance of AT 13-15, 17 makes Attic origin likely. The following may also belong here: UT 27, 67.

Young Men

AT 11   Terracotta mask from   Athens N.M.   Vari, Attica   3rd/2nd cent.B.C.
a vessel

Mask 14: eyes rimmed, exaggerated raised eyebrows broken above forehead (which may imply speira).

Ref. Simon 185 n.103; *AJA*, 7 (1903), 333, no.62, pl.XI, 6.

Note Pottery does not go later than Megarian bowls.

AT 12   Terracotta mask   a) Heidelberg TK 98
                                     b) Munich 991

H. a) 0,058 m., b) 0,075 m.

Youth (15), raised brows, ivy wreath, wavy hair, full modelling.

Ref. a) Luschey, *Ganymed* 76, fig.5-7; *Welt der Griechen* fig.29;
          G.T.P., no.C 1.
       b) Krien, *J.O.A.I.*, 42 (1956), 110, fig.51

Note Acc. to Luschey clay is Attic.
       XT 10 is also very like this.

AT 13   Terracotta head   Munich, S.L.318   ?Olbia

Bald man, clean shaven with large wreath (?20). Well modelled. Perhaps not dramatic.

Women

AT 14   Terracotta mask   Munich, S.L.334   Olbia
H. 0,065 m.

Bald head with ivy wreath: ?20 or rather 29.

Ref. Krien, *J.O.A.I.*, 42 (1956), 112, fig.55; Sieveking, *Samml. Loeb,
       Bronzen, Terrakotten u. Vasen*, pl.24/4; Simon, 181, n.7; D. B.
       Thompson, *Hesperia* 26 (1957), 116, dating 4th to 3rd cent. B.C.

AT 15   Terracotta mask   Bonn

Mask of old woman (28): sleepy eyes; fully modelled cheeks
Ref. Bieber, *HT*, fig.276; Luschey, *Ganymed*, 77; G.T.P., no.C 2

AT 16   Terracotta mask   Copenhagen, NM. Inv.Chr.viii,922

Elderly woman (37): raised brows, fillet with large bow on forehead.
Ref. Breitenstein, no.599; Luschey, *Ganymed*, 77, fig.8 (takes as no.29);
       RB xxxii, 132, no.31; G.T.P., no.C 3

Slave

AT 17   Terracotta mask   Leningrad   S. Russia (Mithridates Mountain)
          Mask 26: pupils *not* bored; very careful modelling.
          Ref. Simon 188 n.10; *CR* 1882/3, 83 nr.1, pl.8,1

AT 18-25 Late Hellenistic terracottas from the Agora.   Most of these are dated
          by context.   The statuettes are all small and may have been made in
          used moulds, but small rather mean little slaves appear elsewhere also
          in the first century B.C. (Corinth, Delos, Myrina).   19 is a very fine
          fragment of a 2nd century mask, perhaps the *pornoboskos*;   the modelling
          is hard and the pupils are bored.   Two late heads, 21 and 25, hetaira
          and youth, have sharp noses and staring pierced eyes.   (UT 58 may be
          compared with AT 19;   UT 81 with AT 21, UT 69 with AT 24).

AT 18   Terracotta mould   Athens, Agora T 2572   Agora,   2nd cent. B.C.
                                                              Deposit D 17:11
          H. 0,045 m.
          Mask with wavy hair coming to peak, raised brows, hooked nose (10 rather
          than 13).

AT 19   Terracotta mask   Athens, Agora T 2450   Agora C 16-17
          H. 0,04 m.
          Bald mask with knit brows, eyes outlined with bored pupils (8, 23 or 25).
          Note Probably 2nd cent. B.C.   Cf. DT 12

AT 20   Terracotta statuette   Athens, Agora T 607   Agora F 14   2nd/1st cent.B.C.
          H. 0,057 m.
          Leading slave (22), with wide, rather shallow trumpet, brown hair and beard,
          pink chiton and white himation over left shoulder.

AT 21   Terracotta mask   Athens, Agora T 623   Agora F 14   2nd/1st cent.B.C.
          H. 0,055 m.
          Little hetaira (39); hard rimmed eyes with pierced pupils. Break suggests
          long hair and therefore that this head was female.
          Note Found with Pergamene sherds, cf. Robinson, *Agora V, Roman Pottery*, 11.

AT 22   Terracotta mask   Athens, Agora T 1625   Agora,   1st cent. B.C.
                                                              Cistern N 20:4
          H. 0,057 m.
          Maiden (33).   Long parted hair, sloping brows, red on hair and lips, traces
          of blue in eye.

AT 23   Terracotta   Athens, Agora T 2501   Agora,   Late 2nd
                                                            Fill C 18:3   cent. B.C.
          H. 0,062 m.
          Seated slave (22): peaked speira, eyes not bored, deepish trumpet, right
          elbow rests on left hand, right hand to chin.
          Note Cf. CT 2; DT 19

AT 24   Terracotta   Athens, Agora T 125   Agora G17 (no useful context)
         H. 0,063 m.

         Slave (22) with himation over shoulder: eyes not bored, peaked speira,
         deepish twisted trumpet

AT 25   Terracotta head   Athens, Agora T 2439   Agora C19,   1st cent.B.C./
                                                          post-Sullan drain   1st A.D.
         H. 0,034 m.

         Head with staring pierced eyes, traces of peaked hair, smooth brows: (13)

Vases

AV 1-10   West slope ware.   The Agora examples are securely dated.   AV 3 and 10
           are included because they seem to belong to the same fabric.   The types
           are not later than the first quarter of the third century B.C.   AV 1
           is an old man in the Middle Comedy tradition (mask A) and may in fact
           be taken from a Middle Comedy mould.   AV 5, 6, 10 show clearly the wide
           trumpet mouth of the New Comedy slave.   ZV 3 should be included here
           as it seems to be an Attic import in Tarsus.

Old Men

AV 1   Handle mask   Athens, Agora P 11238   Agora, well at   3rd Cent. B.C.
                                                          B 13:7

         Man with narrow pointed beard (perhaps Middle Comedy A).
         Ref. *W.A.M.*, no.C 10.   Cf. P 50, P 1086, P 16149.
         Note Possibly a Middle Comedy mould is re-used (cf. *Middle Comedy*, AV 2).

AV 2   Handle mask   Athens, Agora P 1443   Agora   3rd cent. B.C.
         Old man's head with full beard (perhaps Papposilenos rather than 3).
         Ref. *W.A.M.*, no.C 15

AV 3   Handle mask   Athens, N.M. (?)   Haliartos   3rd cent. B.C.
         Mask of Pornoboskos (8) from handle.
         Ref. *B.S.A.* 32 (1931-2), 194, fig.9

Slaves

AV 4   Handle mask   Athens, Agora P 6303   Agora, Cistern   275-25 B.C.
                                                          at E 14:1

         Slave with low speira, deepish wide trumpet with raised edges (22)
         Ref. Howland, *Agora IV*, 237; *W.A.M.*, no.C 11.   Cf. P 11234, 26053

AV 5   Handle mask   Athens, Agora P 16243   Agora, Cistern   About 250 B.C.
                                                          at N 21:4
         Wreathed slave with deepish trumpet (?25)
         Ref. *W.A.M.*, no.C 12.   Cf. P 599, 600, 18698, 23080

AV 6   Handle mask   Athens, Agora P 25991   Agora, well   250/200 B.C.
                                                          at F 17:3

        Slave with wide deepish trumpet (?27)
        Ref. W.A.M. no.C 13

AV 7   Handle mask   Athens, Agora P 16245   Agora, cistern   275 B.C.
                                                          filling: N 21:4

        Mask of bald-headed slave (25)
        Ref. W.A.M., no.C 14

AV 8   Handle mask   Athens, N.M. 2310   Athens   3rd cent. B.C.
        Slave mask (22) with large mouth
        Ref. Watzinger, *Ath.Mitt.,* 26 (1901), 79f., 91, no.27,J; cf. Thompson,
            Hesperia, 3 (1934), 315, no.A 32

AV 9   Handle mask   Athens, N.M. 2217   Athens   3rd cent. B.C.
        Slave mask with large mouth
        Ref. Watzinger, *Ath.Mitt.,* 26 (1901), 79f., 94, no.26; cf. Thompson,
            Hesperia, 3 (1934), 332, no.B 4

AV 10   Mask from shoulder of   Cambridge   ? Attica   3rd/2nd cent.
        vase (black glaze out-   B.C.
        side;   red inside)
        H. 0.06 m.

        Wreathed slave with bang of hair over ears; sharp eyelids; wide twisted
        trumpet (25)
        Ref. Perhaps cf. West Slope, H. Thompson, *Hesperia* 3 (1934), no.D 25-6

Groups of Masks

AV 11-24   Megarian bowls. Moulds found in the Pnyx (AV12, 21) prove that these were
           made in Athens. Only one find spot (as also for West Slope ware) is quoted
           for types of which several examples survive. The types are not later than
           the third quarter of the third century B.C., although the vases themselves
           last into the second century. In particular they establish the leading
           old man's mask with full hair, short nose, and a large square beard for
           Attica in the late third century (cf. CS 1, FT 1, NP 19, NS 1, 28 below).

AV 11   Bowl   Athens, Agora P 21045   Agora, Middle Stoa   2nd
                                                          building fill   cent.B.C.

        Fully modelled old man's mask and leading slave mask repeated: 3, 22
        Ref. W.A.M., no.C 24

AV 12   Mould   Athens, Agora,   Pnyx   225/200 B.C.
                                 Pnyx P 280

        Normal old man; girl with parted hair and locks down to chin level: 3, 33
        Ref. G. R. Edwards, *Hesp.Supplt.* 10 (1956), 96, pl.39, no.24; *W.A.M.,*
            no.C 25.   For girl's mask cf. Watzinger, *A.M.,* 26 (1901), 60 n.19.

AV 13   Bowl   Athens, Agora P 20946   Agora, fill over floor   3rd/2nd
                                                                    of square building   cent. B.C.

Leading slave mask (hair striated, deepish smooth trumpet) alternating
with pseudokore mask: 22, 34

Ref. *W.A.M.*, no.C 26

AV 14   Bowl   Athens, Agora, Pnyx P 406   Pnyx   225/200 B.C.

Three slave masks (shock over ears, wide deepish trumpet, twisted) and one
female mask with short hair: 25, 33

Ref. G. R. Edwards, *Hesp.Supplt.* 10 (1956), 98, pl.41, no.47 takes as satyr
      masks. *W.A.M.*, no.C 27

AV 15   Bowl   Athens, Agora P 22191   Agora, brick building   2nd cent.B.C.
                                                                    beneath Stoa of Attalos

Masks of wavy-haired slave, with smooth rimmed trumpet; delicate youth;
wavy-haired old man; and maiden: 27, 13, 4, 33

Ref. *W.A.M.*, no.C 28

    Old Men

AV 16   Bowls.   Athens, Agora, P 65,   Agora, Komos Cistern etc.   225-200 B.C.
                            P 404, P 405, P 4084,
                            P 19780, P 23052

Masks of leading old man (3)

Ref. H. A. Thompson, *Hesperia*, 3 (1934), 356, nos.C 22-3, D 49; *W.A.M.*, nos.
      C 16, 18, 19

AV 17   Bowl   Athens, Agora, Pnyx P 367, P 18666   Pnyx   225/200 B.C.

Square-bearded old man, rather indistinct (3)

Ref. G. R. Edwards, *Hesp.Supplt.*10 (1956), 95, pl.38, 39, 41, nos.22, 23, 25,
      45, 49; *W.A.M.*, no.C 17

AV 18   Bowl   Yale University, 1913.198   ?3rd cent. B.C.

Bearded mask with Erotes (3)

Ref. Baur, *A.J.A.* 45 (1941), 234, pl.13. On dating cf. *Tarsus* I, 30, 159, 163,
      late C III to early C I.

AV 19   Bowl (?)   Madrid 19682

Old man with rich hair and full long beard (4)

Ref. Laumonier, *Terres cuites du Musée archéologique de Madrid*, pl.15

    Slaves

AV 20   Bowl   Athens, Agora P 18663,   Agora, Komos Cistern etc.   225/200 B.C.
                            20986, 24812

Repeated slave masks

Ref. *W.A.M.*, no.C 20

AV 21   Krater mould   Athens, Agora, Pnyx   Pnyx   200/175 B.C.
                               P 345, P 346

Leading slave mask (22): peaked speira, mass of hair over ears, deepish
wide trumpet with raised edges

Ref. G. R. Edwards, *Hesp.Suppl*. 10 (1956), 106, pl.49, no.117-8; *W.A.M.*
        no.C 21

AV 22   Bowl   Athens, Agora P 590   Agora M 16:4   175/150 B.C.

2 masks of slaves (22) with flying Erotes: wideish round trumpet with very
narrow edge.   Hair comes right down over ears; no peak.

Ref. H. A. Thompson, *Hesperia* 3 (1934), 379, D 35; *W.A.M.*, no.C 22

AV 23   Bowl   a) Athens, Agora P 17085   a) Agora, Cistern   200-150 B.C.
                               b) Athens, N.M.   Channel, L-M 19:1

Repeated mask of bald-headed slave (Maison): 25, shock of hair over ears,
deepish rounded trumpet, twisted.

Ref. *W.A.M.*, no.C 23; Watzinger, *A.M.*, 26 (1901), 60, no.20; Simon, 188
        n.11

Note Cf. perhaps DT 7.   Perhaps from same mould as AV 14 above.

AV 24   Bowl   Cambridge, GR 4.1921   ?   250/100 B.C.

Slave mask (22) held by woman: peaked speira, deepish trumpet with raised
edge, raised brows

Ref. *C.V.*, II, pl.29.3; 30.21; p.50, fig.7

Group of Masks

AV 25-33   Braziers.   The commonest masks on terracotta braziers are a) satyr masks
            with wild hair, b) Papposilenos with ivy-wreath, c) head with *pilos* and
            shut mouth, probably Hephaistos.   The animal ears of a) and b) are
            sometimes clearly marked.   Other braziers, however, have comic masks
            and these are included here.   Conze argued that Attica was the centre of
            distribution (see on AV 26) and examples have been found in the Agora
            (H. A. Thompson, *Hesperia* 3 (1934), 392, no.D 76; 421, no.E 150).   A
            firm date about the middle of the 2nd century B.C. is given by the Agora
            examples and by AV 27, 32, 33.   AV 25 has an interesting and unique
            grouping of *agroikos*, *hetairidion*, and 'little housekeeper'.   The style
            is hard; the eyes (of both sexes) are large and rimmed, with pierced
            pupils.   The following detached masks should perhaps have been included
            here: ET 40, TT 12, NT 15, UT 74.

AV 25   Terracotta brazier   Mykonos   Delos, N. of   2nd Cent. B.C.
                                                         Sacred Lake

Masks of Agroikos (14), Hetairidion (39), little housekeeper (30): bored
pupils

Ref. Marcadé, *B.C.H.*, 76 (1952), 623, fig.25; *C.R.A.I.*, 1911, 871; Rumpf,
        A.E., 1953/54, 121ff., interprets as *pseudokore*; *G.T.P.*, no.C 5

Old Men

AV 26   Terracotta mask on brazier   Athens N.M.   Athens   2nd Cent. B.C.

Mask 8; pierced pupils

Ref. Simon 192 n.6a; Konze, *J.d.I.*, 5 (1890), 130, dates mid-second century
and suggests Athens as centre.

AV 27   Terracotta mask on brazier   Mykonos Museum   Delos   2nd cent. B.C.

Mask 8, with elaborate wreath

Ref. Simon 192 n.6a; Konze, *J.d.I.*, 5 (1890), 130, no.821

AV 28   Terracotta mask on brazier   Alexandria   Hadra   2nd cent. B.C.

Mask 8

Ref. *Annuaire du Musée Greco-Romain* III, 1952, pl.xii, 4

AV 29   Terracotta brazier   Syracuse   2nd cent. B.C.

Mask 4: speira with straight furrows, hanging locks, long beard pointed at
the bottom

Ref. Simon 194 n.59; Kekulé, p.53, fig.115

Young Men

AV 30   Low terracotta brazier   Berlin, Terr.   Priene, House   ?2nd cent.
                                            Inv.8661   West of XXII   B.C.

Mask of youth with wavy peaked hair, raised brows, bored pupils, locks below
ears, set in garland

Ref. *Priene*, 319, 461, fig.567, no.212

Slaves

AV 31   Terracotta brazier   Delos   Delos   ?2nd cent.B.C.

Slave masks (27) (but published as satyr masks)

Ref. *Archaeological Reports*, 1958, 14, fig.19; *B.C.H.* 83 (1959),713

AV 32   Terracotta from brazier   Corinth   Corinth,   2nd cent.B.C.
                                                                 South Stoa, Well xix

Slave (27): wavy hair very rough, deep twisted trumpet

Ref. Weinberg, *Hesperia*, 18 (1949), 152, pl.17 no.23

Note Dated 205-150 B.C. by coins of Ptolemy V and VI

Women

AV 33   Terracotta brazier   Delos B 7372   Delos, House   2nd cent.B.C.
                                                                 of the Herm

Mask 33, with shortish hair, smooth brows, bored pupils, set in a garland

Ref. J. Marcadé, *B.C.H.*, 77 (1953), 584 fig.77; p.512 gives inscription of
88 B.C.; p.602, unguentaria; p.596, amphora stamps 150/100 B.C.

Vases: Late Hellenistic from the Agora

AV 34   Terracotta mask   Athens, Agora P 19991   Agora, Area D 17

H. 0,030 m.

Slave mask with wreath (22): speira, wide trumpet. Yellow buff clay,
probably ornament on a pot.

Note Probably 2nd cent. B.C.

AV 35   Terracotta mask   Athens, Agora P 4199   Agora, Area C-G 13-16   2nd/1st
                                                                                    cent.B.C.
H. 0,030 m.

Slave mask with wreath; probably not bald; wide, twisted, shallow trumpet.
Grey ware, black glaze

Ref.   cf. H. A. Thompson, *Hesperia*, 3 (1934), 426; H. Robinson, *Agora V*;
         Roman Pottery, 13

AV 36   Terracotta mask   Athens, Agora T 3441   Agora, Area I 11
          from utensil

H. 0,053 m.

Comic Slave (22): coarse reddish clay, reddish glaze; outlined bulbous
eyes, raised brows, peaked speira, deepish trumpet.

BOEOTIA

Terracottas

BT 1-18   1-3 are well dated by find-spot.   1 confirms the wearing of knee-length
            chiton by youth and slave very early in the New Comedy period; the group
            is a most interesting anticipation of the marble relief in Napes (below
            NS 25).   4-7 are reliably dated by style and should not be much later
            than the Attic group AT 11-16.   The treatment of the eyes (cf. above on
            AT 2) in 3 and 4 is repeated by ET 11 and ST 25, which should therefore
            be contemporary.   7 belongs to a recognizable group of Tanagra figures;
            the provenance and dating of 8-13, 18 is much less certain.   10 and 11
            have even heavier lids and longer, narrower eyes than 5; but they must
            be male, 10 because of the raised eyebrows, 11 because of the cap hair.
            18 is the not very common *agroikos* mask.

            Doubts have been expressed as to whether the masks associated with
            14-17 are genuine or belong to the figures (14, the mask looks later, 15,
            the mask is a forgery); the figures themselves appear to be Tanagra
            statuettes of the third century B.C.   In the late Hellenistic and Roman
            period (MT 7, 44, NT 10, AT 51, ZT 55, NB 9, NS 26, UB, 28, IS 22), as in
            Early Hellenistic jewellery (AJ 1-2), the association of a boy or Eros
            with a mask is found, and for this reason these figures are included
            here.

BT 1   Terracotta group   Thebes   Halai, Boeotia   335/280 B.C.
                                                   (Grave 29)

         H. 0,125 m.

         Youth with wavy hair, large nose, hand over head, knee-length chiton,
         supported by small slave in thigh-length chiton

         Ref. H. Goldman and F. Jones, *Hesperia* XI (1942), 409, pl.23

BT 2   Terracotta mask   Thebes   Halai, Boeotia   335/280 B.C.
                                                   (outside Grave 244)

         H. 0,078 m.

         Slave: deep rounded trumpet, bald, with ivy wreath: mask 25

         Ref. H. Goldman and F. F. Jones, *Hesperia* XI (1942), 409, pl.20; *P.C.F.*,
              fig.91; *G.T.P.*, no.C 52

BT 3   Terracotta   Unknown   From Elatea,   3rd cent. B.C.
                                                   Temple of Athena Kranaa

         H. 0,045 m.

         Delicate youth (16?): rimmed eyes, *not* bored;   smooth brows;   remains of
         hair below ears

         Ref. P. Paris, *B.C.H.*, 11 (1887), 406, 443, pl.3 fig.10; *G.T.P.*, no.C 55

         Note A Middle Comedy statuette (Middle Comedy, BT 13) comes from the same
              deposit,   Like BT 4.

BT 4   Terracotta mask   Athens, N.M.   Thebes Kabeirion

         Delicate youth (16?); large, rimmed eyes, even brows

         Ref. Germ.Inst. neg. Kab.317; Wrede, *A.M.* 53 (1928), 91.

         Note Early Hellenistic. Like BT 3

BT 5   Terracotta mask   Athens, N.M.   Thebes Kabeirion

         Hair broken off, but probably 15: largeish nose, raised brows, wreath

         Ref. Germ.Inst. neg. Kab.317; Wrede, *A.M.* 53 (1928), 91.

         Note Early Hellenistic.   Cf. AT 12

BT 6   Terracotta head   Athens, N.M.   Thebes Kabeirion

         Lampadion head (42)

         Ref. Germ.Inst. neg. Kab.383; Winter, *T.K.*, 421/6.

         Note Early Hellenistic.   (Earlier than DT 2)

BT 7   Terracotta statuette   London, British Museum C 309   ? Tanagra

         H. 0,212 m.

         Muse carrying mask of first pseudo-kore (34)

         Ref. Walters, *Catalogue*, no.C 309.

         Note Early Hellenistic

BT 8   Terracotta statuette   Bonn D 5   Boeotia

H. 0,15 m.

Slave with child: mask 22.   Peaked hair;   goggle eyes;   semicircular
trumpet;   short chiton

Ref. Bieber, *D* no.89b pl.73/2;   *H.T.*[2], fig.152;   Winter, 423/9;   *P.C.F.*,
fig.121

Note Early Hellenistic

BT 9   Terracotta mask   Berlin 7589   Tanagra

H. 0,095 m.

Mask 6 with pointed hat

Ref. Simon 193 n.32;   Robert, fig.38

Note Probably third century.   Cf. eyes with BT 4.   Survival of Middle
Comedy, Mask A

BT 10   Terracotta mask   Vienna 1898   Boeotia

H. 0,053 m.

Youth (15)? Fat face;   raised brows, evanescent eyes;   elaborate wreath
with hair descending below it

Note Perhaps 2nd cent. B.C.   Cf. DT 1

BT 11   Terracotta mask   Vienna 1552   ? Tanagra

H. 0,047 m.

Youth (13):   cap hair with peak;   evanescent eyes

Note Probably Early Hellenistic

BT 12   Terracotta mask   Copenhagen, NC. Inv.911   ? Tanagra

Young episeistos (16) with wreath: fat face, bored pupils, smooth brows,
hair descending below wreath

Ref. V. Poulsen, *Terres Cuites*, pl.31, 49

BT 13   Terracotta mask   Copenhagen, N.M.5390   Thebes, (acquired in Athens)

H. 0,067 m.

Smooth brows, large outlined eyes;   peaked striated speira falling to level
of ears (11)

Ref. Breitenstein, no.538, takes as concubine

BT 14   Terracotta statuette   Leiden I 98/5 no.6   ? Tanagra

H. 0,148 m.

Boy with wreath in longish chiton, seated on altar, holding mask of wavy-
haired old man (4)

Ref. Anita Klein, *Child Life*, pl.18c and note 222 gives other examples.

Note For the mask cf. TT 3, it should perhaps be regarded as a satyr.

BT 15   Terracotta statuette   Vienna, 1261   Tanagra

H. 0,16 m.

Youth holding mask of slave (27)

Ref. Winter, *T.K.*, 243/1; *Arch.Ep.Mitt.Ost.* 3 (1879), 131 f.

Note Mask almost certainly a forgery

BT 16   Terracotta statuette   Copenhagen 3255   Tanagra (acquired in Athens)

H. 0,140 m.

Standing boy in wreath with bearded mask, slave of late C IV type

Ref. Breitenstein no.555

BT 17   Terracotta statuette   Cambridge, Fogg Museum, Kahnweiler 33

Eros seated with cock and comic mask with swung brows and pointed beard beside him (?27). (Very pale clay)

BT 18   Terracotta mask   Paris, Louvre MNB 506   Tanagra

Youth (14) with striated peaked speira, hard brows, bulbous eyes, small nose

Note Early Hellenistic?

CORINTH

Jewellery

CJ 1   Bronze mirror   BM 295   Corinth   Early 3rd cent. B.C.

Muse with slave mask (27) and Eros

Ref. Züchner, *Klappspiegel*, no.144 fig.48; *G.T.P.*, no.C 53

Lamps

CL 1   Terracotta lamp   Corinth 837   Corinth   Early 1st cent. B.C.

Mask 8: shock of hair at either side, big beard slightly pointed (?). Grey clay; black glaze

Ref. Broneer, *Corinth*, IV, 2, no.335, figs.30, 88.

Note Type XIX. Probably import from Asia Minor

Sculpture

CS 1   Marble statue   Corinth C.S.13   Corinth

Muse seated with old man's mask (3) on her left knee; crook in right hand

Ref. *Corinth* IX, 24, no.13. Cf. Zagreb, Reinach *RS*, IV, 179,3. Cf. Bie in Roscher sv. *Musen*

Note Probably copy of an original of the late 4th cent. B.C.

Terracottas

Only 1 and 2 come from excavations in Corinth

CT 1   Terracotta statuette   Corinth Museum   Corinth   250 B.C.
                                  1904   Deposit VI

H. 0,141 m.

Actor holding kore mask (33), draped for playing female part

Ref. *Corinth* XII, no.336, photo.3651; G. R. Davidson, *Hesperia* 11 (1942),
        117, no.44

CT 2   Terracotta statuette   Corinth Museum 4234   Corinth

H. 0,04 m.

Wavy-haired slave wrapped in cloak, deepish rounded trumpet with narrow
flat edges, raised brows;   right hand clasping left arm (27)

Ref. *Corinth* XII, no.427, photo.4271

Note Not before first century B.C.   Cf. AT 24

CT 3   Terracotta statuette   Berlin 7644   Corinth

H. 0,10 m.

Old man, bald-headed, long himation, right hand wrapped in it

Ref. Robert, fig.43; *T.K.*, 420/4

Note Perhaps Early Hellenistic.   Survival of Middle Comedy, Mask F.

CT 4   Terracotta mask   Athens NM   Corinth

H. 0,6 m.

Mask (9): wreath with depressed dots, swung brows, bulbous eyes

Ref. Simon 192 n.12; Martha 529, pl.VI,6.

Note Survival of Middle Comedy, Mask F

MAINLAND GREECE

Terracottas

XT 1-24   Other mainland terracottas (Corfu is included as belonging to the
           West of Greece rather than to the Cyclades, and in any case the Corfu
           attributions mark the place of collection rather than the find spot).
           The provenances are certain except for 8, 9, 16, 17, for which they
           are very doubtful;   they are only included here because of these
           doubtful provenances.   8 and 9, which are known in several copies,
           are not unlike the early group of Myrina terracottas;   they continue
           in an altered form the Middle Comedy tradition of cooks and porters.
           21-22 are a pair;   these masks on disks are otherwise known from
           Italy (IT 38 etc.) and some are much later;   but the disk MT 23 should
           be 2nd cent. B.C.   The early seated slave in Cambridge (UT 36) may
           belong here;   UT 76 is not unlike XT 13.

XT 1   Terracotta plaque   Kavalla   Amphipolis
         0,10 x 0,10 m.

         Masks: old man with slightly peaked striated speira, uneven brows, full
         straight beard (3); first pseudokore (34); slave (27?) with straight,
         striated hair, pointed trumpet; youth with striated hair falling to ears,
         raised brows (?10); girl with short parted hair (33); old woman with
         confused hair and haggard cheeks (?36)

         Ref. *To Ergon*, 1958, 74; *B.C.H.*, 83 (1959), 711, fig.4

         Note Early Hellenistic

XT 2   Terracotta statuettes   Kavalla   Amphipolis

         Three examples of slaves seated on square altar with hands folded and
         crossed legs: peaked speira, oval trumpet with a distinct point (27?)

         Ref. *To Ergon*, 1959, 39, fig.37; *B.C.H.*, 84 (1960), fig.2

         Note Not before 2nd cent. B.C.

XT 3   Terracotta statuette   Kavalla   Amphipolis

         Slave standing wrapped in cloak, right hand to mouth, chiton girt below
         fat stomach: receding peaked hair with shock over ears, deep rounded
         trumpet (22)

         Ref. *To Ergon*, 1959, 39, fig.37; *B.C.H.*, 84 (1960), fig.2

XT 4   Terracotta mask   London, British   Corfu?
                                 Museum, C 46

         Flatterer (17): red clay; pupils and iris depressed; swung brows; hard
         modelling of brows and hair

         Ref. Walters, *Catalogue*, 192

         Note Probably 2nd cent. B.C.

XT 5   Terracotta head   London, British   Corfu?
                                 Museum, C 45
         H. 0,81 m.

         Hetaira (39): elaborate wreath with ivy leaves, hair falling in locks in
         front of ears; head completely closed

         Ref. Walters, *Catalogue*, 192

         Note Early Hellenistic

XT 6   Terracotta mask   Delphi   Delphi

         Mask (41): hair in *sphendone*; depressed pupils, round face

         Ref. Simon 197 n.50; *Fouilles de Delphes*, V, XXIV, 2, 206 n.684

         Note Early Hellenistic

XT 7   Terracotta mask   Epidaurus   ?Epidaurus

         Leading old man (3)

XT 8   Terracotta   a) Berlin 7042   Megara
                            b) Cambridge GR 85d 1937

H. 0,15 m.

Maison with basket containing goose (25): bored pupils, semicircular trumpet

Ref. a) Robert, fig. 24; Bieber, *H.T.*[1] fig. 98; *H.T.*[2] fig. 156; *D.*, no. 86;
            P.C.F., fig. 81; *G.T.P.*, no. C 56
        b) *Burlington Fine Arts Club*, pl. 84, fig. 77; Simon 188, n. 1b

Note Late third to early second century B.C.

XT 9   Terracotta statuette a) Berlin 7087   a) Megara
                       b) Vienna Inv. 1287   b) Athens
                       c) London, V.& A. 617/84 c) Tanagra

Porter with bedding on shoulders: mask 25

Ref. Bieber, *D.* no. 88; Winter, *T.K.* 415/1; Simon 188, n. 2

Note Not before 2nd cent. B.C.

XT 10 Terracotta mask   D.M. Robinson collection   Mekyberna

H. 0,44 m.

Wavy hair, perhaps with wreath, raised eyebrows, sharp eyelids, well-modelled fattish face (15)

Ref. *Olynthus* XIV, pl. 37, no. 94 and pl. 39, no. 110

Note Early Hellenistic. Very like AT 12

XT 11 Terracotta mask   Nessebur (Bulgaria)   Messembria

Pan: raised brows; roughly striated hair; small beard

Ref. *Bulgaria To-day* 1960, 4, 30

Note Perhaps 3rd cent. B.C.

XT 12 Terracotta mask   Nessebur (Bulgaria)   Messembria

Wavy-haired slave (27): roughly striated hair; deep smooth trumpet, swung brows; bulbous, rimmed eyes

Ref. *Bulgaria To-day* 1960, 4, 30

Note Perhaps 3rd cent. B.C.

XT 13 Terracotta mask   Nauplia 14228 (5932) ?   ?

Mask 27: staring eyes, *not* bored; wavy hair; semicircular smooth trumpet

Note Perhaps 3rd cent. B.C.

XT 14 Terracotta mask   Nauplia 14229 (3441)   ?

Mask 10: sharpish eyelids, *not* bored; raised brows; striated front edge to speira

XT 15 Terracotta head   Nauplia 3289   ? Asine

Leading slave with wreath; small eyes, wide apart, deepish trumpet.
Pink clay (22)

XT 16   Terracotta statuette   Munich, S.L.190(?)   Greece

Slave; smooth hair; small bulbous eyes; very deep, smooth trumpet (22): right hand in mouth; himation over shoulder

Ref. Sammlung Loeb, II, pl.79

XT 17   Terracotta mask   Copenhagen ABb 327   ?Greece

H. 0,079 m.

Slave mask with bored eyes wide apart; wide twisted trumpet(?22). Broken off above forehead

Ref. Breitenstein, no.629

Note Perhaps 2nd cent. B.C.

XT 18   Terracotta mask   Berlin   Dardanelles

H. 0,055 m.

Mask 27 with *pilos*

Ref. Simon 193 n.33, compares YT 10; Robert fig.16

Note Probably 2nd cent. B.C.

XT 19   Terracotta statuette   Sarajevo   ?Thrace

Slave with shortish hair (22)

Ref. Bulanda, fig.58, no.169

Note Probably 2nd cent. B.C.

XT 20   Terracotta mask   Athens N.M.76039   Thrace
                                     (Stamboule collection)

Girl with parted hair (?44)

Note Probably 2nd cent. B.C.

XT 21   Terracotta mask on disk   Berlin 6623   Selymbria

Mask (12): high speira of corkscrew locks, corkscrew locks below, smooth brows.   Pairs with XT 22

Ref. Simon 182 n.24d; Bieber *D.* no.67; *R.B.* xxix, 128 no.12; *P.C.F.*, fig.55a; *G.T.P.*, no.C 67a

Note Late Hellenistic

XT 22   Terracotta mask on disk   Berlin 6622   Selymbria

Mask 41: small corkscrew locks below parted hair.   Pairs with XT 21

Ref. Simon 197 n.66, pl.VI/2; *B.D.* no.67; *P.C.F.*, fig.55b; *G.T.P.*, no.67b

Note Late Hellenistic

XT 23   Terracotta mask   Paris, Louvre C.A.1941   Greece

Large, wreathed mask: swinging brows, pierced pupils; completely flat, narrow trumpet with sharp corners (?22)

Ref. Musée Guimet Exhibition, 224

Note Not clear whether this is slave or satyr.   For stylization of trumpet cf. NP 4, 13, 22.   Probably Roman.

XT 24   Terracotta mask   Paris, Louvre C.A.2299   Kertch

Kore with ornament at parting of long hair; eyes pierced; closed
mouth (perhaps not dramatic).   Orange, red clay

Ref. Musée Guimet Exhibition, 226

Note Probably Roman

DELOS

Lamps

DL 1   Terracotta lamp lid   Delos A 1713   Delos, street E. of
H. 0,04 m.   Sanctuary of Apollo

Mask with pointed beard: perhaps 27

Ref. *Delos* 23, no.1285

Note Cf. D. B. Thompson, *Gnomon* 31 (1959), 636 on lamp lids.
Probably 1st cent. B.C.

DL 2   Terracotta lamp lid   Delos A 719   Delos
H. 0,04 m.

Slave mask (22): striated speira down below ears; bored pupils;
striated semicircular trumpet

Ref. *Delos* 23, no.1286

DL 3   Terracotta lamp lid   Delos A 6690   Delos, high valley of
                                                    Inopos
H. 0,04 m.

Slave mask (22): speira; bored pupils

Ref. *Delos* 23, no.1287

Note Perhaps same mould as DL 2

DL 4   Terracotta lamp lid   Delos A 3973   Delos, N.E. of Museum
H. 0,035 m.

Slave mask (25): wreath, probably bald, wide, flat trumpet, squashed
nose

Ref. *Delos* 23, no.1288.   Cf. AV 34-5

Mosaics

DM 1-2   The Maison des Masques is dated early in the second century B.C.
The house may have been used as a meeting place for theatrical companies.
The masks show how standardized practice had become and corroborate the
view that Pollux' list derives from a good Hellenistic source.   The
leading old man (3) has the differentiation of brows indicated by a sharp
nick in the line of the brows, which does not appear in the old men's
masks on Megarian bowls but is seen on an old man from Ruvo (TT 19) and

on some leading slave masks (e.g. DT 10).   Both old men have a full
square beard as on the Megarian bowls.   The wavy-haired slave (27)
has a deeper, shaggier trumpet than the leading slave.   The pornoboskos
is noticeably like a Papposilenos (cf. above on braziers).   The young
men have staring eyes and haggard cheeks as in some of the terracottas
(e.g. DT 4, 5).

DM 1   Mosaic masks   Delos   Delos, House of masks   Early 2nd.
                                                                                 cent.B.C.

Masks 3, 4, 8, 11, 16, 22, 27, 29, Pan, Satyr.   The masks from the borders
of a mosaic carpet, at one end 27, 29, Pan, 16, 3;   at the other Satyr, 11,
4, 8, 22

Ref. Simon 93; 192 n.9;   184 n.82c;   190 n.43b;   191 n.64a;   193 n.47;
        194 n.61;   199 n.11; Chamonard, *Delos*, XIV, pl.IV/VI;   *G.T.P.*, no.
        C 61a

DM 2   Mosaic   Delos   Delos, House of masks   Early 2nd
                                                                                 cent.B.C.

Slave (25) in wreath, yellow himation, blue chiton, dancing before flute
player on rock

Ref. Chamonard, *Delos*, XIV, pl.VII;   *G.T.P.*, no.C 61 b

Terracottas

DT 1-28 The terracottas are divided into 1-16 dated by their find spot, 17-28
            undated.   The undated terracottas are unlikely to be after 69 B.C.
            when Delos was enslaved by pirates.   2-3, 27 are large wall-masks like
            those from Priene (ZT 20-24) etc.   DT 17 is the soldier (see Introduction).
            The soldier's slave is bearded and wears the *causia* (DT 22).   The not
            very numerous figurines may be divided into two main types: stout and
            lively like early and 2nd century Myrina (4, 17, 20, 21), meagre and dull
            like 1st century Myrina and Athens (6, 19).   10 and 23 probably come from
            vases, but it seemed unnecessary to make a separate category DV,   parti-
            cularly as braziers found in Delos have been included under AV;   these two
            heads may be compared to AV 34-5.

            The early terracottas have affinities with UT 47.   The 2nd century
            terracottas have affinities with UT 12, 58, 82, 83, 92, 94;   the 1st
            century terracottas with UB 3, 8, 30, UT 37, 38, 42, 62, 63, 68, 75.   These
            affinities may be no more than an indication of date for the terracottas
            and bronzes of unknown origin.

    a) Dated

DT 1   Terracotta mask   Delos A 930   Delos: Kabeirion   Early 2nd
            H. 0,075 m.   cent.B.C.

            Broken: could be *kore* or *hapalos*, probably *kore* (33)

            Ref. Delos 23, no.1240, takes as *kore*

DT 2   Terracotta mask   Delos A 3302   Delos, house to   2nd cent.B.C.
                                                   E. of house of columns

H. 0,155 m.

Young hetaira with *tainion* (39)

Ref. *Delos* 23, no.1235; wall mask. Compares DT 25. Cf. also AT 9, BT 6

DT 3   Terracotta mask   Delos A 3301   Delos, house E.   2nd cent.B.C.
                                                   of house of columns

H. 0,11 m.

Mask wreathed; ?*hapalos* (13)

Ref. *Delos* 23, no.1236, belongs to preceding: takes as feminine.   Cf.
        no.1237, from road near Apollo sanctuary.   Perhaps cf. BT 12

DT 4   Terracotta statuette   Delos A 3348,3374   Delos, cistern in   After 166 B.C.
                                                   Establishment of
H. a) 0,075 m.   Poseidoniastai
    b) 0,03 m. (head only)

Figure with long hair, in himation and chiton with short sleeves; right hand
on chest; peaked hair with long falling locks; eyes rimmed with depressed
pupils.   Probably Mask 16

Ref. *Delos* 23, nos.1217, 1218, well compares Bieber, *D.*, no.141 = MT 20.
        On date, *Delos* 23, 26.   Cf. also AT 18

DT 5   Terracotta mask   Delos A 3376   Delos, Establishment   After 166 B.C.
                                                   of Poseidoniastai
H. 0,085 m.

Head with long hair; raised swinging brows; bored pupils; hollow cheeks.
Perhaps Mask 15

Ref. *Delos* 23, no.1233, takes as either freedman or old man (Bieber, *D.*,pl.25/1)

Note The haggard face, however, can be seen on the mosaic.   Probably too much
       hair for the *Kolax* 17; therefore the first *Episeistos* (15)

DT 6   Terracotta statuette   Delos A 3320   Delos, room of   After 166 B.C.
                                                   Poseidoniastai
H. 0,123 m.

Slave (22) seated on square altar with *os columnatum*, right elbow on left hand.
Smooth hair, deepish round trumpet.   Square vent.

Ref. *Delos* 23, no.1219.   Cf. also AT 23

DT 7   Terracotta mask   Delos A 3943   Delos, E. of wall   About 100 B.C.
                                                   of Triarius
H. 0,06 m.

Bald, swinging, joined brows, protruding eyes.   Shock of hair.   (Nothing
preserved below eyes)

Ref. *Delos* 23, no.1234

Note Unclear whether *pornoboskos* (8) or *maison* (25): cf. AV 23

DT 8   Terracotta head   Delos A 3893   Delos, E. of wall   About 100 B.C.
                                                   of Triarius
H. 0,028 m.

Head of slave, perh. 22: straight hair line, semicircular trumpet

Ref. *Delos* 23, no.1227

71

DT 9   Terracotta head   Delos A 3941   Delos, E. of wall   About 100 B.C.
                                                   of Triarius
        H. 0,027 m.

        Head of slave, with *speira* and rather pointed trumpet (27)

        Ref. *Delos* 23, no.1228.   Cf. DT 22 below

DT 10   Terracotta mask   Delos A 3942   Delos, E. of wall   About 100 B.C.
        (from vase?)   of Triarius

        H. 0,065 m.

        Head of slave with wreath: striated hair behind wreath, uneven brows with
        sharp nick to right of nose, deepish rounded trumpet (22)

        Ref. *Delos* 23, no.1231 says *oulos* cf. Robert, fig.37.   Cf. also AV 6

DT 11   Head of terracotta   Delos A 3940   Delos, E. of wall   About 100 B.C.
        statuette   of Triarius

        H. 0,024 m.

        Slave (27)

        Ref. *Delos* 23, no.1223

        Note Note likeness to DT 19

DT 12   Terracotta mask   Delos A 3650   Delos, Road of Stadium   Not before
                                                                          100 B.C.
        H. 0,08 m.

        Head of slave: very fierce brows;   semicircular trumpet mouth;   bored pupils,
        squinting (25)

        Ref. *Delos* 23, no.1232, takes as *pornoboskos*;   but the beard is too short.
             Cf. AT 19, MT 30

DT 13   Terracotta mask   Delos A 3639   Delos, Road of Stadium   Not before
                                                                          100 B.C.
        H. 0,058 m.

        Broken: bored eyes: hetaira rather than *hapalos*

        Ref. *Delos* 23, no.1241.   Cf. AT 21

DT 14   Head of terracotta   Delos A 3453   Delos, Agora of Italians   After 100 B.C.
        statuette   (not after 69 B.C.)

        H. 0,06 m.

        Slave (?25), head turned to right;   bald;   shock of hair over ears;   semicircular
        smooth trumpet

        Ref. *Delos* 23, no.1220, compares Bieber, *D.*, no.154 = MT 30.   Cf rather AT 23

DT 15   Terracotta head   Delos A 3455   Delos: W. of Agora   ?100-69 B.C.
                                                   of Italians

        H. 0,035 m.

        Head of slave, very rough.   Smooth hair;   wideish trumpet with upper side twisted.
        Perhaps 22

        Ref. *Delos* 23, no.1226.

        Note For style cf. above DT 6.   Not unlike AV 4

DT 16   Terracotta mask   Delos A 2478   Delos: N.E. of *analemma*   ?1st cent.B.C.
                                                  of the theatre

H. 0,055 m.

Fragment of head with raised brows and marked pupils

Ref. Delos 23, no.1248.

Note Probably like DT 12

b) Undated: Youths

DT 17   Terracotta   Mykonos 147 (50)   Delos

Soldier (15): pseudo-onkos with wavy hair falling below chin level; contorted
brows; sleeves; chlamys pinned on right shoulder; girt chiton; sandals

Ref. Bieber, *D.* no.57; *H.T.*, fig.207; Rumpf, in *Mimus u. Logos,* 164; *P.C.F.,*
        fig.50; *G.T.P.,* no.C 62; Laumonier, *Delos* 23, no.1216.

Note Not before 2nd century

DT 18   Terracotta mask   Delos A 3642   Delos

H. 0,035 m.

Broken: pricked pupils, hard lids, smooth brows: 13 or 16

Ref. Delos 23, no.1242, takes as feminine, but eyes are too wide open

Note For eyes cf. ST 13 and YT 9

Slaves

DT 19   Terracotta statuette Delos A 2079   Delos
                               Delos (unnumbered)

H. 0,09 m.
Head of statuette, H. 0,025 m.

Slave (?27), very wide mouth, short chiton, himation over left shoulder, held
out by right hand

Ref. Delos 23, no.1221, 1222

Note Likeness to DT 11 suggests a date early in the 1st century B.C.   For
        proportions cf. AT 23 etc.

DT 20   Terracotta statuette Delos A 2077   Delos, theatre

H. 0,075 m.

Bald old slave with large ears and short chiton: himation over left shoulder

Ref. Delos 23, no.1224, cf. Winter, *T.K.* 433/3 (caricature); Robert, 18,
        fig.38

Note Perhaps Early Hellenistic

DT 21   Terracotta statuette Delos A 2007   Delos, West of the Lake

H. 0,11 m.

Man (headless) with heavy girding of himation round middle; wineskin or
bundle round shoulders held by both hands

Ref. Delos 23, no.1225

DT 22   Terracotta head   Delos A 3701   Delos

H. 0,03 m.

Head of slave with deep trumpet (27) wearing *causia*

Ref. *Delos* 23, no.1229

Note Very like DT 9.   Cf. *W.A.M.*, n.46 on *causia*

DT 23   Terracotta mask (from vase?)   Delos A 3759   Delos: S. of Hera sanctuary

H. 0,035 m.

Head of slave (27): striated hair with shock over ears, wide trumpet with
top edge twisted.   Yellow brown clay

Ref. *Delos* 23, no.1230

DT 24   Terracotta mask   Delos A 1977   Sanctuary of Hagne Aphrodite

H. 0,045 m.

Fragmentary nose

Ref. *Delos* 23, no.1243

Note Perhaps tragic?

Women

DT 25   Terracotta mask   Berlin 5165   Delos

H. 0,115 m.

Mask (?42) with hair knotted at back of head and handkerchief round it

Ref. Simon 120, 196 n.37; Robert, fig.77; *Delos* 23, 265, pl.106, 8

Note Perhaps Early Hellenistic

DT 26   Terracotta mask   Delos A 613   Delos, N. of Sanctuary of
                                                             Apollo
H. 0,11 m.

Wreathed hetaira mask, fattish face, snub nose: perhaps mask no.44

Ref. *Delos* 23, no.1238

DT 27   Terracotta mask   Mykonos 155 (62)   Rheneia

H. 0,07 m.

Wreathed hetaira: fat face, perhaps mask no.38

Ref. *Delos* 23, no.1239

Note Suspended against wall, like DT 2-3.   *Delos* takes as procuress.
          Style very like DT 1

DT 28   Terracotta mask   Delos A 1867   South of *oikos* of Naxians

H. 0,035 m.

Female head with longish hair, parted: pierced pupils, incised outline (33)

Ref. *Delos* 23, no.1247, takes as *kore*, comparing Winter, *T.K.* 421/6 = BT 6

CYPRUS

Lamps

KL 1   Terracotta lamp   Nicosia, Cyprus Museum, J 3347   Cyprus

Relief, leading slave mask (22) on body of lamp: peaked speira, wide shallow rounded trumpet

Ref. Cf. Howland, *Agora Lamps*, Type 46

Note Probably 2nd cent. B.C.

Terracottas

KT 1   Terracotta statuette   Nicosia, Cyprus   Cyprus
    1934-vii-12-3

Pornoboskos (8): rimmed eyes, wreath, elaborate cloak

Ref. G.T.P., no.C 58

Note Early Hellenistic

KT 2   Terracotta mask   London, British   Salamis, Cyprus
    Museum, A 436

Second Episeistos (16); small and very fine: pierced pupils, smooth brows

Ref. Walters, *Catalogue*, 66

Note Probably 2nd cent. B.C.

KT 3   Terracotta head   Nicosia, Cyprus   Cyprus
    D212, 1935

Slave (22) with twisted eyebrows; cap hair; bulbous eyes with depressed pupils; deep trumpet nearly pointed

Note Probably Early Hellenistic

KT 4   Terracotta head   Nicosia, Cyprus Museum   Salamis theatre

Both brows raised and furrowed; pupils flat; wavy hair, striated pointed trumpet (27 rather than 4)

Ref. V. Karageorghis, *B.C.H.*, 84 (1960), 288 fig.66

Note Probably 2nd cent. B.C.

KT 5   Terracotta mask   Bowdoin College   Salamis, Cyprus
    WAB. 1902, 42
H. 0,045 m.

Ivy wreath: hair with striations which run round forehead (22?). Deepish trumpet beard

Ref. K. Herbert, *C.J.* 55 (1959), 98, fig.13

Note Published as satyr mask. Probably 2nd cent. B.C.

KT 6   Terracotta mould   Nicosia, Cyprus   Cyprus
    1939 ix-27-4

Wimpled hetaira (41)

Note Early Hellenistic. Style not unlike AT 9

OTHER ISLANDS

Amphora handle

YA 1   Benachi Collection   Cos

Gem impression of slave (25?)

Terracottas

YT 1-12   Even where provenances are safe, local manufacture is not certain.
4 may be a slave with a deep trumpet rather than an old man.   11
is a young man walking (perhaps mask 10) and 12 a slave with fat
legs; both seem to come from weak moulds; the conception should
be Early Hellenistic.   The attitude of YT 11 is not unlike that of
NT 27.

YT 1   Terracotta head   London, British Museum,   Kalymnos
                                 C 469

H. 0,091 m.

First pseudo-kore (34), ivy wreath, eyebrows and eyelashes black.
Pink clay

Ref. Walters, *Catalogue*, 234

Note Probably Early Hellenistic.   (Cf. also below YT 11 and 12 from
Kalymnos.)

YT 2   Terracotta statuette   Athens N.M.3983   Eretria

H. 0,20 m.

Youth wrapped in large cloak

Ref. Simon 182 n.26d; Winter, *T.K.*, 429/2:

Note Replica of MT 17.   Head with smooth speira does not belong.
Probably 2nd century B.C.

YT 3   Terracotta statuette   Athens, N.M.4794 (P 1956)   Eretria   ?

Slave seated on altar with volutes; head wreathed; semicircular trumpet;
elaborate folds between legs (25?)
Note Same body as London, 1910.1.6.16, *P.C.F.*, fig.134

YT 4   Terracotta mask   London B.M. C81   Melos

H. 0,124 m.

Bearded mask (27) with dotted wreath, short pointed beard striated;
globular rimmed eyes; knotted brows

Ref. *P.C.F.*, fig.136

Note Cf. perhaps AT 1 or AT 5.   Early Hellenistic

YT 5   Terracotta   Berlin 5166   Melos

Mask of slave (27): peaked striated hair; bored pupils; semicircular striated
Ref. Bieber, *H.T.*[1], fig.267; *D.*, pl.105/2, no.169   trumpet

Note ?Late 2nd cent. B.C.

YT 6   Terracotta statuette   Copenhagen 483   Melos (acquired in Athens)
        H. 0,091 m.

        Seated slave, face very distorted and unclear;   square altar;   left hand
        on seat, right hand against breast

        Ref. Breitenstein, no.618

        Note Late Hellenistic.   Cf. AT 23

YT 7   Terracotta statuette   Copenhagen, NM,   ?Rhodes
                                  Inv.7658

        Man in sleeved chiton with big himation over it: *no* head

        Ref. Breitenstein, no.324

        Note Probably 2nd cent. B.C.

YT 8   Terracotta head   Copenhagen, NM   Rhodes
                                  Inv.7658

        Head with very full hair above forehead, pointed beard

        Ref. Breitenstein, no.324

        Note Head does not belong to body but is similar fabric.   Early Hellenistic.
               Perhaps survival of Middle Comedy type AA.

YT 9   Terracotta mask   Thera   Thera   3rd/2nd cent.B.C.
        Mask 16:   elaborate wreath;   eyes rimmed, very full wavy hair below ears

        Ref. Simon 186 n.128b;   *Thera*, III, fig.168 and p.172

        Note Context contained good Hellenistic terracottas.   Probably Early
               Hellenistic

YT 10   Terracotta head   Thera   Thera
        Mask (27?):   pointed hat.   Depressed pupils, deep trumpet *not* striated

        Ref. Simon 193 n.33, cf. XT 18;   *Thera*, III, 178 fig.180/1

        Note No context.   Probably Early Hellenistic

YT 11   Terracotta statuette   London, B.M.,C 476   Kalymnos   ?2nd cent. B.C.
        H. 0,205 m.

        Young man with speira (probably 10) walking in cloak draped over left shoulder.
        Pink clay

        Ref. Walters, *Catalogue.*

        Note Worn example: draping of cloak like MT 20 and NT 27;   head like MT 21

YT 12   Terracotta statuette   London, B.M.   Kalymnos   ?2nd cent. B.C.
                                  56.8.26.245

        Head missing.   Man walking, himation down to knees;   fat legs.   Probably
        slave

Vases

YV 1   Relief hydria   Brussels R 408   ?Crete   3rd cent. B.C.
       Kore mask (33)
       Ref. *C.V.* Brussels, Belgium, pl.47/2

YV 2   Terracotta vase (?)   London, B.M.,C 420   Mytilene
       H. 0,0445 m.
       Leading slave mask (22).   Detailed modelling;   glaze paint on clay above
       mask.   Peaked, striated speira;   striated nearly pointed trumpet
       Ref. Walters, *Catalogue*, 227

YV 3   Terracotta rhyton (?) London, B.M.,C 419   Mytilene
       H. 0,132 m.
       Leading slave (22): striated peaked speira, bored pupils, deep rounded
       trumpet;   mouth forms orifice
       Ref. Walters, *Catalogue*, 227
       Note Probably 2nd cent. B.C.

YV 4   Terracotta mask   Vienna, 409   Rhodes
       (? from vase)
       H. 0,039 m.
       Slave mask (22?): hair striated back from forehead, wide shallow twisted
       striated trumpet
       Ref. Not before 1st cent. B.C.

ASIA MINOR

MYRINA

Terracottas

MT 1-49   The Myrina series is extremely lively and varied: the main group (2nd
          cent.) may be the result of some single inspiration like the Attic comic
          terracottas of the second quarter of the fourth century.   Only 1-7 are
          dated: 1 and 2 by the finding of the same signatures Sodamos and
          Nikostratos in dated contexts, 3-7 by other finds in the tombs in which
          they were discovered.

          The undated terracottas are divided into Old men 8-14, Young men 15-24,
          Slaves 25-44, Women 45-49.   Within each category statuettes precede
          masks;   slaves are further subdivided into standing, seated, masks.
          Provenances of many are certain, and the rest are convincing.   The main
          group belongs to the second century: 1, which is dated, is inseparable
          from 15, and both figures appear on the Dioskourides mosaic (NM 2), which
          probably derives from a third century original.   (This raises the

question of the relation of these terracottas to painting)[1] 2, which
is dated, is inseparable from the lively slaves such as 27-30 (the deep
trumpet noted on DM 1 is extremely clearly seen on MT 2); for the
running slave too an earlier example can be quoted: 27 is very like
AT 6, which is firmly dated in the third century. The main group may
therefore be strongly influenced by earlier Attic terracottas. It may
be right to distinguish from the main group an earlier group which is
more akin to Tanagras in the compacter build of the figures and the
avoidance of loose limbs: 8, 25, 26, 36, 37, 38. A later group is
fixed by Tomb C in the late first century and shows the same slurred
forms and meagre figures as contemporary terracottas from Athens and
Delos: 3-7, 16, 24, 34, 35, 40, 44, 48, 49.

The early group has affinities with UT 48, 72, 73; the middle group
with UB 1, 4, UT 61; the late group with UT 39, 42, 54, 96.

The hard sharp angle at the top of the trumpet on MT 26 and 27 is
found again on XT 23 and on Campanian wall-paintings, e.g. NP 4, 13, 22.

a) Dated

MT 1   Terracotta statuette   a) Berlin 7969   Myrina   2nd cent. B.C.
                                b) Froehner Collection
                                c) Bamneville Collection

Tympanum player: mask 13

Ref. Bieber, *H.T.*, fig.241; *D.*, no.142; Robert, *Masken*, fig.87; Simon
        183 n.58; *P.C.F.*, fig.114; *T.K.*, 426/6, quotes Froehner replica
        signed *Sodamou*, cf. Burr, 25 and no.33.

Note Robert takes as lyre player rather than tympanum player (wrongly?)

MT 2   Terracotta   Berlin 7820   Myrina   2nd cent. B.C.
H. 0,235 m.

Man wearing hat, short chiton, himation, carrying bedding, sword, and
flask, mask (27). Right hand bored. Signed NIKO. High pedestal with
curved profile

Ref. Bieber, *D.*, no.85; *H.T.*[1], fig.96; [2], fig.154; *T.K.*, 427/6; *P.C.F.*,
        fig.110; Robert, fig.17; D. B. Thompson, *Hesperia* 21 (1952), 144
        dates late 2nd cent. B.C. at earliest

MT 3   Terracotta statuette   Paris, Louvre 94   Myrina, Tomb C ?1st cent.B.C.
H. 0,17 m.

Youth in short chiton, calling someone away, right arm extended. The head
has wavy hair but no pseudo-onkos; if dramatic, 16 rather than 15

Ref. Simon 182 n.25; *Myrina* no.321, pl.45/1; Winter, *T.K.* II, 430/3;
        D. Burr, p.6 n.7, dates Tomb C late 1st cent. B.C.

MT 4   Terracotta statuette   Paris, Louvre 214   Myrina, Tomb C 1st cent.B.C.
H. 0,17 m.

Slave perorating: mask 23: short chiton, right arm raised, cloak; shock
of hair over ears, high scalp (?bald), semicircular trumpet

Ref. Simon 189 n.29; *Myrina* no.319, pl.45/7; Robert, fig.34; Winter, *T.K.*
        II, 425/3; *G.T.P.*, no.C70

[1] Other cross-connections with Italian painting noted below are: NP 4, 6 (with 22, 23), 8,
23-5. 27, 38.

MT 5   Terracotta statuette   Paris, Louvre 37   Myrina, Tomb C   1st cent.B.C.
       H. 0,165 m.

       Slave standing: hand to ear; elbow on hand.   Mask 22(?): small bulbous eyes;
       striated hair with striated peaked speira, deep twisted striated trumpet;   traces
       of red;   rectangular vent

       Ref. Winter, *T.K.*, 425/4; *Nécropole de Myrina*, pl.45/9, no.320

MT 6   Terracotta   Paris, Louvre 265   Myrina, Tomb C   1st cent. B.C.
       H. 0,165 m.

       Mask 22 or 25, with semicircular trumpet and large wreath;   seated on altar;
       right hand raised, left hand straight out;   short chiton

       Ref. Simon 190 n.47b; Winter, *T.K.* II 425/5; *Myrina*, no.318, pl.45/8

MT 7   Terracotta statuette   Paris, Louvre 79   Myrina   1st cent.B.C.
       H. 0,155 m.

       Boy with pigtail, and cloak over left shoulder, holding mask.   Oval vent

       Ref. *Myrina*, pl.18/1, no.299, with bibliography on p.343.   p.95, Tomb 101,
               with Samian ware

   b) Undated

      Old Men

MT 8   Terracotta statuette   Athens, N.M. 5056 (Misthos 257)   Myrina
       H. 0,19 m.

       Pornoboskos (8) in long chiton with very elaborate wreath, holding sistrum in
       right hand

       Ref. *T.K.*, 426/1; Philadelpheus, pl.24

       Note Possibly Early Hellenistic

MT 9   Terracotta statuette   Paris, Louvre 199   Myrina
       H. 0,195 m.

       Pornoboskos (8): large wreath, cloak, thong in hand

       Ref. Robert, fig.33; Bieber, *D.*, no.146; *P.C.F.*, fig.106; *G.T.P.*, no.C 65;
               Simon, 192 n.4; *T.K.*, 426/2; *Myrina*, no.316, pl.46/4

       Note 2nd cent. B.C.

MT 10 Terracotta statuette   London, B.M. C 520   Myrina
       H. 0,192 m.

       Leno (8): one shoulder bare, big himation over arm, large wreath with streamers
       falling on to shoulders, tall twisted figure, sandals

       Ref. Simon 192 n.5

       Note 2nd cent. B.C.

MT 11 Terracotta mask   Athens, N.M. (Misthos)   Myrina
       Pornoboskos

       Ref. Philadelpheus, *Pelina Eidolia*, pl.25

       Note 2nd cent. B.C.

MT 12   Terracotta head   Cambridge GR 88e 1937   ?Myrina

H. 0,44 m.

Knotted brows; bald, wrinkled forehead; bulbous eyes; red on mouth.
Leno

Note 2nd cent. B.C.

MT 13   Terracotta mask   Athens NM.5315 (Misthos 93)   Myrina

H. 0,05 m.

Mask 7?: very wrinkled; peaked curly hair; eyes outlined, pupils bored;
very short beard in trumpet.   Dark red clay

Ref. Simon 95, 194 n.71; Martha, no.936, pl.VI.4

Note Simon suggests survival of Middle Comedy type.   Perhaps it is more
likely to be the curly-haired slave (Pollux no.24)

MT 14   Terracotta   Athens NM.5040 (Misthos 529)

H. 0,13 m.

Mask of bald, bearded man with bored pupils; closed mouth

Ref. Bieber, *H.T.*, fig.252; *D.*, no.162; Simon 88 n.39; Robert, *Masken*
fig.37; *P.C.F.*, fig.107

Note Simon rightly doubts if this is dramatic

Young Men

MT 15   Terracotta statuette   Athens NM.5060 (Misthos 543)   Myrina

H. 0,19 m.

Youth with castagnets (10?); much colour

Ref. Bieber, *D.*, no.155; *H.T.*, fig.240; Simon 55 n.57; *T.K.*, 426/5;
Germ.Inst. N.M.194

Note Perhaps Kolax (17) rather than (10): brows very strongly twisted;
wreath obscures baldness.   Very like MT 1.   2nd cent. B.C.

MT 16   Terracotta statuette   Paris, Louvre 383   Myrina

H. 0,16 m.

Youth in short chiton and chlamys: right hand raised in surprise: mask
probably 16 rather than 15.   Cf. on MT 3

Ref. Simon 186 n.130; Winter *T.K.*, 430/2; *Myrina*, no.322, pl.45/4

Note Very like the statuettes from Tomb C.   1st cent. B.C.

MT 17   Terracotta statuette   a) Paris, Louvre 529   Myrina
                                  b) Vienna, Inv.1564
                                  c) Athens NM.5025

H. 0,22 m.

Soldier (15), wrapped in large cloak, corkscrew locks falling from pseudo-
onkos

Ref. Bieber, *H.T.*[1], fig.204-5; *D.*, no.56; Simon 49 n.26; *P.C.F.*, fig.49;
G.T.P., no.C 68; *T.K.*, 429/5; Germ.Inst. neg.N.M.1125

Note The Vienna example has the right arm forwards.   2nd cent. B.C.

MT 18   Terracotta statuette   Athens N.M.5059 (Misthos 476)   Myrina

H. 0,20 m.

Mask 17: Kolax wrapped in cloak without aryballos, strigil

Ref. Simon 181 n.3

Note For head cf. AT 4.   2nd cent. B.C.

MT 19   Terracotta statuette   Athens N.M.5027 (Misthos 544)   Myrina

H. 0,19 m.

Parasite (18), carrying aryballos and strigil; bored pupils

Ref. Simon 44, 181 n.1; Robert, fig.52; Bieber, *H.T.*, fig.249; *D.*, no.144; *P.C.F.*, fig.120; *G.T.P.*, no. C 69; Germ.Inst. neg.NM.1127

Note The body is a free replica of MT 18.   2nd cent. B.C.

MT 20   Terracotta statuette   Athens N.M.5045 (Misthos 542)   Myrina

H. 0,22 m.

Man in large cloak (?10 or 19)

Ref. Simon 64; Robert, fig.98; Bieber, *D.*, no.141; *H.T.*, fig.230; *P.A.P.S.* 103 (1959), 381; *P.C.F.*, fig.113; *G.T.P.*, no.C 66; Germ.Inst. neg., NM.1124

Note Simon interprets as 19, but it is difficult to see a valid distinction from 10.   2nd cent. B.C.

MT 21   Terracotta mask   Leipzig   ?Myrina

Mask 10: peaked speira, raised brows, bored pupils, very smooth and worn

Ref. Simon 183 n.59; pl.V,2

Note Perhaps 2nd cent. B.C.

MT 22   Terracotta mask   Boston 01.7752   Myrina

H. 0,143 m.

Striated speira, no peak, no falling locks, elaborate wreath, smooth brows (?13)

Ref. Burr, no.114; Bieber, *H.T.*[1], fig.257; Webster, *Greek Terracottas*, fig.34

Note 2nd cent. B.C.

MT 23   Terracotta disk   Athens N.M.5043 (Misthos 525)   ?Myrina

H. 0,14 m.

Mask of young man with wavy hair, wreathed (16)

Ref. Philadelpheus, pl.25

Note Pairs with MT 42.   Perhaps 2nd cent. B.C.

MT 24   Terracotta mask   Paris, Louvre 279   Myrina

H. 0,115 m.

Mask of wreathed youth with large plain pseudo-onkos (16).   Smooth brows; bored pupils; White slip; red paint.   Two suspension holes: inscribed

Ref. *Myrina* pl.48/1, no.347

Note Probably 1st cent. B.C.

Slaves: 1) Standing

MT 25   Terracotta statuette   Constantinople 465   Myrina

H. 0,115 m.

Slave walking with stick with short, round crook: probably mask 22

Ref. Simon 191 n.57; Winter, *T.K.*, 425/1; Mendel 2743

Note Possibly Early Hellenistic

MT 26   Terracotta statuette   Athens 5055 (Misthos 429)   Myrina

H. 0,145 m.

Slave of Comedy: mask 27?: walking, cloak over left shoulder, hands to
breasts, chiton to thigh, girt under stomach, red face, small eyes

Ref. *T.K.*, 425/2; Robert, fig.89; Bieber, *H.T.*, fig.214; Simon, 190 n.42d;
Germ.Inst. NM 1123

Note Possibly Early Hellenistic

MT 27   Terracotta   Athens N.M.5057 (Misthos 539) Myrina

H. 0,21 m.

White-haired slave, hurrying (21): chiton; fringed himation over shoulder
and rolled at waist; uneven brows

Ref. Bieber, *D.*, *no.153*; *H.T.*, fig.234; Robert, fig.90; *T.K.*, 427/7;
Philadelpheus, pl.24; German Inst., N.M.1670

Note Cf. AT 6.   2nd cent. B.C.

MT 28   Terracotta   Athens N.M.5048 (Misthos 540)   Myrina

H. 0,20 m.

Gesticulating curly-haired slave (24)

Ref. Robert, fig.22; Bieber, *D.*, no.150; *H.T.*, fig.236; Simon 189, n.32a;
G.T.P., no.C 71; *T.K.*, 427/4; Germ.Inst. neg. N.M.1126

Note 2nd cent. B.C.

MT 29   Terracotta statuette   a) Boston 01.7679   Myrina
                                   b) Athens, N.M.   Myrina

H. 0,187 m.

Walking slave (22): short chiton, sandals, much colour; right arm raised,
left arm deformed

Ref. Bieber, *H.T.*, fig.213; Burr, no.113; 'Princeton', fig.37; *T.K.*, 425/6

Note 2nd cent. B.C.

MT 30   Terracotta statuette   Athens N.M.5058 (Misthos 60)   Myrina

H. 0,19 m.

Running slave: mask 25.   Both arms forward; cloak over back; chiton girt
above and below stomach; edge of mask clearly shown behind

Ref. Bieber, *H.T.*, fig.235; Simon 188 n.5; Pickard-Cambridge, *Dithyramb*,
fig.45; Bieber, *D.*, no.154; Robert, fig.27; *P.C.F.*, fig.129; *T.K.*,
427/5; Germ.Inst. neg. NM 1124

Note Perhaps cf. DT 12.   2nd cent. B.C.

MT 31   Terracotta statuette   Lyon, Faculté des Lettres, 1540   Myrina
H. 0,195 m.

Slave running: right hand raised; cloak; chiton girded above and below
stomach (head missing)

Note Perhaps a variant of MT 30.   2nd cent. B.C.

MT 32   Terracotta statuette   Berlin 7953   Myrina
H. 0,195 m.

Cook (22): wreath, semicircular trumpet, himation girt round hips, arms
level with breasts

Ref. Bieber, *H.T.*, fig. 248; Robert, *Masken*, fig. 26; Bieber, *D.*, no. 143;
Simon 71 n. 4; Lietzmann, *Hellenistisch-romische Kultur*, 420, Pl. III, 2;
P.C.F., Fig. 124; *T.K.*, 426/4

Note 2nd cent. B.C.   Winter takes as tympanist

MT 33   Terracotta statuette   a) Montpellier, Faculté des Lettres, 100   Myrina
H. 0,195 m.   b) Bammeville Collection
H. 0,150 m.

Slave: bending forward with arms stretched out; himation girt round his
waist; ?ends of wreath appear on both shoulders, but head badly battered

Ref. b) Froehner, 1893, no. 111

Note 2nd cent. B.C.

MT 34   Terracotta statuette   a) Paris, Louvre 124   Myrina
b) Lecuyer
H. 0,175 m.

Slave standing: wig-like hair (?27); wide mouth; hands crossed in front
of stomach; feet close together.   Traces of white slip.   Round vent

Ref. *Nécropole de Myrina*, pl. 46/5, no. 317 (Pottier notes replica in Lecuyer
Collection); Winter, *T.K.*, 425/7; Robert, fig. 91

Note Cf. DT 19.   Late 1st cent. B.C.

MT 35   Terracotta statuette   Vienna, 1512   ?Myrina
H. 0,102 m.

Slave (27?) wearing wreath; uneven brows, bulbous eyes with depressed pupils;
himation over left shoulder held by left hand, right hand before stomach

Ref. Winter, *T.K.*, 423/2; Schneider, *A.A.*, 1892, 119, no. 155

Note Probably 1st cent. B.C.   Cf. UT 96

MT 36   Terracotta statuette   Adolphseck, Schloss Fasanerie   ?Myrina
Slave (27) wearing women's clothing?

Ref. Brommer, *Antike Kleinkunst*, fig. 2

Note Probably Early Hellenistic

2) Seated

MT 37   Terracotta statuette   Paris, Louvre MNC 525   Myrina
H. 0,12 m.

Slave seated on square altar: both hands under cloak on left side; legs crossed

Ref. *P.C.F.*, fig.104; Robert, fig.40; Winter, *T.K.*, 425/8; Simon 193 n.34

Note Robert takes as sphenopagon.   Probably Early Hellenistic

MT 38   Terracotta statuette   Paris, Louvre CA 1540   ?Myrina

Slave (22) with semicircular, deep rounded trumpet, peaked speira, with hair falling below ears; enormous horned wreath; seated on altar with hands between legs

Ref. Bieber, *Record of the Art Museum, Princeton*, 9 (1950), 10, fig.5

Note Probably Early Hellenistic

MT 39   Terracotta statuette   Athens 5029 (Misthos 428)   Myrina
H. 0,18 m.

Seated slave (22): wreath, right arm raised, left hand to hip, legs crossed; cloak; chiton girt above and below stomach.   Round seat separate

Ref. Bieber, *H.T.*, fig.271; Simon 189 n.32b; *T.K.*, 427/3; Rumpf, *Mimus u. Logos*, 166; Robert, *Masken*, fig.21; *P.C.F.*, fig.125; Germ.Inst. NM 1672

Note 2nd cent. B.C.

MT 40   Terracotta statuette   Lyon, Faculté des Lettres, 1550   Myrina
H. 0,06 m.

Slave (27): wavy hair from highish onkos; even raised brows; rimmed eyes; button nose; deepish trumpet; arms folded with left hand on right elbow; cloak round shoulders; chiton girt below stomach.   ?Seated (legs missing)

Note Not before 1st cent. B.C.

3) Masks

MT 41   Terracotta mask   Athens, French School   Myrina

Slave: speira; deepish striated trumpet; raised brows; small bulbous eyes

Ref. *Nécropole de Myrina*, pl.45/6

Note Perhaps cf. DT 22.   Late 2nd cent. B.C.

MT 42   Terracotta disk   Athens, N.M.5037 (Misthos 526)   Myrina
H. 0,13 m.

Mask of leading slave (22)

Ref. Philadelpheus, pl.25

Note Pairs with MT 23.   Perhaps 2nd cent. B.C.

MT 43   Terracotta statuette   a) Boston 01.7706   Myrina
                                  b) Athens, N.M.5101 (Misthos 49)
H. 0,263 m.

Nike holding wreathed slave mask (sleepy eyes, deepish trumpet) in left
hand and scroll in right hand

Ref.   a) D. Burr, *Terracottas from Myrina*, 60, no.70; Luschey, *Ganymed*,
            84 n.93; Kleiner, *Tanagrafiguren*, 211
       b) Burr, *loc.cit.*;   *T.K.*, 188/4; Philadelpheus, pl.11

Note   a) 2nd cent. B.C.

MT 44   Terracotta statuette   Paris, Louvre 176   Myrina
H. 0,15 m.

Boy in necklace and chiton holding slave mask with wavy hair, raised brows,
semicircular deepish trumpet.   Oval vent

Ref.   *Myrina*, pl.43/1, no.300

Note   Early 1st cent. B.C.

Women

MT 45   Terracotta statuette   Athens 5032 (Misthos 427)   Myrina
H. 0,18 m.

Courtesan in peplos: mask 41 rather than 44

Ref.   *T.K.*, 428/5; Bieber, *H.T.*, fig.246; *D.*, no.157; Robert, *Masken*,
            fig.64-5; Simon 111, 116, 195 n.1; *P.C.F.*, fig.149; *G.T.P.*, no.C 75;
            Germ.Inst. N.M.1123

Note   2nd cent. B.C.

MT 46   Terracotta statuette   a) Paris, Louvre CA 1348   Myrina
                                  b) Lost: once Smyrna Market
H. 0,20 m.

Mask 41:   woman in mitra and chiton: right hand half raised, left hand
down

Ref.   b) Simon 198 n.100;   *T.K.*, 428/4; Robert, fig.79

MT 47   Terracotta   Boston 01.7753   Myrina
H. 0,118 m.

Female comic mask with ear-rings; 'Wimpled courtesan' (41).   Bored pupils

Ref.   Burr, no.115; Bieber, *H.T.*, fig.285; Webster, *Greek Terracottas*,
            fig.35

Note   Late 2nd century

MT 48   Terracotta mask   Paris, Louvre 315   Myrina
H. 0,15 m.

Mask of hetaira in mitra; bored pupils.   Three suspension holes

Ref.   *Myrina* pl.48/2, no.353

Note   Perhaps 1st century B.C.

MT 49   Terracotta mask   Paris, Louvre 502   Myrina

H. 0,11 m.

Mask of girl: perhaps melon hair; bored pupils

Ref. Myrina, pl.48/5, no.348

Note Perhaps 1st cent.B.C.

ASIA MINOR: OTHER SITES

Amphora handle

ZA 1   Amphora handle   Rhodes   Sinope   3rd/2nd cent. B.C.
(Iphis, son of Hestiaios)

Pornoboskos (rather than Papposilenos)

Note Date given by Miss V. Grace

Lamps

ZL 1   Terracotta lamps   London, B.M. 356 etc.   Knidos   Late 2nd cent.B.C.
(black)

Masks of slave (22), old man (3)

Ref. British Museum Catalogue of Lamps, no.384, fig.61, no.358, pl.9. Cf.
    Howland, *Agora IV: Greek Lamps*, 126-7, 170-1, Type 40A

Note   The slave (no.356) has a peaked speira and a deep smooth
    trumpet; 365, 384 the same but a much shallower trumpet; 358 the
    same with flying hair and cheeks emphasized; 368, 380, 381, the
    trumpet is much more pointed at the bottom. The old man, 357, is
    very like the old man on Megarian bowls.

ZL 2   Bronze lamp with   Berlin, Misc.Inv.10050   Priene, House   Late 3rd
two spouts   N. of no.XVII   cent.B.C.

0,25 x 0,115 x 0,09 m.

Wreathed slave mask (22 or 25): slightly uneven brows, narrowish eyes,
semi-circular trumpet beard, perhaps bald

Ref. Priene, 322 (cf. 328 for coins of Chares etc.), 384, fig.486

ZL 3   Terracotta lamp   Berlin, Terr.Inv.8697   Priene   Late 2nd/early
                                                                      1st cent. B.C.

Women's masks and slaves' masks

Ref. Priene, 451, no.180, fig.560, Class II,B (Broneer, Type xviii;
    Howland, Type 49)

ZL 4   Terracotta lamp   Berlin, Terr.Inv.8715   Priene,   2-3 B.C.
                                                   Roman grave

Bearded, wreathed mask: fruit on the forehead; wings above

Ref. Priene, 279, 451, fig.562, no.192 (coin date)

Note In spite of wings included here because of likeness of mask to old men's
    mask in Pompeii etc. The lamp is Broneer, Type xxi.

ZL 5   Terracotta lamp   Adana Museum   Tarsus, Middle   Late 1st cent.
                                                          Level, Hellenistic   B.C.
                                                          & Roman Unit

Two bald slave masks on nozzles (25): shock of hair over ears, wide rounded
trumpet

Ref. Goldman, 31, 33, 36, 92, 108, fig.97, no.131: Group XI = Broneer, Type xxi

ZL 6   Terracotta lamp-lid   Leiden (Case 6),   ?Asia Minor
                                    L, K-A, 350

Maison mask (25)

Ref. Cf. D. B. Thompson, *Gnomon* 31 (1959), 634, on Delos no.1285

Note Cf. DL 2.   1st cent. B.C.

   Mosaic

ZM 1   Mosaic   Berlin   Pergamon,   Early 2nd cent.
                                                          Royal Palace   B.C.

Three-quarter mask of dark-haired girl wearing ivy-wreath

Ref. Rumpf, *MuZ.*, pl.56/4; Kaverau, *Pergamon* V, 1, pl.12-15; B. Brown,
        Ptolemaic paintings and mosaics, 72f.; Rumpf, *A.E.*, 1953/4, 124 takes as
        Second Pseudokore (35) but may rather be young hetaira (39)

   Sculpture

ZS 1   Marble relief   Vienna University,   Kremna (Asia Minor)
                                    18.12.1884

Bearded man (4)

Note Probably Late Hellenistic

ZS 2   Marble masks from frieze   Berlin   Pergamon, Upper   Late 2nd cent.B.C.
                                                          Agora,Middle Gymnasium
        H. 0,17 m.   Terrace

Masks 16, 26 set in ivy sprays: bored pupils

Ref. Simon, 186 n.124, 188 n.9; Winter, *Pergamon*, VII, 2, 315 fig.404d,e;
        Rumpf, *Symbola Coloniensia*, 98; *B.D.*, no.166; *B.H.T.*, fig.273; Robert,
        fig.28; *P.C.F.*, fig.53c; *G.T.P.*, 72

Note The beardless mask is so badly damaged that only the outline can be seen

ZS 3   Marble relief   Berlin   Pergamon, door   Late 2nd
                                                          of theatre   cent. B.C.

Alternating *pornoboskos* (8) and wavy-haired old man (4)

Ref. *Pergamon*, IV, i, 13, fig.1; VIII, no.236

Terracottas, in alphabetical order of find spots

Amisos

(1-2, 5-6 are large wall masks like 20-24 from Priene)

ZT 1   Terracotta mask   Helbing Collection   Samsun

H. 0,145 m.

Mask 10: hair in rough striations; raised brows

Ref. Simon 183 n.56; Helbing 283, pl.16

ZT 2   Terracotta mask   Munich Inv.5401   Samsun

H. 0,13 m.

Mask of youth: mask 13.   Smooth brows; sharp eyelids; bored pupils; wreath; fat face

Ref. Bieber, *H.T.*, fig.255; *D.*, no.164; Simon 184 n.80a; *P.C.F.*, fig.115; Krien, *Jahreshefte*, 42 (1956), 112, fig.52

Note Not unlike BT 10.   Very careful and elaborate like UT 27.   2nd cent. B.C.

ZT 3   Terracotta mask   Berlin 8886   Samsun

H. 0,056 m.

Mask 13

Ref. Simon 184 n.80

ZT 4   Terracotta mask   Berlin 8885   Samsun

H. 0,066 m.

Mask 15

Ref. Simon 186 n.132

ZT 5   Terracotta mask   Paris, Louvre CA 1958   Samsun

Mask of youth (16): sharp eyelids, wreath, smooth brows, corkscrew locks below wreath

Ref. Bieber, *H.T.*, fig.256

Note Found with ZT 6.   Probably wall masks like ZT 20

ZT 6   Terracotta mask   Paris, Louvre CA 1938   Samsun

Mask of courtesan 'Little Torch' (42): parted hair, locks in front of ears

Ref. Bieber, *H.T.*, fig.287

Note Found with ZT 5.   For style, cf. DT 1.   Perhaps 2nd cent. B.C.

ZT 7   Terracotta mask   Berlin 31169   Samsun

H. 0,075 m.

Mask (41): evanescent eyes

Ref. Simon 197 n.69, pl.XII,3

Note Like ZT 6 in style

ZT 8   Terracotta mask   Unknown   Samsun

Slave (22) with cap on head?

Ref. Helbing, *Auction Catalogue* 1913, pl.8, no.284

ZT 9   Plastic vase   Unknown   Samsun

Slave lying down by *askos*:   mask 22

Ref. Simon 190 n.51; Helbing, *Auction Catalogue* 1913, pl.12, no.249

Ephesos

ZT 10   Terracotta mask   Berlin 7597.32   Ephesos

H. 0,04 m.

Mask of old nurse (30)

Ref. Bieber, *H.T.*, fig.278; Robert, *Masken*, fig.83-4; *T.K.*, 428/6;
        Pickard-Cambridge, *Dith.*, fig.30; *Festivals*, fig.147; Simon p.30
        (caricature, *not* Comedy); 199 n.9b

Note Perhaps not dramatic, but stylization of brows and mouth derives
        from dramatic masks. Early Hellenistic

Halikarnassos

ZT 11   Terracotta mask   London, British Museum, C 518   Mausoleum

H. 0,51 m.

Wrinkled old woman (29?): pupils bored

Ref. Walters, *Cat.*, 242

Larisa: perhaps later than the destruction date of 280 B.C.

ZT 12   Terracotta mask   Unknown   Larisa

H. 0,082 m.

Mask of slave (22): hard striation, goggle eyes with bored pupils and ducts

Ref. *Larisa* III, 115, pl.9, 21 (cf. p.41 for dating in 3rd century); *G.T.P.*,
        no.C 63

Note Early Hellenistic.   Cf. ZT 22

ZT 13   Terracotta mask   Unknown   Larisa

H. 0,0571 m.

Mask of hetaira (38?): fat face with elaborate wreath; eyes sleepy; side
locks; white face, red hair, red outlines to mouth and eyes; blue and
white on wreath

Ref. *Larisa*, III, no.117, pl.9, 22

Note Early Hellenistic

Lebanon

ZT 14   Terracotta head   Beirut, Kn.1116   Kharayeb,Lebanon   3rd/2nd cent.B.C.
Slave mask (27) with peaked hair and shock over ears;   wide, twisted trumpet
Ref. Chehab, *Bulletin du Musée de Beyrouth*, X-XI, 75, pl.11, 6 (limiting dates
given by coins)

ZT 15   Terracotta mask   Beirut University 534   ?
H. 0,10 m.
Maison mask (25):   rimmed eyes, bored pupils, semicircular twisted trumpet
Ref. Simon 188 n.6, pl.IX,2
Note Like DT 12 etc.   Probably 2nd cent. B.C.

Pergamon

ZT 16   Terracotta statuette   Berlin P 178   Pergamon
H. 0,118 m.
Bald slave (25):   uneven brows, bulbous eyes, smooth oval trumpet, himation
over left shoulder and down to knees.   Small plinth
Ref. *Pergamon*, I, 259, fig.15;   Robert, fig.92
Note Early Hellenistic, cf. Middle Comedy, ET 1

ZT 17   Terracotta statuette   Berlin P 191   Pergamon
Headless slave;   himation round waist;   carries something round his neck
which ends in both hands: animal?   wineskin?   bundle?
Ref. *Pergamon*, I, 259, fig.16
Note Probably Early Hellenistic.   Cf. above DT 21

ZT 18   Terracotta head   Berlin (Humann)   Pergamon
H. 0,04 m.
Slave (22):   striated hair and semicircular trumpet, even brows, small eyes
with bored pupils
Ref. Bieber, *H.T.*, fig.269;   Simon 77 n.42e;   *Pergamon*, I, 261, fig.20
Note Probably Late Hellenistic

ZT 19   Terracotta head   Berlin P 213   Pergamon
Slave head: knotted brows;   inscribed pupils;   square trumpet with teeth
showing
Ref. *Pergamon*, I, 261, fig.19
Note Late

Priene

20-24, Wall masks from a house built in the first half of the 2nd century B.C.

ZT 20   Terracotta mask   Berlin 8568   Priene, House A   Before 150 B.C.

[This and the following masks alternated with bull's heads on the walls]

H. 0,20 m.

Pornoboskos (8).   Bald, small, glowering eyes (bored).   Elaborate modelling.
Flowing beard (pink)

Ref. Priene 361, fig.447;   Simon, 192 n.1;   Robert, fig.30.   On dating Burr,
        Terracottas from Myrina, 16, n.4;   *Priene*, 323, 328, 424, 429

ZT 21   Terracotta mask   Constantinople 1566   Priene, House A   Before 150 B.C.

H. 0,105 m.

Fragmentary youth with furrowed brow, raised hard eyebrows, outlined eyes with
bored pupils, hair showing beneath ears

Ref. Priene, 361, fig.449;   Mendel, 2249

Note Perhaps cf. DT 5 but also UT 15

ZT 22   Terracotta mask   Berlin 8570   Priene, House A   Before 150 B.C.

H. 0,185 m.

Slave (22) with striated speira;   smooth deepish trumpet;   bored pupils (later
stopped)

Ref. Priene, 361, fig.448

Note Cf. MT 30, ZT 12

ZT 23   Terracotta mask   Berlin 8569   Priene, House A   Before 150 B.C.

H. 0,125 m.

Slave (27) with furrowed brow;   outlined eyes with bored pupils;   trumpet
mouth with curly overlapping hair, dark brown

Ref. Priene, 361, fig.450

ZT 24   Terracotta mask   Constantinople 1514   Priene, House A   Before 150 B.C.

H. 0,145 m.

Woman with parted hair, bored pupils;   yellow face;   brown in hair;   blue in
pupils;   red on lips

Ref. Mendel, 2248;   *Priene*, 361, fig.446;   Rumpf, *A.E.*, 1953-4, 122 takes as
        mask 44 (hetaira's maid)

Note Cf. TT 13

ZT 25   Terracotta head   Constantinople 1390   Priene

H. 0,65 m.

Woman with mitra and back hair (42): incised pupils.   White on face;   red
brown on hair;   red mouth, white teeth

Ref. Priene, 360;   Mendel, 2239, pl.7, 6

Note Probably 2nd cent. B.C.

ZT 26   Terracotta statuette   Constantinople 1609   Priene

H. 0,05 m.

Slave (27) with chin on right hand, right elbow on left hand;   rimmed eyes
(not bored);   striated, peaked wig hair, semicircular trumpet.   Red clay
with mica

Ref. Priene, 360, fig.445;   Mendel, 2149

Note Cf. DT 19.   Probably 1st century B.C.   (Note also Mendel 2235-2238,
of which no illustration).

Seleucia

ZT 27   Terracotta mask   Toledo 7142   Seleucia (Tigris)   143 B.C.-79 A.D.
                                                         III, Room 31

H. 0,028 m.

Caphair with striated edge, smooth brows, evanescent eyes: ?*hapalos* (13)

Ref. Van Ingen, *Figurines from Seleucia*, no.1360, pl.73, 531, taken as female

Note Probably Late Hellenistic

ZT 28   Terracotta mask   Cleveland 32.543   Seleucia (Tigris)   143 B.C.-79 A.D.
                                                          III, Room 31

Parted wavy hair, bound by narrow fillets, ?*hetairidion*

Ref. Van Ingen, no.1363, pl.73, 533

Note Probably Late Hellenistic

Smyrna

ZT 29-38, 49 can only be dated stylistically.   They are very like the Myrina series,
and 29 may be an import.   Most of them are probably 2nd cent. B.C., but 30, 31, 36 go
with the later groups of Myrina, Delos, and Athens.   UT 5 probably belongs to and
UT 92 has affinities with the 2nd cent. group.   UT 38 has affinities with the later
group.

ZT 29   Terracotta statuette   Vienna, Inv.1567   Smyrna

H. 0,205 m.

Running slave of Comedy (27).   Left arm bent;   right hand to mouth

Ref. Bieber, *H.T.*, fig.215;   *T.K.*, 427/8

Note Cf MT 2.   2nd cent. B.C.

ZT 30   Terracotta statuette   Heidelberg TK 130   Smyrna

Slave with wreath (22):   peaked speira, sleepy eyes;   brows slightly uneven;
semicircular trumpet;   wrapped in cloak

Ref. Luschey, *Ganymed*, 78, figs. 9 & 10;   Simon 78, 190 n.42b

Note Probably late 2nd or early 1st cent. B.C.

ZT 31   Terracotta head   Boston 01.7642   Smyrna

Slave (22): very large wreath with hair showing below;   wide, twisted trumpet

Ref. 'Princeton' fig.42

Note Probably late 2nd or early 1st cent. B.C.

ZT 32   Terracotta mask   Berlin 6335   Smyrna

H. 0,85 m.

Mask (8) held by ugly dwarf

Ref. Simon 192 n.2; Robert, fig.31

Note Perhaps 2nd cent. B.C.

ZT 33   Terracotta mask   Berlin 8206   Asia Minor

H. 0,77 m.

Mask (8) wreathed, held by ugly dwarf

Ref. Simon 192 n.3; Robert, fig.32

Note Robert takes as a replica of ZT 32, except that the mask is wreathed

ZT 34   Terracotta mask   Athens, N.M.5447   Smyrna

Leading slave (22)

Paris,
ZT 35   Terracotta mask   Louvre, CA 1437   Smyrna

a) Tettix (26);   b) Leading slave with neatly striated peaked hair (22)

Note Probably late 2nd cent. B.C.   With b) cf. perhaps DL 2

ZT 36   Terracotta head   Paris, Louvre CA 1408   Smyrna

Wavy-haired slave (27): bored eyes;   smooth edges to trumpet

Note Cf. DT 19.   Probably 1st cent. B.C.

ZT 37   Terracotta mask   Berlin 6330   Smyrna

Mask (29): very hard modelling; bored eyes

Ref. Simon 129, 199 n.8; pl.XII, 2

Note Cf. ZT 21 for style.   2nd cent. B.C.

ZT 38   Terracotta mask   Oxford, Ashmolean Museum   Smyrna

Female mask: melon hair with *lampadion* (42)

Ref. *P.C.F.*, fig.157; *G.T.P.*, no.C 74

Note 3rd/2nd cent. B.C.

Tarsus

ZT 39   Terracotta statuette   Adana Museum   Tarsus

Mask has longish beard; probably wavy-haired old man (4) as beard is too big for a slave: hand to chin, fold of himation just shows across breast

Ref. Goldman, *Tarsus* I, 345, fig.234, nos.265/6

Note Probably 1st cent. B.C.   But cf. ZT 55 below

Troad

[Mrs. D. B. Thompson showed me photographs of these which she is publishing]

ZT 40   Terracotta mask   Troy, A 8   ?2nd cent.B.C. or later

H. 0,048 m.

Perhaps wreath rather than speira;   swinging knotted brows;   pierced pupils;   small
nose;   considerable trumpet

Ref. D.B.T., no.127

Note Cf. DL 2.   Probably 1st cent. B.C.

ZT 41   Terracotta mask   Troy, M 10   ?Roman

Slave mask (22):   red on hair;   orange on face;   buff and blue on wreath,
which hangs down over ears.   Two hang-holes at top.   Broken below top of
trumpet.   Eyes with indented pupils;   outlined

Ref. D.B.T., no.128.

Note D.B.T. cf. Priene fig.448 (= ZT 22).   Presumably the date is not compelling

ZT 42   Terracotta mask   Troy A 5

H. 0,056 m.

Little hetaira: smooth brows;   evanescent lids, pierced pupils (39)

Ref. D.B.T., no.129

Note D.B.T. cf. Delos 1241, = DT 13, and Agora T 623, = AT 21

Asia Minor (unspecified where)

ZT 43   Terracotta head   Munich, S.L.332   Asia Minor

Cleanshaven head with raised brows, bulbous eyes and rich hair, in *pilos* (15)

Ref. Sieveking, *Sammlung Loeb*, *T.B.u.V.*, pl.24/2

Note Middle Comedy tradition.   Cf. Middle Comedy, AT 96.   Perhaps 3rd Cent. B.C.

ZT 44   Terracotta statuette   Leiden I 94/6 no.4   ?Asia Minor

Slave (22), seated on altar;   longish chiton

Note Perhaps 1st cent. B.C.

ZT 45   Terracotta mask   Leiden L, K-A, 98 (store room)   ?Asia Minor

Slave mask (22)

Note Perhaps 1st cent. B.C.

ZT 46   Terracotta mask   Leiden L, K-A, 574

Wavy-haired slave (27):   pricked pupils, deepish trumpet

Note Cf. MT 2.   Probably 2nd cent. B.C.

ZT 47   Terracotta head   Munich   Asia Minor

        H. 0,035 m.

        Maison (25):   eyes rimmed, not bored, semicircular trumpet

        Ref.   Simon 188 n.8b;   *Sammlung Loeb* II 87, 5

        Note   Perhaps 2nd cent. B.C.

ZT 48   Terracotta head   Munich, S.L.225   Asia Minor

        Slave (27):   wreath of leaves;   wrinkled brow;   raised eyebrows;   eyes
outlined with bored pupils;   semicircular twisted trumpet with curly hair inside

        Ref.   *Sammlung Loeb*, II, pl.87/6

        Note   Cf. perhaps ZT 23.   2nd cent. B.C.

ZT 49   Terracotta mask   Berlin 5128   Smyrna

        H. 0,045 m.

        Slave (25):   raised brows;   bulbous eyes with depressed pupils;   very wide,
smooth trumpet

        Ref.   Robert, fig.100

        Note   Perhaps 2nd cent. B.C.

Vases

ZV 1   Handle of brown cup   Berlin, Terr.Inv.8573   Priene, House XXVII   2nd cent.B.C.

        Bald mask with long spade beard, eyes scarcely marked (?pornoboskos or
papposilenos)

        Ref.   *Priene*, 410 no.53, fig.536, takes as Silen mask, perhaps rightly

ZV 2   Glazed pottery   Adana Museum   Tarsus, Middle Level,   250-20 B.C.
                                                                    Middle Hellenistic Unit

        Slave mask (22):   striated hair, round trumpet (much deeper than ZL 5)

        Ref.   Goldman 219, fig.125c (local variant of West Slpe ware)

ZV 3   Glazed pottery   Adana Museum   a) Tarsus,Top Level   a) 150-50 B.C.
                                                                Hellenistic-Roman unit
                                                                   b) Tarsus chance find   b) 3rd cent.B.C.

        Masks of wreathed young man (13):   smooth brows, narrow eyes, short hair, fat
cheeks

        Ref.   Goldman, *Tarsus* I, 218, fig.124, a) no.109 local variant of West Slope ware,
            b) Attic import

ZV 4   Head vase with spout   Calvert coll.   ?Troas
        and handle above

        H. 0,10 m.

        Wreathed leading slave: wide, shallow, striated trumpet, striated hair

        Ref.   *T.K.*, 427/1

        Note   Probably Late Hellenistic

ZV 5   Green-glaze ware   Amsterdam 2967   Asia Minor

Maison mask (25) in relief: semicircular trumpet.   Formation of ear suggests that he may rather be a satyr

Ref. *Algemeene Gids*, no.1691, bought at Smyrna

Note Perhaps late 1st cent. B.C.

EGYPT

Bronze

EB 1   Bronze statuette   Princeton 48.68   ?

H. 0,193 m.

Slave seated on square altar (22):   large wreath, peaked hair with shock over ears, wide twisted trumpet, bored pupils;   hands clasped, ring round neck

Ref. 'Princeton', fig.38; Bieber, *Record of Art Museum*, 9 (1950), 5ff. (style Alexandrian of the 2nd cent. B.C.); *Hellenistic Sculpture*, 96, figs.382-3; Jones, *Ancient Art*, 57

Note For the head cf. NB 2

EB 2   Bronze statuette   Vienna, 281   ?Egypt

Slave (22):   right hand to chin, left hand to thigh, probably seated; peaked speira, semicircular trumpet with flat edge

Ref. Sacken-Kenner, no.528;   Sacken, pl.47/4;   Reinach, *R.S.*, II, 558/5

Note Late Hellenistic or Roman

Ivory

EI 1   Ivory plaque   London, Mustaki Collection   Alexandria

Old man's head (3) set in swags

Note Perhaps 2nd cent. B.C.

EI 2   Bone plaque   Alexandria   Canopus

Wreathed youth with smooth brows and long hair, *onkos*.   ?Dionysos

Ref. Breccia, *Monuments*, I, 80 pl.44, 3, cf. Strzygowski, *B.S.A.A.*, 5, 1-99

Lamps

EL 1-29   Lamps found in Egypt can only be dated by comparison with lamps from other sites;   the tentative dates are based on parallels particularly in Broneer's catalogue of lamps found at Corinth (*Corinth*, IV 2) and Howland's catalogue of lamps found in the Agora (*Agora*, IV).   Some of these lamps are probably imports.   Certain groups go together: EL 4-7;   9-12;   13-17 (and within this very closely 15-17);   20-22;   25-6.   27-29 are lanterns. (UL 3 and 4 may be compared with EL 24).

EL 1   Terracotta lamp   Mustaki Collection   Alexandria

Slave wearing thigh-length chiton, sitting cross-legged between two spouts, head pillared on hand (27)

Note Probably 2nd cent. B.C.

EL 2   Lamp   Amsterdam (case 76)   ?Egypt

Reclining comic slave (22)

Note Probably 2nd cent. B.C.

EL 3   Lamp, 3-spouted   Frankfurt   Fayoum

Slave masks between spouts: straight speira, wide trumpet

Ref. Kaufmann, *Ägyptische Terrakotten*, fig.129; *Koroplastik*, pl.69, no.729

Note Not unlike the bronze lamp, ZL 2.   For general type cf. Knidos lamps, ZL 1.   2nd cent. B.C.

EL 4   Terracotta lamp   Benachi Collection   Egypt

Slave mask (27)

Ref. cf. Broneer, *Corinth*, IV, 2, Type XI

Note Mid-third century B.C., or rather later

EL 5   Terracotta lamp with Benachi Collection   Egypt
       double bottom

Leading slave mask on subsidiary spout: peak hair, swinging brows, striated trumpet (22)

Ref. Broneer, *Corinth*, IV, 2, Type XI; Howland, Type 46c, no.600 (3rd cent. B.C.). But this looks much later

EL 6   Terracotta lamp   Ann Arbor, Michigan   Purchased in Tunis
                            University 196

Very weak impression of slave mask on the spout

Note Same type as EL 4 above

EL 7   Terracotta lamp   London, Mustaki Collection   Alexandria

Slave mask (27)

Note Same type as EL 4 above

EL 8   Lamp   Frankfurt   Fayoum

Leading slave (22) with peaked speira and wideish round trumpet, on inner end of spout

Ref. Kaufmann, *Ägyptische Terrakotten*, fig.127; *Koroplastik*, pl.69, no.739

Note Not unlike Knidos lamps (ZL 1).   2nd cent. B.C.

EL 9   Terracotta lamp   Benachi Collection   Egypt

Wreathed slave mask (27)

Ref. Cf. Howland, *Agora* IV, Type 47c (late 3rd to end of 2nd cent. B.C.)

EL 10   Terracotta lamp   Oxford 1953.738   Egypt

Wreathed slave mask (27)

Note Perhaps from same mould as EL 9

EL 11   Terracotta lamp (small)   Mustaki Collection   Alexandria

Slave head (27) with mouth as orifice

Note Perhaps from same mould as EL 9

EL 12   Terracotta lamp (small)   Mustaki Collection   Alexandria

Slave head (27) wreathed with mouth as orifice

Note Very like EL 9

EL 13   Terracotta lamp   Benachi Collection   Egypt

Wreathed slave mask (27)

Ref. Cf. Broneer, *Corinth*, IV, 2, Type XVI; Howland, *Agora* IV, Type 47c

Note Earlier than the type with triangular nozzle.   2nd cent. B.C.

EL 14   Terracotta lamp   Oxford 1953.737   Egypt

Wreathed leading slave mask forms body.   Red clay: spout with semicircular nozzle

Note Cf EL 13, but this is rather later.   Semicircular nozzle as in Broneer Type XIII, Howland Type 40A.   Late second to early first B.C.

EL 15   Terracotta lamp   Benachi Collection   Egypt

Mask of bald slave (25) on top of lamp

Note Whitish clay. Probably still in the time of long-nozzled lamps: therefore *not* later than 1st cent. B.C.

EL 16   Terracotta lamp   Egypt

H. 0,09 m.

Mask of bald slave (25) on top of lamp

Ref. Graindor, pl.24, 72

Note This appears to be duplicate of EL 15.   Graindor dates Ptolemaic

EL 17   Terracotta lamp   Ann Arbor, Michigan   Karanis (surface find)
                                University 22329

Mask of bald slave (25) on top of lamp

Note Duplicate of EL 15

EL 18   Grey terracotta lamp   Ann Arbor, Michigan   ?Egypt
                                University, 421

Rough slave mask very badly preserved in ?ivy spray ornament between two spouts

Note Bought in Rome, 1893.   Like Broneer, Type XVIII.   Late 2nd or early 1st cent. B.C.

EL 19   Mask below handle of lamp   Dresden, Sieglin Collection

         H. 0,05 m.

         Maison (25).   Grey clay.   Rimmed eyes with slight depression for pupils.
         Shock of hair

         Ref. Sieglin, II, 3, pl.38/6

         Note May be lamp lid, like DL above.   1st cent. B.C.

EL 20   Terracotta lamp   Benachi Collection   Egypt

         Slave mask (27) with deep striated trumpet coming to a point

         Ref. cf. Broneer, *Corinth*, IV, 2, Type XX (1st cent. B.C. to 1st cent. A.D.)

EL 21   Terracotta lamp   Alexandria   Canopos

         Slave mask with wide mouth, bald, perh. wreathed (25).   Ring handle on
         forehead;   spout below chin

         Ref. Breccia, *Monuments de l'Égypte Gréco-Romaine*, I, 1926, 76, pl.42, 15

         Note Cf. EL 20 for type

EL 22   Terracotta lamp   Fouquet Collection 427   Lower Egypt

         H. 0,112 m.

         Slave (22?), peak-hair, wrinkled brow, raised eyebrows;   bored pupils;   striated
         trumpet.   Brown clay: MAPΩN

         Ref. Perdrizet, pl.86, no.427

         Note Cf. EL 20

EL 23   Lamp   Benachi Collection   Egypt

         Two slave masks: wreathed *episeistos* (27), leading slave (22)

         Ref. cf. Broneer, *Corinth*, IV, 2, Type XXI (50 B.C.-25 A.D.);   Howland, Type
                 43E (50-1 B.C.)

         Note The leading slave mask is like the earlier type on Knidos lamps ZL 1

EL 24   Terracotta lamp   Alexandria 23137   Fayoum

         H. 0,09 m.

         Slave mask (22);   striated peaked hair all round, trumpet with flat striated
         edge, slightly bored eyes.   Mask from body of lamp;   palmette handles;   round
         spout

         Ref. Breccia, *Terrecotte*, ii, pl.109, 631, p.53, no.352

         Note Cf. UL 4.   Not unlike Broneer, Type XXI.   Late 1st cent. B.C.

EL 25   Lamp   Benachi Collection   Egypt

         Slave mask (22) and another at bottom of 20-wick lamp Sarapeum(?)

         Ref. cf. Walters, *B.M.Cat.*, no.446, pl.15, which has very weak impressions
                 of slave masks

         Note Probably Late Hellenistic

EL 26   10-wick oblong lamps with   Ann Arbor, Michigan   Fayoum
         mask on handle for 11th wick   University 22167, 22169

         a) 22167;   wreathed Maison mask
         b) 22169:   wreathed Dionysos head with shut mouth

         Ref.   Askren Collection.   Cf. EL 25

EL 27   Terracotta lantern   Benachi Collection   Egypt

         Seated slave (22) with hands on knee: elaborate headdress

EL 28   Terracotta lantern   a) Schreiber Collection   Alexandria
                                      b) Frankfurt   Fayoum

         Wreathed Mask 16:   low relief on a terracotta lantern, smooth brows, wide
         rimmed eyes, hair below ears.   Cf. ET 11

         Ref.   a) Simon 183 n.62b;   Sieglin, II, 2, pl.liii, 7
                  b) Kaufmann, *Ägyptische Terrakotten*, 116, fig.83.   cf. Loeschke,
                     Bonner Jb, 1910, 399f.

EL 29   Terracotta lantern   Benachi Collection   Egypt

         Mask of elaborately wreathed slave

Sculpture

ES 1 is included here because the heads of Chronos and Oikoumene have been
identified with Ptolemy IV and his wife, and the work may have been made for
Alexandria: writing and sculptural style give a date in the late 2nd cent. B.C.
(cf. above AS 3).

ES 1   Marble relief by Archelaos   London, B.M. 2191   2nd cent. B.C.
        of Priene

        'Comedy' in mask 42

        Ref.   Schefold, *Bildnisse*, 148;   Bieber, *Hellenistic Sculpture*, 127ff., fig.497;
                 P.C.F., fig.194;   *G.T.P.* no.A 78, pl.12;   P.M. Fraser, *Boeotian Tombstones*,
                 182, n.45

Terracottas

ET 1-61

1-5 *Dated* terracottas from two tombs of late 4th/early 3rd cent. B.C.   ET 2
has the small eyes and large beard of some early New Comedy slaves.   ET 3 is
not unlike a terracotta in Leipzig, UT 85.

6-60 *Undated*. Stylistic dates are suggested where possible.   They may give the
date when the type originated rather than the date of the actual object.   Some,
particularly of the early terracottas, are probably imports, e.g. 11, 28, 41.
Terracottas from the Fayoum are generally later than terracottas from Alexandria;
but many of them are Hellenistic or at least Hellenistic in origin.   **6-10** *Old
men*, in mask order.   UT 106 probably belongs here.   **11-22** *Young men*.   13 has a
peculiarly hard treatment of brows and eyes, which recurs on other largeish masks,
e.g. 19, 22, 49.   UT 15 probably belongs to this group.   **23-54** *Slaves*.   23 is a

group of slave and woman; a slave who has broken a pot is being rebuked by
his mistress; face of slave and scene recall phlyax vases.   24-36, statuettes
(UT 59 has some likeness to ET 27).   36-53 heads, arranged according to provenance.   44 has the curious petal-like formation of the eyelids which is found
in terracottas of the Augustan period.   53 is a mould for masks, possibly rather
like the masks on the stem of the trumpet, 54.   55-6 *Women*.   58-9 *Plaster heads*,
probably derive from metal vessels.   UT 19 may belong to these.   60-1 *Fayence
heads*, multi-coloured and therefore probably dating from the 3rd cent. B.C., cf.
satyr masks on early Queen jugs.   The pale green/blue EV 15 should not be much
later.

1) Dated

ET 1	Terracotta mask	Alexandria 15915	Chatby	Late 4th/3rd cent. B.C.

H. 0,04 m.

Mask (3): very square beard

Ref. Simon 193 n.45; Breccia, *Terrecotte*, 65, no. 363 pl. xlvi, 11; *Necropoli*,
no. 498, pl. 74, 234; *G.T.P.*, no. C 64

ET 2	Terracotta mask	Alexandria 24129	Hadra (Ezbet el Makhlouf)	Late 4th/early 3rd cent. B.C.

H. 0,065 m.

Slave with big *speira*, small button eyes, good modelling, biggish trumpet, but
lower part broken off (27)

Ref. Adriani, *Ann.Mus.Gr.Rom.*, 3 (1935-9), 97f., pl. 34/4; *W.A.M.*, n. 99

Note Dated by pottery. Unguentaria at least as early as Group B (H. A. Thompson,
Hesperia, 3 (1934), 330f.)

ET 3	Terracotta mask	Alexandria 24130	Hadra (Ezbet el Makhlouf)	Late 4th/early 3rd cent. B.C.

Kore with parted striated hair down to chin, sloping brows (33)

Ref. *W.A.M.*, n. 99; Adriani, *Ann.Mus.Gr.Rom.*, 3 (1935-9), 97f., pl. 34/5 from
same tomb

ET 4	Terracotta mask	Alexandria	Hadra	Late 4th/early 3rd cent. B.C.

H. 0,05 m.

Head with very full hair; finely striated, perhaps *kore* (33)?

Ref. Adriani, *Ann.Mus.Gr.-Rom.*, 3 (1935-9), 100, pl. 44, 5.   From same tomb

ET 5	Terracotta head	Alexandria	Hadra	Late 4th/early 3rd cent. B.C.

H. 0,045 m.

Sharp nose; evanescent eyes; large wreath; veil. Presumably *hetaira* (38?)

Ref. Adriani, *Ann.Mus.Gr.-Rom.*, 3 (1935-9), 100, pl. 44, 5.   From same tomb

2) Undated

Old Men

ET 6   Terracotta statuette   a) Alexandria 9629   Said to be from Egypt
                                b) Berlin 4715
        H. 0,15 m.

        Seated man with mask of maiden, legs crossed, and hands crossed on knee

        Ref. a) Breccia, *Terrecotte*, I, 64, no.351, pl.38,5
                b) Bieber, *H.T.*, fig.416; Robert, *Masken*, fig.104/5, p.83; *W.S.*,
                   69 (1956), 115

        Note Attitude and clothing suggest a slave and Robert explains as mask 22
                in spite of long beard.   Early Hellenistic

ET 7   Terracotta mask   Fouquet Collection 425   Lower Egypt
        H. 0,95 m.

        Old man's mask (3).   Speira: wrinkled brow, furrowed cheeks, one eyebrow
        raised higher than the other, eyes with v. slightly sunk pupils, full beard

        Ref. Perdrizet, pl.86, no.425

        Note Cf AT 2.   Early Hellenistic

ET 8   Terracotta mask   Berlin, Rubensohn Collection   Egypt
        H. 0,062 m.

        Mask (3)

        Ref. Simon 193 n.44a

ET 9   Terracotta mask   Stuttgart   Alexandria
        H. 0,075 m.

        Mask 8: good modelling

        Ref. Simon 192 n.8; Sieglin, II, 2, pl.LIV, 9

        Note Early Hellenistic

ET 10   Terracotta mask   Fouquet Collection 426   Fayoum
        H. 0,110 m.

        Old man's mask (8).   Bald, both brows raised; outlined eyes, no inscription;
        very long beard

        Ref. Perdrizet, pl.86, no.426

        Note Early Hellenistic

Young men

ET 11   Terracotta mask   Oxford 1886.478   Naukratis
        Youth with outlined, ball eyes (16)

        Note Early Hellenistic.   Cf. BT 3 and 4

ET 12   Terracotta mask   London, B.M., 1910.12.11.1   Oxyrhynchos

Delicate youth (13), wreathed: seems to come from a vessel

Note Early Hellenistic. This may rather be a hetaira like ET 5

ET 13   Terracotta mask   Dresden   Alexandria

Youth (13) mask with very hard modelling of brows

Ref. Sieglin, II, 2, pl.LI, i

Note Cf. ET 19.   Probably Early Hellenistic

ET 14   Terracotta head   Rome, Vatican, Coll.Grassi, B 2   Fayoum

Perhaps delicate youth (13), striated hair; smooth brows; bored pupils;
v. wide mouth

Ref. Faccenna, *Rendiconti P.A.*, 29 (1956), 194, pl.1, no.35, takes as tragic
and compares Sieglin II, 2, pl.50,2; pl.51, 3

Note Late Hellenistic or Roman

ET 15   Terracotta mask   London, B.M., C627

H. 0,038 m.

Mask 14: speira, small turn-up nose, pupils sunk, mouth shows inside mask
mouth

Ref. Simon 185 n.105; *Naukratis*, I, pl.15, fig.15

ET 16   Terracotta head   Mustaki Collection   Alexandria

Head with raised brows, wearing wimple; possibly *agroikos* (14) dressed as
woman?   Red clay painted red, black brows.   Early Hellenistic, if genuine

ET 17   Terracotta head   Alexandria 9621   Alexandria

Youth (?15) with onkos

Ref. Breccia, *Terrecotte*, i, no.362, pl.38/3

Note Cf. DT 17, perhaps 2nd cent. B.C.

ET 18   Terracotta head   Rome, Vatican, Coll.Grassi B 3   Fayoum

Well-haired head with sharp, depressed eyes, hooked nose.   Probably soldier
(15)

Ref. Faccenna, *Rendiconti P.A.*, 29 (1956), 196, pl.8, 45

Note Late Hellenistic or Roman

ET 19   Terracotta head   Alexandria 9831   Alexandria

Youth with wrinkled forehead and swinging brows (?*kolax*), bored pupils

Ref. Breccia, *Terrecotte*, i, pl.46, 7

Note Cf. ET 13.   Probably Early Hellenistic

ET 20   Terracotta mask   Alexandria 16228   Alexandria

H. 0,04 m.

Mask 18: snub nose, bald, much modelling of face

Ref. Breccia, *Terrecotte*, i, no.375, pl.xlvi;   Simon 181 n.4

Note Probably Early Hellenistic, if an actor at all

ET 21   Terracotta mask   Dresden   Alexandria

H. 0,057 m.

Mask 19: very careful modelling

Ref. Simon 185 n.102; Sieglin II, 2, pl.55/1, p.74

Note Early Hellenistic

ET 22   Terracotta mask   Schreiber Collection   Alexandria

H. 0,093 m.

Mask 20: very heavy treatment of brows and cheeks

Ref. Simon 183 n.46; Sieglin II, 2, pl.99/3; p.74

Note Cf ET 13.   Probably Early Hellenistic

Slaves

ET 23   Terracotta group   Mustaki Collection   Alexandria

Slave with small turn-up nose, pointed beard, with broken pot; woman (shut mouth) holding distaff

Note Middle Comedy tradition.   Early Hellenistic

ET 24   Terracotta statuette   Fouquet Collection 433   Sa-el-Hagar

H. 0,115 m.

Wreathed *episeistos* slave (27), bulbous outlined eyes, smooth trumpet, himation down thighs; walking with basket in right hand

Ref. Perdrizet, pl.88, no.433

Note Early Hellenistic

ET 25   Terracotta statuette   Bircher Collection   Egypt

Bald-headed Maison (25) with sheep round his shoulders, himation rolled round his middle falling to his knees

Ref. Graindor, *Terres-cuites de l'Egypte Greco-Romaine*, pl.II, 10

ET 26   Terracotta statuette   Fouquet Collection 435   Memphis

H. 0,104 m.

Slave (25) walking: chiton, himation round waist and down to knees; knotted brows; eyes with inscribed pupil; striated edges to trumpet; large knife in right hand, bundle of sticks (?) over left shoulder

Ref. Perdrizet, pl.87, no.435

ET 27   Terracotta statuette   Athens, V.Grace Collection   Egypt

Fat slave (27?): long wreath, pointed, striated trumpet, probably not bald; wine jar in left hand; small right hand clutching cloak

Note Late Hellenistic.   Perhaps cf. MT 35 etc. for style, TT 8 for subject

ET 28   Terracotta statuette   Mustaki Collection   Alexandria

Slave wearing *pilos* sitting cross-legged on altar (22): small eyes, smooth trumpet.   Pale pink clay

Note Early Hellenistic

ET 29   Terracotta statuette   Fouquet Collection 429   Memphis
         H. 0,093 m.

         Seated slave (22).   Cap hair; small eyes; smooth trumpet; hands crossed
         on breast; decent chiton; legs crossed

         Ref. Perdrizet, pl.87, no.429

         Note Probably Early Hellenistic

ET 30   Terracotta statuette   Fouquet Collection 432   Memphis
         H. 0,55 m.

         ?Wreathed maison (25): globular, outlined eyes; hands crossed on breast;
         seated

         Ref. Perdrizet, pl.87, no.432

         Note Probably Early Hellenistic

ET 31   Terracotta statuette   a) Alexandria 9611   Fayoum
                                   b) Fouquet Collection 430   Fayoum
                                   c) Vienna, Inv. V 1981   Alexandria
         b) H. 0,152 m.

         Slave (22) seated cross-legged on altar with head pillared on hand; slave
         mask beside him.   Striated hair; depressed pupils; narrow striated edge
         to semicircular trumpet

         Ref. a) Breccia, *Terrecotte*, 64, no.350, pl.36,6
                 b) Perdrizet, pl.88, no.430
                 c) Webster, *Wiener Studien*, 59 (1956) 115

         Note Probably 2nd cent. B.C. or later

ET 32   Terracotta statuette   London, British Museum,   Egypt
         (black)   G 166

         Slave (22) seated on altar: arms folded; chiton girt above and below
         belly, stippled; speira; raised brows; largeish striated trumpet, semicircular

         Note Perhaps 2nd cent. B.C.

ET 33   Terracotta statuette   Alexandria 23237   Fayoum
         H. 0,105 m.

         Slave seated, cross-legged, hands clasped under chin, head up, on square altar:
         even speira, deep possibly pointed trumpet

         Ref. Breccia, *Terrecotte*, ii, pl.76, 390, p.52, no.345

         Note Late Hellenistic

ET 34   Terracotta figure   Rome, Vatican, Coll.Grassi, A 6   Fayoum
         Leading slave (?) with hand up to mouth

         Ref. Faccenna, *Rendiconti P.A.*, 29 (1956), 196, pl.10, 62

         Note Late Hellenistic or Roman

ET 35   Terracotta statuette   Amsterdam 7134   Alexandria
         Leading slave (27): peaked speira, wide twisted trumpet; right hand under
         cloak, left hand raised

         Ref. *Algemeene Gids*, no.366

ET 36   Terracotta statuette   Alexandria 6515   Alexandria

Wreathed slave (?seated). Very wide mouth with striated edge; sunk pupils;
brows raised

Ref. Breccia, *Terracotte*, 1, pl.37, 5

Note Cf. AV 10.   Perhaps 2nd cent. B.C.

ET 37   Terracotta head   Alexandria 9624   Alexandria

Wreathed slave with deep wide mouth (22?): raised brows, sunk pupils.
Very shiny clay

Ref. Breccia, *Terracotte*, 1, pl.48, 14

Note Probably 2nd cent. B.C.

ET 38   Terracotta mask   Dresden   Alexandria

H. 0,059 m.

Maison (25)

Ref. Simon 188 n.8a; Sieglin II, 2, pl.xl.1

Note Probably 2nd cent. B.C.

ET 39   Terracotta mask   Alexandria 16780   Alexandria

Slave: bored pupils; evenly stylized brows; knot of hair above forehead.
?*Tettix* (26)

Ref. Breccia, *Terracotte*, 1, no.363, pl.37, 1

Note Cf. ZT 23.   Probably 2nd cent. B.C.

ET 40   Terracotta head   Alexandria 9362, 9626, 9627, 9631,   Alexandria
                                   9790, 10740, 16223, 19590

Slave: probably 27

Ref. Breccia, *Terracotte*, 1, 363, pl.37/4,6,8; 38/2,4,7,9; 46/2,17

Note Cf. AV 32.   Probably 2nd cent. B.C.

ET 41   Terracotta head   Oxford (no no.)   Naukratis
         (Fragment)

Slave with uneven, twisted brows, goggle eyes, finely striated hair (27).
Slave rather than old man because the wavy-haired old man has even brows

Note For treatment of brows, cf. DT 11.   Probably Early Hellenistic

ET 42   Terracotta head   London, B.M., C 640   Naukratis

H. 0,51 m.

Wavy-haired slave (27): wide slightly twisted trumpet

Ref. Walters, *Cat.*, 261

Note Late Hellenistic

ET 43   Terracotta head   Oxford (no no.)   Naukratis
         (?from vase)

Leading slave (22): peaked striated hair, depressed pupils, semicircular
trumpet

Note For style cf. DL 2.   Probably 1st cent. B.C.

ET 44 Terracotta mask   London, B.M., C 641   Naukratis

H. 0,76 m.

Leading slave (22): orange flesh, red lips and eyelids, grey eyeballs; petal eyelids; wideish rounded trumpet

Ref. Walters, *Cat.*, 261; *Naukratis*, I pl.15, fig.14 (brought in by workmen: probably Egypt, not necessarily Naukratis)

Note Probably Early Roman

ET 45 Terracotta head   Alexandria 10706   Kom-el-Sciugefa

Leading slave (22): striated wig hair, twisted trumpet mouth

Ref. Breccia, *Terrecotte*, 1, no.346, pl.47/13

Note Cf. DT 19.   First cent. B.C.

ET 46 Terracotta head   London, B.M., C 647   Fayoum

H. 0,51 m.

Leading slave (22), with wreath: semicircular trumpet, fat face

Ref. Walters, *Cat.*, 262

ET 47 Terracotta mask   Rome, Vatican, Coll. Grassi B 5   Fayoum

Leading slave (22): wrinkled brow, outlined squinting eyes with bored pupils, shallow striated trumpet

Ref. Faccenna, *Rendiconti P.A.* 29 (1956), 196, pl.8, 44

Note Late Hellenistic

ET 48 Terracotta   Berlin 30082   ?Egypt

H. 0,15 m.

Mask 22

Ref. Simon 190, n.41c

ET 49 Terracotta mask   Benachi Collection   Egypt

Leading slave (22): only eye, brow, and front of hair preserved

Note Life-size.   Very hard modelling of ridges.   Perhaps Early Hellenistic. Cf. ET 13

ET 50 Terracotta mask   Benachi Collection   Egypt

Slave mask (22): bored pupils and iris; semicircular twisted trumpet; peaked hair

ET 51 Terracotta mask   Benachi Collection   Egypt

Leading slave (22): bored pupils and iris; semicircular trumpet; peaked hair

ET 52 Terracotta head   Benachi Collection   Egypt

Head of bald slave, maison (25): semicircular twisted trumpet

Note Cf. MT 30.   Probably 2nd century

ET 53   Terracotta mould   Benachi Collection   -

Four masks: one broken away, one a youth with striated peaked speira, two
slaves with peaked speira and wide mouths

ET 54   Terracotta trumpet   Mustaki Collection   Alexandria

Slave mask (22) alternating with other heads on stem

Women

ET 55   Terracotta statuette   Marseille, Musée Borély,   ?Alexandria
                                 Froehner 2592

H. 0,088 m.

Comic slave (22) in female clothing; yellow head-dress, blue chiton, white
himation

Note Head does not belong.   Body possibly Hellenistic

ET 56   Terracotta mask   Frankfurt   Fayoum

First pseudokore.   Evanescent eyes (34)

Ref. Kaufmann, *Ägyptische Terrakotten*, 75

Note Probably Early Hellenistic

ET 57   Terracotta head   Alexandria 6618   Alexandria

Woman with straggly hair: knot on back of hair perhaps is handle of mask;
bored pupils (36?)

Ref. Breccia, *Terrecotte*, 1, pl.46, 10

Note Late Hellenistic

Plasters and fayence

ET 58   Plaster mask   Alexandria   Alexandria

Mask 5

Ref. Simon 192 n.30; Breccia, *Terrecotte*, 1, pl.58,1

Note Late Hellenistic or Augustan

ET 59   Plaster head   University College   Egypt
                                 London GA 52

Maison head with shallow twisted trumpet (25)

Note Late Hellenistic or Augustan

ET 60   Fayence head   Amsterdam 467 (?)   Egypt

H. 0,036 m.

Tettix mask (26): pale greenish face, brown hair, brows, eyelids, beard;
oval trumpet with wavy hair

Note Early Hellenistic

ET 61   Fayence head from vessel   Mustaki Collection   Alexandria

        Slave mask (27): green hair, black eyes, pale yellow face

        Note Early Hellenistic

[Add also EV 15 below]

Vases

EV 1-15   For fayence heads, which probably come from vases, see under terracottas:
        EV 15 is a complete fayence dish.   Only 1-3, the early black glaze
        skyphoi, which are like Attic black glaze, are dated.   The vases which
        comprise whole figurines are classed together, 4-7.   EV 8 has a parallel
        in UT 49.

1) Dated

EV 1   Black glaze kantharos   Alexandria 10481   Alexandria   Late 4th/early
                                                 (Chatby)   3rd cent. B.C.

        Leading slave masks on handles: deepish rounded trumpet, even speira (22)

        Ref. Breccia, *Necropoli*, p.65, no.170, pl.54, 105

EV 2   Black glaze kantharos   Alexandria 19268   Alexandria   Late 4th/early
                                                 (Chatby)   3rd cent. B.C.

        Masks on handles (probably same as preceding)

        Ref. Breccia, *Necropoli*, p.65, no.171, pl.54, 106

EV 3   Handle mask of black   Alexandria   Hadra   3rd/2nd cent.
        glaze skyphos   B.C.

        H. 0,058 m.

        Slave with low speira and shock of hair over ears, very wide twisted trumpet
        with narrow smooth edges (22)

        Ref. Adriani, *Ann. Mus. Gr.-Rom.*, 3 (1935-9), 113, pl.45,4

        Note Found with early Megarian bowls and Hadra vases

2) Undated

EV 4   Terracotta plastic vase   Alexandria 23295   Fayoum
        H. 0,05 m.

        Slave mask (22): above head mouth of jug: whole vase was comic actor.
        Striated peaked hair and wide twisted trumpet with striated edge; pupils
        not bored; brows raised

        Ref. Breccia, *Terrecotte*, ii, pl.76, 393, p.53, no.348. Cf. *Delos* 23,
            1221-2 = DT 19

        Note Probably 1st cent. B.C.

EV 5   Terracotta head from vase   Mustaki Collection   Alexandria
         Slave head (27) with small spout above
         Ref. Like EV 4.   Probably 1st cent. B.C.

EV 6   Plastic vase   Fouquet Collection 431   Fayoum
         Slave (22) with wreath, hands clasped, seated on altar decorated with swags.
         Pupils depressed; narrow striated trumpet.   Orifice above hand: handle
         from shoulder to head
         Ref. Perdrizet, pl.88, no.431
         Note Late Hellenistic

EV 7   Plastic vase   Fouquet Collection 434   Fayoum
         H. 0,155 m.
         Wreathed slave (22) squatting, with bundle on the ground.   Wide twisted
         trumpet
         Ref. Perdrizet, pl.87, no.434
         Note Probably Late Hellenistic

EV 8   Terracotta vase   Alexandria 8083   Fayoum
         H. 0,07 m.
         Slave mask, ?bald, wreathed, wrinkled brow, depressed pupils, shock of hair;
         ?round trumpet.   Orifice in shape of *polos*
         Ref. Breccia, *Terrecotte* ii, pl.76, 392, p.53, no.349, takes as lamp
         Note Late Hellenistic

EV 9   Relief jug (?)   Schreiber Collection   Alexandria
         H. 0,118 m.
         Leading slave (22): green clay; rimmed eyes, with depressed pupils;   peaked
         speira, striated, semicircular trumpet with narrow striated edge
         Ref. Sieglin II, 3, pl.37/1
         Note Perhaps 1st cent. B.C.

EV 10   Moulded cup   Alexandria   Canopus
         Slave mask, bald, wreathed (25);   mouth for mouthpiece;   handle behind ear
         Ref. Breccia, *Monuments*, I, 78, pl.43,3

EV 11   Head vase, cup with floral stem   Frankfurt   Fayoum
         Leading slave (22).   Bored pupils;   striated hair
         Ref. Kaufmann, *Ägyptische Terrakotten*, fig.124/1

EV 12   Head vase, cup with floral stem   Frankfurt   Fayoum
         Leading slave (22)
         Ref. Kaufmann, *Ägyptische Terrakotten*, fig.124/4

EV 13   Terracotta head   Heidelberg   Athens
         (vase or lamp)

         Head, bald, large ears, wide mouth;   band round forehead and across head.
         Red glaze on red clay

         Ref. Sieglin II, 3, 81 fig.98

         Note Import from Alexandria.   Perhaps not dramatic

EV 14   Embossed mask on Roman pottery   Benachi Collection   Egypt

         Curly-haired youth (12): corkscrew curls over forehead and descending
         cheeks, raised brows

         Note Not before late 1st cent. B.C.

EV 15   Fayence dish (green/blue)   Paris, Louvre C.A.   Egypt
                                              1415

         Slave mask in centre (22): wreath, swinging brows, small dotted eyes,
         semicircular twisted trumpet

         Note Not after 2nd cent. B.C. as fayence seems like early Queen jugs

AFRICA

Bronze

      1 is perhaps not dramatic; cf. YT 12, XB 1, NT 26, UB 25

FB 1   Bronze lamps   ?   Volubilis .   Late 1st
                                                          and Bayasa   Cent. B.C.
         a) Youth with two horns (?Dionysos)
         b) Youth with smooth brows and wavy hair (16)

         Ref. C. Picard, *R.A.* 45 (1955), 63, argues for Alexandrian origin: found
                 in Palace of Juba II.   R. Thouvenot, *Publ. du Service des Ant. de
                 Maroc*, 10 (1954), 217, pl.35-7

FB2   Bronze mask   Hildesheim   Galjub

         Mask (?38): melon hair; bun behind

         Ref. Simon 1 22, 197 n.44; *A.M.* 50 (1925), 186 fig.1; Ippel, *Bronze fund
                 von Galjub*, pl.9, no.38

         Note Probably 2nd cent. B.C. or earlier

Terracottas

FT 1   Terracotta head   Paris, Louvre, MI   Cyrenaica
                                  57 1855

         Leading old man (3).   Eyes outlined

         Note For style cf. AT 19.   Probably 2nd cent. B.C.

FT 2   Terracotta mask   B.M., C749   Cyrenaica

H. 0,105 m.

Little housekeeper (30).   Bored pupils

Ref. *R.B.* XXXII (1949), fig.3; Simon 126, 199 n.1; Webster, *Later Greek Comedy*, pl.4c; *G.T.P.*, no.C73

Note For style cf. AT 19

FT 3   Terracotta statuette   Paris, Louvre CA 3005   Cyrenaica

H. 0,10 m.

Slave seated on altar, drapery round waist falling below knee, chin on hand, shoes; wavy hair (27), semicircular trumpet

Ref. *T.K.* 419/3

Note Proportions suggest 1st cent. B.C.

SICILY AND LIPARI

Terracottas

ST 1-28   Terracottas are arranged under find spots.   Firm dates are given for ST 2, 6, 15.   The considerable group from Centuripe, 3-12, has one firm date 6 in the second century B.C., and the rest seem to belong to the same period.   The Lipari mask 15 continues the Middle Comedy tradition (cf. *Middle Comedy*: mask V), like the female masks on a contemporary Gnathia vase (GV 1).   The Naxos masks 16-17 may have been a set of wall masks like the Priene set (ZT 20ff.).   The three closely similar masks of young men from Syracuse 18-20 may also be a set; 21-2 are later.   25 is a very fine early mask.   UT 26 may be Sicilian.

ST 1   Terracotta mask   Palermo   Alontion (Sicily)

Youth (11):   smooth regular speira, brows slightly raised

Ref. Kekulé, pl.53/1

Note For style cf. ST 4.   Probably 2nd cent. B.C.

ST 2   Terracotta statuette   Gela   Butera, Piano della   280/50 B.C.
                                                     Fiera, Grave xxxi

Marionette with movable legs: bald, slave mask with semicircular twisted trumpet mouth and large ears (25)

Ref. D. Adamasteanu, *Mon. Ant.* 44 (1958), 254, fig.30, dates by fusiform aryballos

Note Compare *Middle Comedy*, IT 4

ST 3   Terracotta mask   London, B.M. D 49   Centuripe

H. 0,45 m.

Delicate youth (13):   pupils pierced;   round eyes;   sharp nose.   Small, very shiny.

Ref. Walters, *Cat.*, 306

Note Perhaps 2nd cent. B.C.

ST 4   Terracotta mask   Carlsruhe   ?Centuripe

H. 0,14 m.

Mask 18: wreath, rimmed eyes with bored pupils, raised brows

Ref. Simon 45, 181 n.6, pl.X,2; Kekulé, pl.53/3

Note Style not unlike ET 13 etc.   Probably 2nd cent. B.C.

ST 5   Terracotta mask   ?Biscari   Centuripe

Young Pan, wreathed

Ref. Kekulé, pl.53/2

Note Probably 2nd cent. B.C.

ST 6   Terracotta statuette   Syracuse   Centuripe   2nd cent.B.C.

H. 0,155 m.

Man in short chiton advancing and making a greeting: if an actor, probably
kolax, but mouth is not emphasized

Ref. G. Libertini, *N.Sc.*, 1947, 269, fig.6a

Note For gesture cf. ZT 29

ST 7   Terracotta statuette   Biscari   Centuripe

H. 0,08 m.

Mask 22; seated; left hand gesticulates; right hand tears hair

Ref. Simon 190 n.47a; *T.K.* II, 424/7; Libertini, *Museo di Biscari*, no.1173,
        pl.106

Note Early Hellenistic

ST 8   Terracotta statuette   Catania   Centuripe

Seated, wreathed Maison (25): shock of hair over ears, wide shallow twisted
trumpet

Ref. Kekulé, pl.52/5

Note Probably 2nd cent. B.C.

ST 9   Terracotta mask   ?Biscari   Centuripe

Wreathed slave (27): shock of hair over ears, wavy hair, pointed trumpet

Ref. Kekulé, pl.53/5

Note Cf. ST 4.   2nd cent. B.C.

ST 10   Terracotta mask   London, British   Centuripe
                                         Museum, D 48

H. 0,45 m.

Leading slave (22), with wreath: pierced eyes, wideish trumpet nearly
semicircular

Ref. Walters, *Cat.*, 306

Note Perhaps 2nd cent. B.C.

ST 11   Terracotta mask   Catania   Centuripe
           Mask (?38): melon hair; bun behind
           Ref. Simon 122, 197 n.45a; Kekulé, pl.53/4
           Note For style cf. ST 5 above.   2nd cent. B.C.

ST 12   Terracotta mask   Palermo   Centuripe
           Lampadion mask (42)
           Ref. Libertini, *Centuripe*, pl.36/4
           Note Early Hellenistic

ST 13   Terracotta mask   Vienna 1865   Girgenti
           H. 0,082 m.
           Youth (13): bored pupils, slightly raised brows, smooth cap hair
           Note Not before 2nd cent. B.C.

ST 14   Terracotta mask   Heraclea Minoa   Heraclea Minoa
                                     Inv.697
           H. 0,09 m.
           Mask 27: wavy hair, semicircular trumpet, pupils bored
           Ref. de Miro, *N.Sc.*, 12 (1958), 276 no.8
           Note Probably Late Hellenistic

ST 15   Terracotta mask   Lipari   Lipari   Early 3rd cent.B.C.
           Mask 35 (very clearly derives from Middle Comedy with high topknot)
           Ref. Simon 197 n.42a; *N.Sc.* 1929, 76 fig.40, found with vases of late
                fourth century and lamps of early third century type; bottom date
                242 B.C.

ST 16   Terracotta mask   Princeton, Art   ?Naxos (Sicily)
                                     Museum 51.85
           Wreathed youth with bored pupils; hooked nose.   Presumably 1st *episeistos*
           (15); too much hair for *kolax* (17)
           Note With ST 17, probably wall masks like ZT 20 ff.   2nd cent. B.C.

ST 17   Terracotta mask   Princeton, Art   ?Naxos (Sicily)
                                     Museum 51.84
           Young hetaira with sharp little nose, bored pupils, wreath on front of head,
           wimple
           Note With ST 16.   The added moustache and beard probably belongs to a
                pornoboskos mask of the same set.   Style not unlike DT 2-3

ST 18   Terracotta mask   Syracuse   ?Syracuse
           Youth (10): outlined eyes, depressed pupils; raised brows, rather high
           striated speira like onkos
           Note 2nd cent. B.C.

ST 19   Terracotta mask   Syracuse   ?Syracuse
         Wreathed youth with fat face (13)
         Note For treatment cf. ZT 2 etc.   2nd cent. B.C.

ST 20   Terracotta mask   Syracuse   ?Syracuse
         Youth (?11): outlined eyes, high striated speira, raised brows
         Note 2nd cent. B.C.

ST 21   Terracotta mask   Copenhagen, NM, Ab 87   Syracuse
         Wreathed youth with fat face.   Sharp nose; bored pupils
         Ref. Breitenstein, no.719
         Note Cf DT 13, AT 21.   Probably 1st cent. B.C.

ST 22   Terracotta head   Syracuse   ?Syracuse
         Slave (22): uneven brows; bored pupils; peaked speira, semicircular
         trumpet
         Note Cf. DL 2.   Not before 1st cent. B.C.

[Add ST 28 below]

ST 23   Terracotta mask   Harvard University   Tyndaris, Sicily
                                  (no number)
         Slave mask with knotted brow, marked pupils, deep square trumpet mouth.
         Coarse work
         Note Probably 2nd cent. B.C.

ST 24   Terracotta head   London, British Museum,   Sicily
                                  1956.2.16.3
         Perhaps rustic youth (14): roughly striated hair, arched brows.   Pinkish-
         yellow clay
         Note Probably 2nd cent. B.C. or earlier.   Not unlike NT 4 in clay and
                 style

ST 25   Terracotta mask   Copenhagen, N.M. 7367   Sicily
         Youth (16), smooth brows, wreath, wavy hair, eyes rimmed
         Ref. Breitenstein, no.720; *R.B.* xxxii, 130, no.16
         Note Style like BT 4 and ET 11.   Probably 3rd cent. B.C.

ST 26   Terracotta mask   Biscari   Unknown
         H. 0,12 m.
         Leading slave with elaborate wreath; globular eyes, outlined, with deeply
         depressed pupils
         Ref. Libertini, *Museo di Biscari*, pl.116, no.1179
         Note Probably 2nd cent. B.C.

ST 27   Terracotta mask   Milan   Sicily

H. 0,09 m.

Bald slave (Maison): pupils with incised circles; big ears; wide twisted mouth

Ref. Sambon, pl.12, no.304

Note Probably 2nd cent. B.C.

ST 28   Terracotta mask   Syracuse   Sicily

Youth with hard swinging brows, bored pupils and iris; large nose (15?)

Note Probably 2nd cent. B.C.

SOUTH ITALY

Glass

TG 1   Glass relief   Naples, Room 90   S. Italy

Slave mask (22) (as TG 2) with crook and thyrsos

Note Late Hellenistic

TG 2   Blue glass relief   Naples, Room 90   S. Italy

Slave mask (22) with thyrsos: neatly striated peaked hair; even, arched brows; semicircular twisted trumpet

Note Late Hellenistic

Jewellery

TJ 1-4   Southern Italy is included with Apulia. TJ 1 is dated by the coins found with it and has an interesting assemblage of early New Comedy masks; TJ 2 is dated by style. The mask of TJ 4 is very like the young Dionysos mask (NS 16 etc.), but the contorted brows show that it is rather the young lover of comedy.

TJ 1   Silver cup   Lost   Tarentum   4th/3rd cent.B.C.

Masks 11? (with straight speira striated, slightly arched brows), 22 (with straight speira, wide and deep rounded striated trumpet), 27 (wreathed with shallow striated pointed trumpet), 33 (with short hair, Pan, Herakles (tragic), Satyr, Papposilenos

Ref. Simon 184 n.87, 192 n.11,51, 195 n.3; Nachod, *R.M.*, 33 (1918), 115; Willeumier, *Tarente*, 338f., pl.7,8; Luschey, *Phiale*, 62, no.13; Q. van Ufford, *B.V.A.B.*, 33 (1958), 43; *G.T.P.*, no.C 8

Note Found with coins of 315-272 B.C.

TJ 2   Bronze mirror   Canosa   Canosa

Muse with slave mask (27) with even speira, deepish pointed trumpet and 3 Erotes

Ref. Züchner, *Klappspiegel*, no.145 fig.43

Note Cf. CJ 1. Züchner dates to 3rd cent. B.C.

TJ 3   Gold pendant   Naples (no no.)   Tarentum

Wreathed, young *episeistos*

Note   Perhaps 3rd cent. B.C.

TJ 4   Carneol   Evans Collection   Tarentum

Young *episeistos* (16) with ivy wreath, contorted brows, curly wavy hair.
Inscription: FORTUNATUS Q.L.

Ref.   Lippold, pl.61/1;   *A.G.* 25, 47

Note   According to Lippold Early Roman, therefore probably 1st cent. B.C.

Terracottas

TT 1-30   Of the terracottas TT 1-3 have good excavation dates.   1 and 2, which
are early, have the longer beards of early New Comedy slaves noted on DM 1,
but are much less obviously in the Middle Comedy tradition than the fierce,
small, compact fourth century Tarentine terracottas.   They have the large
limbs of early Myrina terracottas.   18 from Ruvo with its elaborate
modelling and unpierced eyes should also be early: the nicked eyebrows
recall the leading old man's mask on the Delos mosaic.   25-27, 29 should
also be early.   Of the other terracottas from Tarentum 12 looks very like
the slave masks on Attic braziers and may be an import.   13-14 are from
Apulia but not necessarily Tarentum: 13 is not unlike the earlier Delos
and Priene masks;   14 should probably be excluded as not dramatic.   15
and 19 are unique, but there is no sound reason to doubt them.   23-4, 28
may be of the 2nd cent. B.C., 30 is late.   UT 1, 3, 23, 99 may belong
here.   The special style of TT 15 may be repeated in UT 56, 57, 64.   UT 103-5
are stated to be Tarentine in this publication.

1) Dated

TT 1   Terracotta statuette   Taranto   Tarentum,   3rd cent. B.C.
                                                            Arsenale, Grave 13

Maison (25): fierce brows;   straight hair;   semicircular striated trumpet·
cloak pinned on right shoulder;   basket with bird

Ref.   Bieber, *D.*, no.87;   *H.T.*^{1}, fig.97, ^{2}, fig.155;   *N.Sc.*, 1897, 217;
G.T.P., no.C 9

TT 2   Terracotta statuette   Taranto   Arsenale,   3rd cent. B.C.
                                                            Grave 13

Walking slave with child (mask 22):   deep rounded trumpet;   peaked speira;
cloak

Ref.   Bieber, *D.*, no.89c (pl.73/4);   *N.Sc.*, 1897, 216;   *G.T.P.*, no.C 10;
Negative, Sop. Ant. Taranto, Cat.D, no.1415

Note   Same grave as TT 1 above.   UT 99 may be a replica

TT 3   Terracotta masks   Taranto   Tarentum   Late Hellenistic

Three masks: (*m*) roof tile, peaked hair, deepish trumpet;   (*n*) peaked wavy
hair, pointed trumpet;   (*o*) wild-haired satyr

Ref.   C. Drago, *N.Sc.* 1940, 314, fig.1, m, n, o

Note   Found with alabastron, Hellenistic vases, and terracottas.   Dated by
excavator, first century of the empire

2) Undated

TT 4   Terracotta statuette   Taranto Museum   Tarentum
        Comic actor: ?mask 7. Hands on hips, cloak falling to thighs; cap hair
        and flowing beard
        Ref. Bieber, *H.T.*, fig.212
        Note Probably Early Hellenistic

TT 5   Terracotta mould   London, British Museum,   Tarentum
                                   E 14
        H. 0,55 m.
        Mask of admirable youth (10)
        Note Probably Early Hellenistic

TT 6   Terracotta mask   Taranto   S. Italy
        Mask of youth, probably 13: elaborate ivy wreath, nearly smooth brows, no
        hair visible
        Ref. Bieber, *H.T.*, fig.408
        Note Early Hellenistic

TT 7   Three terracotta masks   Taranto   Tarentum, Via Mazzini 278,
                                                               Grave 4
        Youths, 10: wavy hair with slight peak, bored pupils, slightly contorted brows,
        folds on forehead
        Ref. Krien, *J.D.O.A.I.*, 42 (1956), 108, fig.48
        Note Perhaps 1st cent. B.C.

TT 8   Terracotta statuette   a) Trieste, Museo   Tarentum
                                      Civico 215
                                   b) Harvard University TL 10368.6
        Bald slave (25) with deep, round trumpet beard, hand to mouth, wine jar,
        himation down to knees
        Ref. a), Winter, *T.K.*, 423/6
        Note Cf. ET 27.   Early Hellenistic

TT 9   Terracotta head   Copenhagen, NC Inv.997   Tarentum
        H. 0,035 m.
        Slave (25): bald forehead, enormous shock of hair, broken off below mouth
        Ref. V. Poulsen, *Terres Cuites*, pl.47, 85
        Note Bought from Helbig 1888 as coming from Tarentum.   Early Hellenistic

TT 10   Terracotta mask   Copenhagen, NC Inv.996   Tarentum
        H. 0,045 m.
        Slave or old man: short, roundish beard; rimmed eyes; receding hair
        Ref. V. Poulsen, *Terres Cuites*, pl.47, 86
        Note Bought from Helbig as coming from Tarentum.   Early Hellenistic.   A
        curious piece of which the identification is doubtful

TT 11   Terracotta antefix   Taranto   Tarentum

H. 0,21 m.

Head of slave (27) with receding wavy hair; furrowed forehead and cheeks, uneven striated eyebrows, eyes outlined with depressed pupils, striated moustache and beard which turns up in front

Ref. C. Leviosa, *Arch. Class.* 6 (1954), 247, no.48, pl.77/4

Note Probably Early Hellenistic

TT 12   Terracotta head   Copenhagen, NC Inv.988   Tarentum

Slave (27): peaked, wavy hair, smooth rounded trumpet, spade-shaped

Ref. V. Poulsen, *Terres Cuites*, pl.47, 87; cf. Quagliati, *Taranto*, 49, and *H.T.*, fig.268

Note Bought from Helbig 1888 as from Tarentum.   Cf AV 32, i.e. probably from brazier and possibly import.   2nd cent. B.C.

TT 13   Terracotta mask   Munich, Inv.5404   Apulia

H. 0,085 m.

Mask of slave girl: 44.   Bored pupils; sharp lids

Ref. Bieber, *H.T.*, fig.288a; *D.*, no.178; Simon 111, 197, n.49;   116; Sieveking, *A.A.*, 1917, 30; Rumpf, *A.E.*, 1953-4, 122, n.5

Note Cf. DT 1.   Probably early 2nd cent. B.C.

TT 14   Terracotta mask   Munich, Inv.5403   Apulia

Slave girl: sleepy eyes with sharp lids; naturally formed mouth (?44)

Ref. Bieber, *H.T.*, fig.288b

Note Probably early 2nd cent. B.C.   Probably the mouth excludes this as not dramatic

TT 15   Terracotta mould   London, B.M., E 31   Tarentum

H. 0,13 m.

Fat woman (?) dancing.   Possibly can be taken as slave dressed as woman, cf. TT 27

Ref. *P.C.F.*, fig.144; Winter, *T.K.*, 467/6

Note Very strange hard style.   Perhaps 2nd cent. B.C.

TT 16   Terracotta mask   Reggio   S. Italy

Leno (8)

Ref. Krien, *J.D.O.A.I.* 42 (1956), 110, fig.45

Note Very coarse treatment of brows and locks of beard.   Perhaps 2nd cent. B.C.

TT 17   Terracotta mask   Reggio   S. Italy

Slave (27): peaked striated hair, flat bulbous eyes, semicircular trumpet

Ref. Photo. Sopr. alle antich. Calabria

Note Not unlike DT 23.   Late Hellenistic

TT 18   Terracotta head   London, British Museum, D 59   Ruvo

H. 0,58 m.

Leading old man (4).   Knicked uneven brows, wavy hair, fillet over hair, flowing beard; eyes large and outlined

Ref. Walters, *Cat.*, 308

Note Early Hellenistic

TT 19   Terracotta mask   Ruvo   Ruvo

Mask 5: knicked uneven brows, bored pupils, striated beard

Ref. Simon 193 n.31; Robert, fig.60

Note Perhaps 2nd cent. B.C.

TT 20   Terracotta statuette   London, British Museum, D 325   Ruvo

H. 0,12 m.

Youth in short chiton and himation: large wreath, wavy hair peaked above forehead, large, outlined eyes with depressed pupils.   Perhaps first *episeistos* (15)

Ref. Walters, *Cat.*, 360

Note Probably 2nd cent. B.C.

TT 21   Terracotta antefix   Milan   S. Italy

H. 0,20 m.

Slave (22), flower wreath and fillet; small eyes with depressed pupils, deep twisted trumpet with striated flat edge

Ref. Sambon, no.276, pl.10, takes as satyr, perhaps rightly

Note Not before 2nd cent. B.C.

TT 22   Terracotta mask   Milan   S. Italy

H. 0,16 m.

Slave (?*tettix*): eyes outlined, pupils not bored; very wide, hollow trumpet

Ref. Sambon, no.183, pl.11

TT 23   Terracotta mask   Taranto   Tarentum

Unbearded mask with pseudo-onkos of curly hair, smooth brows, depressed pupils

Note Perhaps 2nd cent. B.C.

TT 24   Terracotta statuette   Taranto   Tarentum

Standing slave, right arm forward, himation round waist and left shoulder, tights, wig hair, deepish pointed trumpet, uneven brows

Note Perhaps 2nd cent. B.C. or earlier

TT 25   Terracotta statuette   Taranto   Tarentum (Villa Beaumont)

Standing man with wavy speira, wedge beard, diadem, wrapped in cloak to knees

Ref. Perhaps still Middle Comedy

TT 26   Terracotta statuette   Taranto   Tarentum (Grave in Contrada
                                                       Tesoro)

Striding slave, wavy hair, deepish pointed trumpet, himation over both hands
and head

Note Perhaps 3rd cent. B.C.

TT 27   Terracotta statuette   Taranto   Tarentum (Grave in Via Pepe)

Dancing slave with wavy hair, deepish pointed trumpet, wrapped in long
himation

Note Perhaps cf. TT 15.   Perhaps 3rd cent. B.C.

TT 28   Terracotta statuette   Taranto   Tarentum (Via Oberdan)

Slave seated on altar, both hands wrapped in himation, right hand raised,
elaborate wreath, perhaps bald, bored eyes, semicircular trumpet

Note Cf. IT 13.   Perhaps 2nd cent. B.C.

TT 29   Terracotta mask   Taranto   Tarentum

Peaked speira, raised brows, small bulbous eyes, deep rounded trumpet: 22

Note Perhaps 3rd cent. B.C.

TT 30   Terracotta mask   Reggio   S. Italy

Wreathed slave with bulbous eyes and very wide trumpet, perhaps bald

Note Late Hellenistic

Vases

TV 1   Canosa vase: confirms TT 1-2 for the type of decently clothed comic slave
          in S. Italy in the third century B.C.

TV 1   Canosa vase   Amsterdam 4712   Canosa   3rd cent. B.C.
          H. 0,172 m.

Pensive slave (22): right hand to chin, legs crossed, chiton well down thigh,
straight speira and falling hair, deepish rounded trumpet with square upper
corners

Ref. *Algemeene Gids*, no.1676.   Cf. Pryce, *C.V.A.*, British Museum, fasc.7,
        on IV D a, pl.13

GV 1-6   The Gnathia vases with masks which can be firmly ascribed to the early
          3rd cent. B.C. for the most part continue the tradition of Middle Comedy
          Gnathia masks, but the mask of the 'full-grown hetaira' (38) on GV 4 and
          the mask of the concubine (37) on GV 3 are new in the Gnathia repertoire.
          The wreathed youth with fattish face on GV 1 dates this type to the
          beginning of the third century.

GV 1   Gnathia oinochoe   Cleveland Museum of Art   300/275 B.C.
        (Ribbed group)   52.16, John L. Severance Coll.

Wreath of ivy leaf and helichryse round belly.   Neck: wreath of vine
leaves, grapes and tendrils from which depend a) ivy spray, b) mask of
woman in mitra with side hair (35), c) red scarf, d) fat boys dancing,
f) mask of woman with hair done in top knot by fillet (35).   Male plastic
mask at base of handle, youth with wavy hair (16) and elaborate wreath

Ref.   *Antike Kunst*, no.46

Note   For male mask cf. ZT 2, BT 10, etc.   For female mask cf. ST 15

GV 2   Gnathia oinochoe   Lecce 4092   Roccavecchia   300/275 B.C.
        (Ribbed group)

Pseudokore mask with spray of hair in front (35)

Ref.   Bernadini, *N.Sc.*, 1934, 194.   No useful context.   *Antike Kunst*,
        3 (1960), 30f.

GV 3   Gnathia oinochoe   Once Ann Arbor,   300/275 B.C.
        (Ribbed group)   Kelsey Museum

Women with wreath of hair (36)

Ref.   *J.H.S.*, 71 (1951), 222, no.8;   *G.T.P.*, no.C 7

GV 4   Gnathia oinochoe   Vercelli, Museo Leone   300/275 B.C.
        (Ribbed group)

Profile female mask: ear-ring.   Parted hair; no wimple (38).   Details
in brown and light golden

Ref.   *Antike Kunst*, no.47;   *G.T.P.*, no.C 29

GV 5   Gnathia oinochoe   a) Manchester, M.W.I. 6949   300/275 B.C.
        (Ribbed group)   b) Francavilla Fontana   b) Francavilla Fontana

Woman with melon hair (39?)

Ref.   a) *J.H.S.*, 71 (1951), 222, no.35;   *G.T.P.*, no.C 6
        b) Drago, *N.Sc.* 2 (1941), 116, fig.1;   *Antike Kunst*, p.30

GV 6   Gnathia oinochoe   Taranto   Francavilla Fontana   300/275 B.C.
        (Ribbed group)

Mask 41

Ref.   *J.H.S.*, 71 (1951), 222, no.17;   *C.V.*, 756/5

PAESTUM

Terracottas

PT 1   Terracotta mask   Paestum, M.N.,   Temple of Hera (1937)
                                  Case 38

Mask of *panchrestos* (10)

Ref.   *G.T.P.*, no.C 14.   Early Hellenistic

PT 2   Terracotta mask   Paestum, M.N., Case 45   Near the Temenos
                                                                   (1952)

        Mask of *hapalos* (13)

        Ref. G.T.P., no.C 17

        Note Early Hellenistic

PT 3   Terracotta mask   Paestum, M.N., Case 38   Temple of Hera
                                                                   (1937)

        Mask of slave (22), wreathed

        Ref. G.T.P., no.C 16.   Early Hellenistic

PT 4   Terracotta mask   Paestum, M.N., Case 38   Temple of Hera
                                                                   (1937)

        Mask of woman with melon hair (39?)

        Ref. G.T.P., no.C 15

        Note Early Hellenistic

CAMPANIA

Bronzes

Included here, although they come from Pompeii, because their Hellenistic dates
seem firm

NB 1   Bronze mask from chest   Naples, M.N. 1280   Pompeii   Late 2nd
                                                                              cent. B.C.

        Mask 15: raised brows, bored pupils; wreath with large ivy leaves; falling
        locks below wreath

        Ref. Simon 186 n.133a; Pernice, *Hell. Kunst in Pompeii*, V, 87, fig.35

NB 2   Bronze brazier   Naples 73018   Pompeii   2nd cent.B.C.

        Mask 27?: smooth peaked hair, corkscrew locks; deep twisted trumpet

        Ref. Pernice,IV, 30, pl.7, dates about 150 B.C.

NB 3   Bronze mask from chest   Naples?   Pompeii   2nd cent.B.C.

        Mask 27: outlined eyes, not bored, striated peaked hair with twisted locks, very
        wide trumpet with narrow edges

        Ref. Pernice, V, 85, pl.50/3

Terracottas

NT 1-21   Campanian terracottas. NT 1 is firmly dated Early Hellenistic. The rest
        are arranged by localities. The Capua series (2-12, 20) is large and varied.
        6, the Sicilian Parasite, and 12, the garrulous wife, are seldom found else-
        where.   11 is a procuress holding a skull - the same basic idea as in the
        later skeleton cups from Boscoreale (NJ 2).   Cross-connections with non-Italian
        series are noted on 6, 10, 14, 15.   UT 53 may belong to the same fabric as
        NT 10.   Perhaps UT 98 belongs here.   UT 117 may belong with NT 13.

1) Dated

NT 1   Terracotta masks   Ponticelli (Naples)   Ponticelli, Tomb 50   Early 3rd
        H. 0,100; 0,090 m.   cent. B.C.

        Mask of youth (10) with smooth speira slightly peaked, brows very much raised,
        outlined eyes and depressed pupils;   and of maiden (39) with small, round, fat
        baby face, melon hair, sharp upper lid, depressed pupils

        Ref. *N.Sc.*, 1922, 274, fig. 15

        Note Found with fusiform aryballoi.   Complex of tombs has much fourth century
        and a little of second half of third century (Giglioli, p. 285)

2) Undated

NT 2   Terracotta statuette   Berlin 7397   Capua
        H. 0,16 m.

        Mask 11?: draped so as to leave chest bare;   hands clasped like Demosthenes

        Ref. Simon 184 n.89;   Winter, *T.K.*, II, 430/5

        Note Probably Early Hellenistic

NT 3   Terracotta head   London, British   Capua
        (fragmentary)   Museum, D 165
        H. 0,60m.

        First youth with wavy hair (15?): hair broken off, largeish nose, evanescent
        eyes, mouth hardly open

        Ref. Walters, *Cat.*, 325

        Note Perhaps 2nd cent. B.C.   Identification doubtful, perhaps not dramatic

NT 4   Terracotta mask   London, British   Capua
                                  Museum, D 167
        H. 0,77 m.

        First youth with wavy hair (15): globular eyes, very high brows, hair falling
        from pseudo-onkos, smallish nose.   Pink clay

        Ref. Walters, *Cat.*, 325

        Note Probably 2nd cent. B.C.   For hair cf. DT 17.   For style cf. ST 24
                    (or earlier)

NT 5   Terracotta mask   London, British   Capua
                                  Museum, D 166
        H. 0,77 m.

        Second youth with wavy hair (16), wreath, arched brows

        Ref. Walters, *Cat.*, 325

        Note Probably 2nd cent. B.C.   Identification very uncertain

NT 6   Terracotta statuette   a) Berlin 7395   a) Capua
        H. 0,14 m.   b) Paris, Louvre   b) ?Myrina
                               c) Hartwig Collection
                               d) Munich, Inv. 5395
                               e) Milan

Sicilian parasite (20): rimmed eyes, pupils *not* bored

Ref. *T.K.*, 430/6; Bieber, *H.T.*, fig. 250; *D.*, no. 145; Simon, 54, 183 n. 49;
     P.C.F., fig. 119; *G.T.P.*, no. C 12

Note Winter's ascription of the Paris example to Myrina is probably unreliable;
     Megara is also suggested.   Probably 2nd cent. B.C.

NT 7   Terracotta mask   London, British Museum,   Capua
                               D 62
        H. 0,82 m.

Leading slave (22?): bulbous eyes, fierce brows, deepish smooth trumpet almost
semicircular, peaked hair with falling shock of hair

Ref. Walters, *Cat.*, 308
Note Probably 2nd cent. B.C. or earlier

NT 8   Terracotta mask   London, British Museum,   Capua
                               D 63
        H. 0,71 m.

Leading slave (22?): bulbous eyes, deepish trumpet lightly striated, almost
pointed; peaked hair with falling shock of hair
Ref. Walters, *Cat.*, 308
Note Probably 2nd cent. B.C. or earlier.   Very like NT 7 but different mouth

NT 9   Terracotta mask   London, British Museum,   Capua
                               D 61
        H. 0,19 m.

Wavy-haired slave (27): semicircular trumpet.   Small, orange
Ref. Walters, *Cat.*, 308
Note Perhaps 1st cent. B.C.

NT 10   Terracotta statuette   Milan, Museo Teatrale   Capua
        H. 0,15 m.

Youth in chiton and himation holding mask of slave (27): peaked hair, deepish
trumpet, hair falling over ears
Note Cf. BT 14-17; MT 7, 44.   Probably 2nd cent. B.C.

NT 11   Terracotta statuette   Vienna, V 1844   ?Capua
        H. 0,13 m.

Old woman (29) with skull
Ref. Bieber, *H.T.*, fig. 107; Webster, *Wiener Studien*, 69 (1956), 114

NT 12   Terracotta statuette   Berlin 7401   Capua

H. 0,13 m.

Garrulous wife (31)

Ref. Bieber, *H.T.*, fig.244;   *D.*, no.156;   *T.K.*, 428/2;   *G.T.P.*, no.C 11

NT 13   Terracotta antefix   Cambridge   Cumae

H. 0,0915 m.

Probably elaborate wreath broken off.   Falling wavy hair;   smooth brows;
depressed pupils;   wideish eyes: young hetaira or delicate youth, perhaps
16

Note Perhaps 1st cent. B.C.   Cf. AT 21 etc.

NT 14   Terracotta mask   Naples   ?Naples

Mask: bald, bored pupils, outlined eyes, striated trumpet about same depth
as semicircular trumpet

Ref. Simon 87, 192 n.13;   Robert, fig.35

Note Perhaps 2nd cent. B.C.   Robert and Simon take as an old man (5 or 1),
        but probably it is a Maison with a deeper trumpet than usual, cf. MT 2.
        Simon says that a terracotta mask from Pompeii (her pl.X,1, top row,
        left) is from the same mould but that clearly is not bald and looks
        like an old man (below NT 30)

NT 15   Terracotta mask   Formerly Collection Bieber   ?Naples

Mask of slave (27): roughly striated hair;   raised brows, shallow pointed
trumpet;   bored pupils

Ref. Bieber, *H.T.*, fig.268;   *J.d.I.*, 32 (1917), 76, fig.43

Note Cf. TT 12;   perhaps also from a brazier like AV 32.   2nd cent. B.C.

NT 16   Terracotta mask   Milan   Naples

H. 0,18 m.

Perhaps hetaira's maid: cap;   turn-up nose;   bored pupils.   One suspension
hole

Ref. Sambon 279, pl.9 (takes as negro).

Note Late Hellenistic

NT 17   Terracotta mask   London, British Museum, D 56   Nola

H. 0,0733 m.

Curly youth (12): high speira with descending corkscrew locks, depressed
pupils, smooth brows, sharply cut nose.   Two pinholes in forehead hair

Ref. Walters, *Cat.*, 307

Note Possibly from disc.   Early Hellenistic.   Cf. IT 39

NT 18   Terracotta water spout   London, British Museum,   Nola
                                    D 180

H. 0,154 m.

Mask of wavy-haired slave (27): wreath, small eyes, very large trumpet for spout

Ref. Walters, *Cat.*, 327

Note Probably Early Hellenistic

NT 19   Terracotta mask   Pompeii, Antiquarium   Pompeii
                                    361/4

Episeistos slave (27)

Note Probably Early Hellenistic

NT 20   Terracotta statuette   Capua (Pasquale)   Capua

H. 0,13 m.

Old man (8) in long chiton, holding a garland

Ref. *T.K.*, 399/9

Note Perhaps 2nd cent. B.C.

NT 21   Terracotta   a) Vienna 2940   Capua
                            b) Berlin 7596

H. a) 0,055 m.
     b) 0,11 m.

Slave with speira without peak, raised brows, bulbous eyes, rounded deepish trumpet, hand to mouth

Ref. Masner 900; *T.K.*, 424/1

Note Probably 2nd cent. B.C.

Vases

NV 1   Plastic vase   Oxford 1927.45   Campania   2nd cent.B.C.
                                                     (Magenta class)

Leading slave lying on amphora (?27): peaked speira, wide trumpet

Ref. Cf. Zahn *ap.* Mercklin, *A.A.*, 1928, 341 for criteria and date

NORTHERN AND CENTRAL ITALY

Coins

IC 1   Coin   British Museum   Rome   67 B.C.

Thalia with mask of comic slave with pointed trumpet and probably wavy hair rather than wreath (27)

Ref. Grueber, *Coins of the Roman Republic in the British Museum*, I, 445

Lamps

IL 1   Terracotta lamp lid   London, British Museum, D 78   Italy
H. 0,032 m.

Leading slave mask (22):   peaked striated speira, semicircular trumpet

Ref. Walters, *Cat.*, 310

Note Cf. ZL 6.   1st cent. B.C. or later

IL 2   Lamp lid   Oxford, Ashmolean Museum 1872.566)
(bought in Rome)

Leading slave: peak hair with locks over ears but no marked speira; depressed
pupils; fat cheeks, wide trumpet with narrow edge.   Whitish clay

Note Cf. DL 2.   1st cent. B.C. or later

Sculpture

IS 1   Marble relief from frieze   Mantua 80   Italy
H. 0,35 m.

Mask of slave: mask 22.   Sharply twisted brows, bored eyeballs;   semicircular
trumpet

Ref. Bieber, *H.T.*, fig.253;   Simon 77, 189 n.38;   Levi, *Sculture*, 80, pl.51

Note Late Hellenistic

Terracottas

IT 1-64   Of other Italian districts and sites Etruria is listed first.   1-3 are
terracottas from a single grave dated by other finds to the end of the third
century B.C.   The rest are arranged by types of mask.   Cross-connections
with non-Italian series are noted on 10, 13, 19.   These three are very
close to Greek terracottas and 29 is a beautifully modelled example of a
unique mask (36).   Many of the Etruscan masks, however, including the dated
group from Vulci (1-3), have coarser and more exaggerated features than
Greek masks, although they can readily be arranged under the same types.
Whether this is due to the artist or to theatre practice is difficult to say.

The Canino group (32-35) is separated from the other Etruscan terracottas
because it is unique in style and presentation of the actors: although Dr
Simon has interpreted the types as Greek, the local manufacturer (and the
local producer?) has gone further from the originals than his other Etruscan
colleagues.   36, however, which may also be Etruscan, is a fine slave of
the traditional type.

ETRURIA

1) Dated

IT 1   Terracotta statuette   Lost   Vulci   Late 3rd cent.
                                                                         B.C.
H. 0,22 m.

Slave (22) with hair coming to peak without speira and wide, smooth trumpet
twisted at top, carrying child and holding mask of Kore (33) with long straggly
hair also over forehead

Ref. Messerschmidt, *R.M.*, 46 (1931), 57, fig.1, dated by pottery etc. about 200
B.C.

IT 2   Terracotta mask   Rome, Museo Torlonia   Vulci   Late 3rd cent. B.C.

Mask 17: wrinkles on nose and forehead; onkos-like hair with incisions; bored pupils

Ref. Simon 182 n.34b; *Annali* 1881 pl.K; Messerschmidt, *R.M.*, 46 (1931), 59

Note Found with IT 1

IT 3   Terracotta mask   Rome, Museo Torlonia   Vulci   Late 3rd cent. B.C.

Slave (22) with wreath; hard brows, bored pupils, striations inside deepish rounded trumpet

Ref. *Annali* 1881, 150, pl.1 (found with IT 2)

2) Undated

Old Men

IT 4   Terracotta statuette   Lost   Marzi (Etruria)

Old man with long mantle running

Ref. Messerschmidt, *R.M.*, 46 (1931), 61 no.1 (compares Winter, *T.K.*, 424/11)

Note Early Hellenistic

IT 5   Terracotta mask   a) Lost   a) Tarquinia
                                 b) & c) Leningrad,   b) & c) Corneto
                                    Botkin Collection
                                 d) London, B.M. D 67   d) Corneto

Man with hair parted and taken up in tail behind forehead band; bulbous eyes; shallowish, striated trumpet mouth, semicircular

Ref. Messerschmidt, *R.M.*, 46 (1931), 68, fig.19, 24, 26, 31

Note Early Hellenistic.   Should perhaps be regarded as slave masquerading as woman

Young Men

IT 6   Terracotta mask   London, British Museum   Corneto
                                 D 171

H. 0,135 m.

Delicate youth (16): wreath with streamers in front of ears, wavy parted hair

Ref. Walters, *Cat.*, 326; Messerschmidt, *R.M.*, 46 (1931), 60

Note Early Hellenistic perhaps

IT 7   Terracotta mask   Leningrad, Botkin Collection   ?Corneto

Mask 10

Ref. Simon 183 n.65

IT 8   Terracotta mask   Leningrad, Botkin Collection   ?Corneto

Mask 10

Ref. Simon 184 n.70

IT 9   Terracotta mask   Leningrad, Botkin Collection   Corneto

Mask 12

Ref. Simon 182 n.24a

IT 10   Terracotta mask   Unknown   Tarquinia/Corneto

Mask 17: bulbous eyes, outlined pupils

Ref. Simon 182 n.34a; Daremberg-Saglio, IV, 1, 410, fig.5597

Note Cf. above AT 4 and below IT 37, UT 16

IT 11   Terracotta mask   Leningrad, Botkin Collection   Tarquinia

Mask 17

Ref. Simon 182 n.34c

IT 12   Terracotta mask   Leningrad, Botkin Collection   Corneto

Mask 18

Slaves

IT 13   Terracotta statuette   Berlin 223   Vulci

H. 0,21 m.

Seated man: mask 24.   Legs crossed; wreath; right hand inside himation; semicircular shovel trumpet

Ref. Bieber, *H.T.*, fig.289; Robert, *Masken*, fig.20; Simon 189 n.31; *T.K.*, 424/12; *P.C.F.*, fig.126

Note Cf. ZT 30.   Probably late 2nd cent. B.C.

IT 14   Terracotta statuette   Leningrad, Botkin Collection   Corneto

Maison (25): very wrinkled forehead; prominent eyes; wide smooth trumpet

Ref. Simon 188 n.8c; Messerschmidt, *R.M.*, 47 (1931), 68, no.16c, fig.25

Note Probably 2nd cent. B.C.

IT 15   Terracotta mask   Leningrad, Botkin Collection   Tarquinia

Mask 22 with *tainia* round head: uneven brows, small eyes with sharp lids, smooth trumpet

Ref. Messerschmidt, *R.M.*, 46 (1931), 65, fig.17

Note Perhaps Early Hellenistic

IT 16   Terracotta mask   Lost   Tarquinia

Mask 22: rimmed eyes, pupils just marked; striated hair coming to peak; high, hard brows, wide twisted trumpet without striations

Ref. Messerschmidt, *R.M.*, 46 (1931), 68, fig.20

Note Perhaps Early Hellenistic

IT 17   Terracotta mask   London, British Museum, D 64   ?Etruria
H. 0,129 m.

Slave: remains of red on face; squinting eyes with pupils just marked;
triangular smooth trumpet; furrowed forehead; perhaps bald

Ref. Walters, *Cat.*, 308

Note Early Hellenistic

IT 18   Terracotta water spout   London, British Museum, D 66   Corneto
H. 0,121 m.

Leading slave (22): wreath; eyes slightly bored and wide apart;   small
nose; deep trumpet to make spout

Ref. Walters, *Cat.*, 308

Note Early Hellenistic

IT 19   Terracotta head   Munich 761   Vulci
H. 0,04 m.

Slave (22): striated hair falling in wig over ears, furrowed forehead,
raised brows, depressed pupils, twisted trumpet with striated edge

Note Perhaps cf. DT 23.   1st cent. B.C. or later

IT 20   Terracotta mask   Lost   Tarquinia
Mask 23: very rough with prominent nose and eyes; smooth trumpet

Ref. Simon 189 n.30; Messerschmidt, *R.M.*, 46 (1931), 67/8, 15p, fig.21

Note Probably 2nd cent. B.C.

IT 21   Terracotta mask   Leningrad, Botkin Collection   Corneto
Mask 25: rimmed eyes, smooth trumpet

Ref. Messerschmidt, *R.M.*, 47 (1931), 65 fig.18

Note Probably 2nd cent. B.C.

IT 22   Terracotta mask   Lost   Etruria
Mask 25 with elaborate wreath of wool: smallish bulbous eyes;   shallow
smooth trumpet

Ref. Messerschmidt, *R.M.*, 46 (1931), 68 fig.22

Note Perhaps 2nd cent. B.C.

IT 23   Terracotta mask   Tarquinia   Italy
Maison mask (25)

Ref. Romanelli, *Tarquinia* (1954), 148, fig.96

Note Perhaps 2nd cent. B.C.

IT 24   Terracotta relief on urn   Palermo 5959 TC   ?Chiusi   3rd cent.
B.C.
Mask 25 between volutes and acanthus palmettes: bulbous eyes, hard arched
brows, very wide twisted mouth

Ref. Simon 188 n.12; *Studi Etruschi* II, 78, no.15, fig.5

IT 25   Terracotta mask   Leningrad, Botkin Collection   Corneto

Mask 27 with squint: striated hair and beard inside trumpet; flaring eyebrows; bored pupils, rimmed eyes

Ref. Messerschmidt, *R.M.*, 46 (1931), 68 fig.27

Note Probably 2nd cent. B.C.

Women

IT 26   Terracotta mask   Geneva Fol, 559   Corneto

H. 0,09 m.

Mask 32

Ref. Simon 196 n.31; Musée Fol., Cat.1, 559

Note Probably 2nd cent. B.C.

IT 27   Terracotta mask   London, British Museum D 58   Corneto

H. 0,15 m.

Mask 41

Ref. Simon 195 n.11.   Cf. Messerschmidt, *R.M.*, 46 (1931), 60

Note Probably 2nd cent. B.C.

IT 28   Terracotta mask   London, British Museum D 101   ? Corneto

H. 0,050 m.

Mask 39 (?): wreath of ivy leaves, melon hair, very young

Ref. Simon 195 n.10

Note Probably 2nd cent. B.C.

IT 29   Terracotta mask   Berlin 7138   Corneto

H. 0,185 m.

Concubine (37)

Ref. Robert, fig.99, takes as 36; Bieber, *D.*, no.173; *H.T.*, fig.282; *P.C.F.*, fig.148; *G.T.P.*, no.C 13; Simon, 111, 116, 197 n.51; Messerschmidt, *R.M.*, 46 (1931), 70, fig.30

Note Early Hellenistic

IT 30   Terracotta mask   Tarquinia   Italy

Hetairidion with melon hair: 39

Ref. Romanelli, *Tarquinia* (1954), 148, fig.96

Note Probably 2nd cent. B.C.

IT 31   Terracotta mask   Leningrad, Botkin Collection   Corneto

Mask (?39): melon hair; bun behind

Ref. Simon 122, 197 n.45b

Note Probably 2nd cent. B.C.

The Canino Group

IT 32   Terracotta statuette   London, B.M. D 225   Canino (Etruria)

Agroikos (14): young man with cloak over left shoulder and knotted under breasts

Ref. Bieber, *H.T.*, fig.412; Simon p.185 n.106

IT 33   Terracotta statuette   London, B.M. D 224   Canino

H. 0,28 m.

Kolax (17): receding hair; raised brows; bored pupils; short cloak; aryballos in right hand, piece of meat in left hand

Ref. Bieber, *H.T.*, fig.410; Allardyce Nicoll, *Development of the theatre*, 78, figs.68-9; Messerschmidt, *R.M.*, 46 (1931), 62; Simon, 51, 182 n.35; *T.K.*, 431/5

IT 34   Terracotta statuette   London, B.M. D 223   Canino

H. 0,26 m.

Mask 18: walking, wrapped in cloak

Ref. Simon 45, 181 n.8; *T.K.*, 431/3

IT 35   Terracotta statuette   London, B.M. D 226   Canino

H. 0,20 m.

Maison (25): short chiton and cloak covering something held in the left hand; semicircular trumpet with striated edge

Ref. Bieber, *H.T.*, fig.411; Rumpf, *Mimus u. Logos*, 170 n.18; Simon, 188 n.8b

Possibly Etruscan

IT 36   Terracotta statuette   London, B.M. D 228   ?Etruria

H. 0,19 m.

Leading slave (27): short chiton and himation, lantern in right hand; big belly girt above and below; fat legs; wreath, eyes wide apart; shock of hair over ears; wedge-shaped trumpet mouth

Ref. *T.K.*, 423/8; Walters, *Cat.*, 343

Note Probably Early Hellenistic

ELSEWHERE

Terracottas from other Italian sites mostly unspecified are grouped under masks. 37 probably comes from the same source as 59 and belongs to the same stylistic group as 10 from Corneto.   An earlier Attic prototype (AT 4) can be suggested for 10 and perhaps for 37 (one of the masks of AJ 1); the worried lover, of which this mask is a fine example, was already known in Attic Middle Comedy and had spread to South Italy before 325 B.C.   (*Middle Comedy* AT 31, OT 1, GV 9. The suggested Attic provenance of UT 20 is perhaps unreliable and it belongs here (but its likeness to one of the masks of AJ 1 must be remembered).   Several parallels to this Italian group for which no reliable find-spot is recorded are noted below (UT 10; 16; 17; 20; perhaps 60; 87). The Pan (43) has parallels in UT 21, 22, 24, 97. Cross connections with non-Italian sites are noted on 38, 40, 42, 46, 53, 58. Other terracottas which may be Italian are UT 18, 25, 103-5. The date of 51 may be regarded as secure as many of these altars are known. The antefixes 46-8, 49, 58, 59 seem to belong to the late 1st cent. B.C. rather than the 1st century A.D., the date of the antefixes noted below in the Roman section, which may be later derivatives of the same types. UT 56-7 probably belong here. 63 and 64 are a pair of old man and slave conversing; it is unlikely that their naked bodies with drapery perilously attached round the hips belong to the heads; if the heads do not belong to the bodies they need not be either contemporary or from the same place. For the head of 63 IL 6 should be compared.

Young Men

IT 37   Terracotta hanging mask   Leiden, M 1897/5.4   ?Italy

H. 0,075 m.

Youth with wreath, striated speira, raised eyebrows and protruding eyes (10?)

Note Cf. IT 10 for style. Not after 2nd cent. B.C.

IT 38   Terracotta mask on disk   Naples 21424   Unknown

Diameter of disk, 0,154 m.

Mask 12: corkscrew hair; bored pupils

Ref. Simon 182 n.24b; Levi, 177, no.783, fig.135

Note Cf. for disks, NT 17, MT 23, XT 21-2. Late Hellenistic

IT 39   Terracotta mask   Naples C.S. 326

Mask 12: corkscrew hair; depressed pupils

Ref. Simon 182 n.24c

Note Cf. IT 38. Perhaps earlier. 2nd cent. B.C.

IT 40   Terracotta mask   Naples (no no.)   Unknown

Mask (12) with high *onkos* and rows of descending locks

Note Probably not tragic, cf. DT 17. Late Hellenistic

IT 41   Terracotta mask of youth   Louvre, Camp.4776   Italy

Hapalos (13): bored eyeballs and iris; smooth brows; striated speira

Note Late Hellenistic or early Roman. Probably wall mask like ZT 24. May pair with IT 61 below

IT 42   Terracotta mask   Copenhagen, N.M.   Unknown

Hapalos (13) with fat face, elaborate wreath

Ref. Breitenstein, no.675

Note Acquired in Italy. Cf. DT 3, 18. Probably 2nd cent. B.C.

IT 43   Terracotta mask   Dresden 1373   Italy

H. 0,118 m.

Young Pan with goat's horns, small pupils

Ref. *A.A.* 1895, 223, no.16

Note Late Hellenistic. Cf. UT 21, 97

Slaves

IT 44   Terracotta mask   London, British Museum, D 68   ?Italy
H. 0,16 m.
Wavy-haired slave (27): red face; nearly life size; striated speira;
bored iris and pupils; fattish cheeks; flat striated trumpet with striated
edges
Ref. Walters, *Cat.*, 309; Messerschmidt, *R.M.*, 46 (1931), 60
Note Late Hellenistic or more probably Roman, cf. AT 32 for period

IT 45   Terracotta mask   Milan
H. 0,14 m.
Slave (22) with wreath and fillet; wide twisted trumpet.   Two hangholes
Ref. Sambon, no.288, pl.11, Saulini Collection
Note Late Hellenistic

IT 46   Terracotta revetment   Cambridge, G.R.32.1896   ?Italy
Leading slave (22): peaked hair striated back from forehead; even twisted
brows; sunk pupils; smooth shallow twisted trumpet
Note Cf. DL 2.   1st cent. B.C. or later

IT 47   Roof tile   Copenhagen, Inv.1163   Italy
H. 0,120 m.
Slave mask (22): peak hair with corkscrew on either side of face; furrowed
forehead, swinging brows; eyes with depressed pupils; wide smooth, twisted
trumpet
Ref. Breitenstein, no.914; cf. Rohden-Winnefeld, 235
Note Late Hellenistic to Roman

IT 48   Terracotta antefix   Copenhagen, Inv.1181   Italy
H. 0,117 m.
Slave with striated hair and corkscrew on either side of face; bored pupils;
swinging brows; (?22)
Ref. Breitenstein, no.945; Campana, pl.99; *N.Sc.* 1912, 349, fig.3 (Ostia)
Note Augustan

IT 49   Terracotta spout   Copenhagen, Inv.1712   ?Italy
H. 0,103 m.
Elaborately wreathed head: knotted brows, bored pupils, shock of hair over
ears; smooth trumpet; (?25)
Ref. Breitenstein, no.925, takes as satyr (but neither ears nor beard satyric);
        compares Rohden-Winnefeld, p.23, fig.7, and p.38
Note Cf. also UT 57.   Late Hellenistic

IT 50   Terracotta mask   Rome, Market

Mask of Maison (25): inscribed pupils, squinting, semicircular trumpet

Ref. Bieber, *H.T.*, fig.261; Simon 188 n.7; Messerschmidt, *R.M.*, 46 (1931),
56 ff.

Note Probably 2nd cent. B.C.

IT 51   Terracotta altar   Copenhagen, Inv.6589   Italy   3rd cent. B.C.

H. 0,110 m.

Slave mask with wreath hanging on either side: crinkled forehead, swinging brows,
wide-set outlined eyes, small squashed nose, smooth twisted trumpet; probably
Maison (25)

Ref. Breitenstein, no.785; cf. Van Buren, *Mon. Am. Ac. Rome*, II, 41, VI, iii,
type B from Rome, Esquiline (he quotes other examples)

IT 52   Terracotta mask   Aquileja   ?

?Mask 25

Ref. Simon 188 n.12; *Guida* 216, fig.162

IT 53   Terracotta statuette   Milan, Museo Teatrale   ?

Slave (27) pulling at cloak with left hand, right hand at waist; peaked hair,
sharp eyes, wide pointed smooth trumpet

Ref. Sambon, no.278, pl.10

Note Not unlike early Myrina, e.g.MT 37.   Perhaps 3rd cent.

IT 54   Terracotta statuette   Milan, Museo Teatrale   ?Italy

H. 0,12 m.

Slave (27): peaked speira, striated; bulbous eyes; shallow trumpet with
jutting rounded edge

Ref. Sambon, no.227

Note Head only should be considered.   Early Hellenistic

IT 55   Terracotta mask   London, British Museum, D 75   Italy

Wavy-haired slave (27): peaked hair with shock over ears, semicircular
trumpet

Ref. Walters, *Cat.*, 309

Note Perhaps Early Hellenistic

IT 56   Terracotta mask   Naples 21052   Unknown

Episeistos slave (27)

Ref. Robert, fig.56

Note Perhaps 2nd cent. B.C.

IT 57   Terracotta mask   Naples 21443   Unknown

Episeistos slave (27)

Note Perhaps 2nd cent. B.C.

IT 58   Terracotta antefix   Leeds, Inv.no.13   Lanuvium

Mask of wavy-haired slave (27): neatly striated peak hair hanging below ears,
bored pupils, semicircular trumpet slightly twisted

Ref. *B.S.R.*, 11 (1929), 102, fig.30, no.38

Note Cf. DL 2. Late Hellenistic. Better and earlier than IT 46 etc.

Women

IT 59   Terracotta hanging mask   Leiden, M 1897/5.5   ?Italy

H. 0,090 m.

First Pseudo-Kore with melon hair (34)

Note Probably from same find as IT 37.   Not after 2nd cent. B.C.

IT 60   Terracotta hanging mask   Leiden, I 1950/6.5   ?Italy

H. 0,112 m.

Woman with fillet tied over hair (39)

Ref. Schaal, *Gr. Vasen in Bremen*, 1933, pl.38a (from Waldmann Collection,
        Bremen)

Note Probably 2nd cent. B.C.

IT 61   Terracotta mask   Paris, Louvre, C 4775   Rome

Smooth hair; band of hair parted in middle of forehead, locks in front of
ears, pierced eyes: young hetaira

Ref. Musée Guimet Exhibition, 227

Note Perhaps goes with IT 41.   Late Hellenistic or Roman

IT 62   Terracotta mask (large)   Paris, Louvre, C 4770   Rome

Female mask, parted hair with seeming onkos, pierced iris and pupils: probably
kore.   Closed mouth, perhaps not dramatic

Ref. Musée Guimet Exhibition, 228

Doubtful

IT 63   Terracotta statuette   Paris, Cab.Med.122 (49)   Italy

H. 0,30 m.

Old man (3?): bare torso, himation round lower part of body and legs

Ref. Bieber, *D.*, no.140; *H.T.*, fig.226; Musée Guimet Exhibition 244

Note Body probably does not belong

IT 64   Terracotta statuette   Paris, Cab.Med.122 (50)   Italy

H. 0,30 m.

Slave (27), bare torso, himation round lower part of body and legs; shock
of wavy hair, rounded trumpet with flattish edges

Ref. *T.K.*, 430/7; Bieber, *H.T.*, fig.227; Musée Guimet Exhibition, 245

Note Body probably does not belong

Vases

IV 1-7   1 is Etruscan.   2-3 with their black glaze are unlikely to be later than
the 3rd cent.   4 has a good deal of colour: it seems to go stylistically
with the main group of Myrina terracottas.   5-7 may perhaps be dated too
late as no.5 was found with what sound like Genucilia plates of the third
century: the masks recall Attic third century masks.

IV 1   Plastic vase   Rome, Vatican Z 129   Etruria   Late 4th/early
                                                                          3rd cent. B.C.

Wreathed maison head (25): one eye open, one nearly shut; wreath; deep rounded
trumpet; hair over ears

Ref. Beazley, *E.V.P.* 190; Trendall, *Vasi Dipinti*, II, 254, no.Z 129, pl.66j;
Alinari 35817, 2

Note Underneath is a squinting head with hooked nose

IV 2   Plastic vase (black)   Sigéan (Pyrenees)   Sigéan   3rd/2nd cent.B.C.
H. 0,136 m.

Slave (22) seated on cubic seat, feet crossed, hands clasped, head back, semicircular trumpet, peaked hair

Ref. *Gallia* 11 (1953), 94, fig.5, dated by pottery to late 3rd/early 2nd cent.
B.C.

IV 3   Plastic vase (black glaze)   New York 12.232.22   ?3rd cent.B.C.

Slave seated on round altar with mouldings top and bottom: head forward; small
eyes; small nose; deepish trumpet.   Hands clasped round knee.   Tights;
shortish chiton with sleeves.   Legs crossed.   Small spout on back

Ref. Museum negative 15723; *Handbook*, 132, n.98; *B.M.M.*, 1913, 158

Note For posture cf. UB 10

IV 4   Terracotta vase   London, B.M. D 322   Italy
H. 0,119 m.

Slave seated on altar; large wreath, slightly bored pupils; very wide twisted
mouth; chlamys over left shoulder; girding above stomach; right hand on altar

Ref. *P.C.F.*, fig.130; Walters, *Cat.*, pl.34

Note Probably 2nd cent. B.C.

IV 5   Italian Megarian bowl   Boston 95.59   Viterbo   100-50 B.C.
by Popilius

Masks of wreathed slaves: semicircular trumpet

Ref. Jones, *Record of Princeton University Art Museum*, 18 (1958), 21f., no.2

Note For the mask cf. AV 5

IV 6   Italian Megarian bowl   London   Italy   100-50 B.C.
by Lapius

Masks of wreathed slaves: very wide, flat trumpet

Ref. Jones, no.14

IV 7   Italian Megarian bowl   Tivoli?   Tivoli   100-50 B.C.

Mask of hetaira with melon hair (shut mouth)

Ref. Jones, no.34; Paribeni, *N.Sc.* 3 (1927), 377, fig.5

THE WEST

Mosaics

JM 1   Mosaic mask   Malta   Malta   1st cent. B.C.

Fragmentary mask with very full beard slightly pointed

Ref. Pernice VI, 8, pl.2,1, interpreted as probably a Silen.   This is
     likely to be right

JM 2   Mosaic masks   Malta   Malta   Early 1st cent.B.C.

Masks of Kore (twice); slave with small eyes and deep twisted trumpet (perhaps
bald); Lykomedian with curly hair and long curly beard

Ref. Ashby, *J.R.S.*, 5 (1915), 34; Pernice VI, 8, pl.2,2-4

Note Pernice compares the Papposilenos mask of the Villa of the Mysteries

Terracottas

JT 1   Terracotta mask   Naples 116710   Calvi

Youth with ivy wreath.   Perhaps *hapalos*

Note Probably 2nd cent. B.C.

JT 2   Terracotta mask   Naples (no no.) Calvi

Slave: 27

Note Probably 2nd cent. B.C.

JT 3   Terracotta mask   Milan, Sforza 661   Calvi

Mask 42: toupet on the forehead

Ref. Simon 120, 197 n.42b, unpublished

Note Probably 2nd cent. B.C.

UNKNOWN ORIGIN

UB, UJ, UL, UT: Bronzes, Jewellery, Lamps, and Terracottas of unknown (or
     doubtful origin.   These are listed in alphabetical order of museums.
     Terracotta lists are first divided into Old Men, Young Men, Slaves, and
     Women, and within these categories are listed in museum order.   Possible
     attributions to places are given on the individual pieces, and have been
     quoted under the relevant sections above.   Except for the lamps, the
     dates can only be given on the style of the objects.   UT 95 ff. are late
     additions.

Bronzes

UB 1   Bronze statuette   Berlin, Private Collection

Slave mask 27: slave by altar, bending back; narrow girding above and below stomach, himation tied round waist

Ref. Simon, 80, 191 n.61a, pl.VIII, 2

Note Simon takes costume as long chiton with small cloak over shoulder, which would make this late Roman.   The costume seems to me the same as is seen on Myrina slaves: 2nd cent. B.C.

UB 2   Bronze statuette   Boston 08.371

Slave (22) seated on altar: oval trumpet

Ref. 'Princeton' fig.35

Note Perhaps 2nd cent. B.C.

UB 3   Bronze statuette   Cassel 238

Slave (27): peaked hair falling as a wig, oval trumpet; feet close together, hands clasped together level with hips, cloak falling from left shoulder. Slender

Ref. Bieber, *H.T.*, fig.415; *Skulpt. u. Bronzen in Cassel*, 74, no.238, pl.45

Note Compare DT 19 etc.   1st cent. B.C.

UB 4   Bronze statuette   Florence 2327

Comic actor (?27): legs apart, right hand to brow, chiton to knees, girt by two narrow strings, above and below stomach

Ref. Bieber, *H.T.*, fig.211

Note The mask suggests an old man but the costume is that of Myrina slaves. Perhaps 2nd cent. B.C.

UB 5   Bronze mask   Carlsruhe 784

Mask (33): smooth hair; corkscrew locks

Ref. Simon 197 n.61

UB 6   Bronze head   Lehmann Collection

H. 0,08 m.

Mask 15: hair freely done; raised brows

Ref. Simon 186 n.133c; *Vente Lehmann*, pl.15 no.112

Note Perhaps Early Hellenistic

UB 7   Bronze statuette   London, B.M. 1626

Seated comic actor: mask 22: deepish trumpet, twisted, peaked hair; legs crossed, left hand supporting right elbow, right hand to beard

Ref. Bieber, *H.T.*, fig.210

Note Late Hellenistic

UB 8   Bronze statuette   Milan

        H. 0,155 m.

        Slave with shock of wig hair, peaked, semicircular trumpet; mantle over left
        shoulder; hands clasped; left foot forward.   Elaborate pedestal

        Ref. Sambon pl.14, no.328; Bieber, *Record of the Art Museum, Princeton*, 9
        (1950), 10, fig.4

        Note Slim proportions like DT 19.   Perhaps 1st cent. B.C.

UB 9   Bronze statuette   New York, Metropolitan
                                        Museum, 17.230.28

        Slave with wreath (22): feet close together, hands clasped on left breast,
        wearing skin cloak (?); semicircular flattened striated trumpet

        Ref. Bieber, *H.T.*, fig.413

        Note Perhaps Early Hellenistic

Jewellery

UJ 1   Golden earring   Basel Market

        Bald winged man with hairy legs holding mask with large spade beard and band
        round top of head

        Ref. Schefold, *Antike Meisterwerke*, no.572

        Note Mask in Middle Comedy tradition.   Early Hellenistic

Lamps

UL 1   Terracotta lamp, single nozzle   Milan

        0,68 m. diameter

        Three-quarter mask of old man (?3): wreathed; striated hair; large eyes
        with bored pupils; twisted trumpet mouth; corkscrew beard below

        Ref. Sambon, pl.5, no.164; Broneer, Type XXI (50 B.C.-25 A.D.)

        Note Cf. IL 5

UL 2   Terracotta lamp   Oxford L.70 (Fortnum Collection)

        Slave mask with wreath: leaf handle

        Note Head reminiscent of Middle Comedy type.   Probably Broneer Type XXI.   Not
                before 1st cent. B.C.

UL 3   Terracotta lamp   Oxford (no no.)   1st cent. B.C.

        H. 0,041 m.

        Slave mask with striated hair, fat face, flat narrow edge to wide twisted trumpet,
        bored eyes (22).   Palmette handle.   Three nozzles

        Note Identical with UL 4.   Broneer Type XXI.   EL 24 is larger and has one
                nozzle

UL 4 Terracotta lamp   Princeton, Art Museum 51.85

H. 0,043 m.

Identical with UL 3

UL 4a Terracotta lamp   Oxford 1941.23   1st cent. B.C.

Slave mask with wavy-hair corkscrew curls and wide twisted trumpet

Note Except for the hair and mouth this is a twin of UL 3

Terracottas

Old Men

UT 1 Terracotta statuette   Boston 01.7891

?Wavy-haired old man with ivy wreath and pointed beard; body wrapped in long cloak

Note Bought in Paris.   Possibly cf. TT 18 for style.   Possibly better taken as slave (27) dressed up.   Early Hellenistic

UT 2 Terracotta statuette   Madrid 3365

H. 0,14 m.

Bald old man with large ears, connected brows, large beard, long himation, stick in right hand.   Ochre clay.   Oval vent

Ref. Laumonier, no.851, pl.100, no.1, compares NT 20

Note Time of Myrina main group.   2nd cent. B.C.

UT 3 Terracotta mask   Madrid 19669

H. 0,078 m.

Man with full spade beard, drooping moustache, full hair, protruding eyes. Yellow clay; red paint

Ref. Laumonier, pl.15, 14, no.55

Note Cf. perhaps satyr mask TT 3.   Probably Italian.   Late Hellenistic

UT 4 Terracotta mask   Vienna, 305
(from vessel)

H. 0,051 m.

Old man's mask (3)

Note Perhaps Late Hellenistic

UT 5 Terracotta mask   a) Vienna, 2944   a) Unknown
                                       b) Lecuyer   b) Smyrna

H. 0,05 m.

Old man with peaked hair and shock over ears, fullish beard (4)

Ref. b) Robert, fig.19

Note Smyrna provenance is likely.   2nd cent. B.C.

Young Men

UT 6   Terracotta mask   Athens, N.M. 1758

Large wreathed *panchrestos* mask

UT 7   Terracotta mask   Athens, N.M. 5797 (1708)

H. 0,11 m.

Delicate youth (13)

Note Probably 2nd cent. B.C.

UT 7a   Terracotta mask   Athens, N.M. 13621

Delicate youth

Note Probably Early Hellenistic

UT 8   Terracotta mask   Athens, N.M.

H. 0,04 m.

Mask 10: raised brows, eyes outlined and pupils depressed; striated peaked
wig hair.   Yellow clay

Ref. Simon 184 n.68; Martha no.933, pl.VI/I

Note Probably 2nd cent. B.C.

UT 9   Terracotta mask   Berlin 6960

H. 0,085 m.

Mask 11: speira striated from middle, furrow on forehead, sharp eyelids,
pupils not bored

Ref. Simon 195 n.1; Robert, fig.68; *P.C.F.*, fig.150

Note Robert takes as woman.   Late Hellenistic

UT 10   Terracotta mask   Cambridge, Fogg Museum 1916.318

Panchrestos (10) with swung brows; large bulbous eyes outlined, *not* inscribed
or pierced

Note Very like IT 37, probably Italian.   2nd cent. B.C.

UT 11   Terracotta mask   Copenhagen, Thorwaldsen Museum,
                                      Room 39, 55

Youth with wreath (10)

UT 12   Terracotta mask   Leiden (Case 8), M 1897/5.2

Youth (15) with *onkos*; perhaps Dionysos?

Note Very like DT 17 except that this has less contorted brows.   Curiously
        glutinous treatment of hair.   Late Hellenistic

UT 13   Terracotta mask   Leiden (Case 8)

Delicate youth (13)

Note Late Hellenistic

UT 14   Terracotta mask (life size)   Leipzig (Kunstgewerbe Museum)

Negro: bored pupils and iris

Ref. Bielefeld, *W. Z. Greifswald*, 4 (1954), 100; Webster, *Wiener Studien*, 69 (1956), 110

Note Good modelling suggests Early Hellenistic date

UT 15   Terracotta mask   London, University College, GA 90

Kolax (17): bored pupils, hard lids, sharp brows

Ref. *R.B.* XXXII (1949) fig.2; Webster, *Later Greek Comedy*, pl.4b; *G.T.P.*, no.C 54

Note Hard style, cf. ET 13, 19, 22, 49. Much of the GA collection is Egyptian. Early Hellenistic

UT 16   Terracotta mask   Madrid 3370

H. 0,075 m.

Wreathed youth: *?Panchrestos* (10): swung brows, bulging eyes. Yellow ochre clay, white slip. Pink added. Two suspension holes

Ref. Laumonier, no.956, pl.101, 2

Note Very like IT 37. Probably Italian. Not after 2nd cent. B.C.

UT 17   Terracotta mask   Madrid 3371

H. 0,09 m.

Kolax (17): finely striated hair; swinging brows; coarse nose; bulging eyes with incised iris and bored pupils. Yellow ochre clay, white slip. Two holes

Ref. Laumonier, no.859, pl.101, no.8

Note Probably belongs with UT 16. Cf. IT 10. Not after 2nd cent. B.C.

UT 18   Terracotta mask   Milan, Mus. Teatr.

Youth (?13): hair slightly peaked, sliping brows, bored pupils

Ref. Sambon, no.300, pl.12

Note Perhaps Italian. Late Hellenistic

UT 19   Plaster mask   Milan

H. 0,10 m.

Mask of youth (?): *oulos*; corkscrew hair, pseudo-onkos; eyes rimmed and not bored

Ref. Sambon, pl.12, no.301

Note Possibly Egyptian, 2nd cent. B.C.

UT 20   Terracotta mask   Munich 739   Athens

H. 0,07 m.

Wreathed youth (10): bulbous, outlined eyes, raised brows

Note Akin to IT 37. Provenance not to be trusted. Probably Italian, not after 2nd cent. B.C.

UT 21   Terracotta mask   Munich 983

H. 0,12 m.

Pan: outlined small eyes, bored pupils; unbearded

Note Cf. IT 43.   Probably Italian.   Late Hellenistic

UT 22   Terracotta mask   Munich 984

H. 0,105 m.

Pan

Note Probably Italian.   Late Hellenistic

UT 23   Terracotta mask   Munich 987

H. 0,055 m.

Delicate youth (13): speira with striations radiating from centre, smooth
brows; bored pupils; closed mouth

Ref. Krien, *J.O.A.I.* 42 (1956), 112, fig.54.   Cf. TT 7

Note Italian.   1st cent. B.C.

UT 24   Terracotta mask   Munich 988

H. 0,12 m.

Pan: bearded

Note Probably Italian.   Late Hellenistic

UT 25   Terracotta mask   Munich 993

H. 0,075 m.

Youth with curly hair (12): pupils marked, smooth brows, corkscrew hair

Note Cf. IT 39.   Italian.   2nd cent. B.C.

UT 26   Terracotta mask   Munich 5399

H. 0,16 m.

Pan or young satyr: rimmed eyes with bored pupils

Note Some affinity with ST 16.   Probably Italian or Sicilian.   Late
Hellenistic

UT 27   Terracotta mask   Formerly Sabouroff

Mask 10: elaborate wreath, eyes *not* bored

Ref. Simon, 55, 183 n.55; pl.V, 3

Note Simon notes likeness to tambourine player of Dioskourides mosaic.   Has
affinities with early Attic terracottas, e.g. AT 12.   Early Hellenistic

UT 28   Terracotta mask   Vienna 1838

H. 0,043 m.

Youth (11): cap hair with slight peak, sloping brows, outlined eyes with
depressed pupils

Note Perhaps 2nd cent. B.C.

Slaves

UT 29   Terracotta mask   Athens, N.M. 4455

Slave: curly-haired mask: receding hair; short round curly beard; knotted wrinkled brows.   Small; careful.   Pink/grey clay.   Perhaps mask 24

Note Probably Early Hellenistic

UT 30   Terracotta mask   Athens, N.M. 13625

Largeish wreathed slave mask (22)

UT 31   Terracotta mask   Berlin, 6958

H. 0,06 m.

Mask 22: right brow raised with sharp nick; deep trumpet

Ref. Simon 190 n.42f; Robert, fig.93

Note Probably Early Hellenistic.   Perhaps cf. AT 5

UT 32   Terracotta mask   Berlin

H. 0,11 m.

Mask of cook 'Tettix'

Ref. Bieber, *H.T.*, fig.274; Simon 73, 189 n.15; Robert, fig.29; *P.C.F.*, fig.92

Note Probably forgery

UT 33   Terracotta mould   Boston, 01.7933

Slave mask (22): striated peaked hair; bulbous eyes, wide, very shallow trumpet, uneven knicked brows

Ref. 'Princeton', fig.39

Note Perhaps 2nd cent. B.C.

UT 34   Terracotta statuette   Brussels Mus. Cinq. 422

H. 0,04 m.

Maison (25)

Ref. Simon 188 n.8d

UT 35   Terracotta mask   Cambridge

H. 0,15 m.

Bald; ivy and helichryse wreath; bored pupil; beginning of trumpet beard; ear turned right over.   Brown clay   (25)

Note Very like satyr, but ear seems to be human.   Perhaps cf. Priene, ZT 22. 2nd cent. B.C.

UT 36   Terracotta statuette   Cambridge, GR 88a 1937

H. 0,096 m.

Slave seated on square altar with left hand to head: small bulbous eyes, peaked speira, deep trumpet; arms crossed; feet crossed (27).   Pink clay

Note For posture cf. *Middle Comedy*, BT 11.   For head cf. Delos, DT 9. Perhaps 3rd cent. B.C.

UT 37   Terracotta mask   Harvard University, TL 10368.5

Leading slave with peaked hair, swinging brows, eyes wide apart, trumpet mouth with twisted top edge

Note Perhaps 1st cent. B.C.

UT 38   Terracotta mask   Compiègne, Musée Vivenel, V 808

Leading slave: peaked striated hair, deep twisted trumpet striated inside

Note Cf. DT 22, ZT 35.   Late 2nd to early 1st cent. B.C.

UT 39   Terracotta statuette   Copenhagen, 965

H. 0,085 m.

Standing slave: chiton down to knees; himation over left shoulder; holding wreath (?) in hands; high, square plinth with moulding.   Prominent, unpierced eyes, smooth hair, deep twisted trumpet

Ref. Breitenstein, no.623; Sabbatini sale cat., no.152

Note Late 2nd to 1st cent. B.C.

UT 40   Terracotta mask   Copenhagen, Thorwaldsen Museum, Room 39, 53

Slave mask (22)

UT 41   Terracotta mask   Copenhagen, Thorwaldsen Museum, Room 39, 54

Slave mask (22)

UT 42   Terracotta statuette   Frankfurt Liebighaus, 484

H. 0,20 m.

Mask 27: standing, with cloak round hips; chin on hand; eyes rimmed, not bored; peaked striated hair falling over ears, wide twisted trumpet

Ref. Simon 190 n.42a, pl.VIII/I

Note Cf. MT 35, DT 19.   1st cent. B.C.

UT 43   Terracotta mask   Leiden, S.V.L., 462

Maison (25): reddish clay

UT 44   Terracotta statuette   Leiden (Case 8)

Maison (25) with hand to mouth

UT 45   Terracotta   Leiden (Case 8)

Leading slave (22); black

UT 46   Terracotta mask   London, British Museum, 1925.11.20.20

Wavy-haired slave (27): straggly hair and short straggly beard, wrinkled nose

Note Probably Roman.   Possibly tragic but no *onkos*

UT 47   Terracotta statuette   Madrid 3314

H. 0,11 m.

Slave with bundle on shoulders, walking with stick: probably wearing cap and
has deep twisted trumpet.   Pink ochre clay.   White slip; added red

Ref. Laumonier, no.847, pl.100, 2

Note Not unlike Delos, no.1224 = DT 20.   Perhaps Early Hellenistic

UT 48   Terracotta statuette   Madrid 3366

H. 0,145 m.

Slave: full hair, swinging brows; bulging eyes, hole in pupil; deep trumpet
beard;   right hand to beard, left hand on roll of himation.   Ochre clay, no
vent

Ref. Laumonier, no.852, pl.100 n.3   Cf. Winter, *T.K.*, 424/2 (= UT 100)

Note Winter says from Calvi but Laumonier gives no provenance.   Like Early
        Myrina group.   Perhaps cf. also NT 21.   3rd cent. B.C.

UT 49   Head, vase or lamp   Madrid 3372

H. 0,14 m.

Slave head with wreath and *polos*: bald, raised brows, very wide trumpet.
Ochre clay, no vent

Ref. Laumonier, no.858, pl.101, no.5

Note Cf. above EV 8.   Late Hellenistic

UT 50   Terracotta mask   Madrid 3373

H. 0,075 m.

Slave (27) rather than old man: wreath of fruit; peaked hair, swinging
brows; bulging eyes; spade beard.   Red clay; two holes; white slip

Ref. Laumonier, no.859, pl.101, no.8

Note Style not unlike UT 16-17, but clay is apparently different.   Probably
        a slave: for the deep beard cf. AT 5.   Not after 2nd cent. B.C.

UT 51   Terracotta mask   Madrid 4046

H. 0,08 m.

Slave head (22): semicircular twisted trumpet, carefully marked teeth,
wrinkles etc.   Yellow-grey clay

Ref. Laumonier, no.862, pl.101, no.7

Note CF. ZT 12, 22.   Early Hellenistic

UT 52   Terracotta mask   Madrid 4047

H. 0,065 m.

Head with careful hair, not too prominent eyes, spade beard, full cheeks.
Probably slave.   Pink ochre clay; white slip, pink paint, one suspension
hole

Ref. Laumonier, no.863, pl.101, 6

Note Perhaps cf. AT 5.   Early Hellenistic

UT 53   Terracotta statuette   Madrid 17224

H. 0,16 m.

Slave, with oval trumpet mouth, evanescent eyelids; wrapped in cloak (like
an orator, but short), legs wide apart.   Two locks over shoulders, hair not
peaked but striated in front.   Ochre clay.   Oval vent.

Ref. Laumonier, no.424, pl.25, 1.   He compares Breccia, *Terrecotte*, 1,
no.342, pl.18, 3 (Alexandria, 18897) without head, from Chatby;   Winter,
T.K., 424 from Canosa.

Note For posture cf. TT 20, YT 2.   For mask cf. NT 10.   Probably Italian.
2nd cent. B.C.

UT 54   Terracotta statuette   Milan, Museo Teatrale

H. 0,14 m.

Cook holding chickens in both hands: mask 25: raised brows; pupils marked,
eyes outlined, semicircular trumpet

Ref. Simon 188 n.3;   Sambon no.224,pl.8;   Robert fig.25.

Note Sambon says Tanagra (formerly Lecuyer collection).   Simon says possibly
from Pergamon.   Goes with late Myrina, 1st cent. B.C.

UT 55   Terracotta mask   Milan

H. 0,15 m.

Bald, furrowed forehead, eyes slightly bored, wide trumpet.   Two suspension
holes

Ref. Sambon, 284, pl.9

Note Late Hellenistic

UT 56   Terracotta mask (roof tile)   Munich 982

H. 0,14 m.

Wreathed slave: corkscrew locks; bored pupils; hard wrinkles; even raised
brows; semicircular trumpet

Ref. Late Hellenistic at earliest

UT 57   Terracotta head   Munich 5020

H. 0,09 m.

Wreathed slave: depressed pupils, hard swung brows, wrinkles; very deep
trumpet

Note Compare UT 56 and more closely IT 49.   Late Hellenistic at earliest

UT 58   Terracotta head   Munich 5021

H. 0,09 m.

Wreathed slave: even hair below wreath; outlined eyes, bored pupils; semicircular trumpet

Note Perhaps cf. AT 19 for eyes.   Late 2nd cent. B.C.

UT 59   Terracotta   Munich 5343

H. 0,075 m.

Standing slave (22): porter with bedding; double girding above and below stomach; deepish striated trumpet

Note Recalls ET 27.   Probably Late Hellenistic

UT 60   Terracotta mask   Munich 5385

H. 0,085 m.

Slave (27): outlined, bulbous eyes; uneven brows; deep striated beard, nearly pointed

Note Possibly goes with the group round IT 37.   Italian, not after 2nd cent. B.C.

UT 61   Terracotta   Munich 5396

H. 0,145 m.

Standing slave with himation over shoulder (22): right hand to chin, left hand holds himation; deep rounded trumpet

Note Not unlike main Myrina group.   Possibly 2nd cent. B.C.

UT 62   Terracotta statuette   Munich 6936

H. 0,215 m.

Leading slave: mask 27?: wig hair with peak, wide twisted trumpet; hands clasped before stomach; cloak falling between legs; slim

Ref. Bieber, *H.T.*, fig.233; *D.*, 149; Simon, 190 n.42c

Note Cf. DT 19.   1st cent. B.C.

UT 63   Terracotta head   Munich 7544

Leading slave (27): bored pupils; peaked speira; raised eyebrows; pointed trumpet

Note Cf. DT 19.   1st cent. B.C.

UT 64   Terracotta head   Munich 7720

H. 0,10 m.

Wavy-haired slave (27): even bushy brows; bored pupils

Note Cf. above UT 56.   Late Hellenistic at earliest

UT 65   Terracotta statuette   Munich 114a (old no.)

H. 0,135 m.

Soldier with chiton, chlamys, and sword: must be batman because of slave mouth: mask 27

Ref. Bieber, *H.T.*, fig.247a; *D.*, no.147; Simon, 67, 186 n.129 accepts as as soldier (15).   But for the batman cf. above DT 22

Note Early Hellenistic

UT 66   Terracotta statuettes   Munich 117 (old no.)

Lovers

Ref. Bieber, *H.T.*, fig.247b;   *D.*, no.148;   Simon 202 n.20 says slave and low hetaira

Note Early Hellenistic

UT 67   Terracotta   Munich, S.L. 201

H. 0,08 m.

Mask 27: peaked striated hair, uneven brows, rimmed eyes;   folds on cheek, pointed trumpet

Ref. Simon 190 n.41b;   *Sammlung Loeb* II, p.17

Note Middle Comedy tradition in modelling of cheeks and deep trumpet. Possibly goes with AT 11-17

UT 68   Terracotta head   Munich, S.L. 224

Slave: bored pupils, wide, twisted mouth almost semicircular

Note Cf. DT 19.   1st cent. B.C.

UT 69   Terracotta statuette   Munich, Private Collection

H. 0,095 m.

Man seated on altar (?22): peaked speira, semicircular trumpet, both hands on altar

Ref. Lullies, *Sammlung gr. Kleinkunst*, no.182

Note Cf. above AT 24.   Late 1st cent. B.C.

UT 70   Terracotta mask   Munich, Private Collection

H. 0,078 m.

Mask of slave (?27): bulbous eyes, *not* bored;   uneven brows with very sharp knick;   deep, smooth trumpet, pointed

Ref. Lullies, *Sammlung gr. Kleinkunst*, no.184

Note Early Hellenistic.   Perhaps cf. AT 5

UT 71   Terracotta head (from vase?)   New York .10.210.60

H. 0,038 m.

Slave with large wreath: wideish shallow trumpet;   bulbous outlined eyes; two holes on top of head.   Yellow clay

Ref. H. McClees, *Daily Life*, 18

Note Perhaps cf. AV 34.   2nd cent. B.C.

UT 72   Terracotta statuette   Paris, Louvre

Seated comic actor: mask 22: speira, deep trumpet, small pellet eyes;   legs crossed, both hands holding cloak over left shoulder;   square altar

Ref. Bieber, *H.T.*, fig.209

Note Recalls earliest Myrina group.   Perhaps 3rd cent. B.C.

UT 73   Terracotta statuette   Princeton, Art Museum 570

Fat slave with peak hair and smooth trumpet; hands crossed on belly; standing with legs wide apart; low narrow girding

Note Same general class as MT 26.   Perhaps Early Hellenistic

UT 74   Terracotta mask from vessel   Princeton 50.69

Slave mask (27): roughly striated hair, bored pupils, plain beard nearly pointed

Ref. 'Princeton', fig. 41

Note Perhaps mask from brazier cf. AV 32 etc.   2nd cent. B.C.

UT 75   Terracotta head   Vienna 1457

H. 0,034 m.

Slave (25): raised brows, shock of hair over ears, wideish twisted trumpet

Note Not unlike DT 14.   1st cent. B.C.

UT 76   Terracotta mask   Vienna 18.36

H. 0,085 m.

Slave (27): beard broken off

Note Cf. slave in Nauplion, XT 13.   Early Hellenistic

Women

UT 77   Terracotta mask   Athens, N.M. 4000

H. 0,06 m.

Mask (?42) with small knot of hair on back of head and small band

Ref. Simon 120, 196 n.36; Martha pl. VI, 5 (82)

Note Early Hellenistic

UT 78   Terracotta mask   Athens, N.M. 5997

Small *pseudokore* mask with wide narrow mouth

Note Perhaps Early Hellenistic

UT 79   Terracotta mask   Berlin, 436

H. 0,09 m.

Mask of old woman (29): ivy wreath; eyes rimmed; deep wrinkles; hard brows

Ref. Bieber, *H.T.*, fig. 275; *D.*, no. 171; Robert, fig. 82; Simon 199 n.6 suggests 'wolfish woman' (Pollux no. 28) doubtfully; *P.C.F.*, fig. 146

Note Perhaps 2nd cent. B.C.

UT 80   Terracotta mask   Boston 95.175

Woman with melon hair and wreath; evanescent eyes; white face (39?)

Note Early Hellenistic

UT 81   Terracotta mask   Cambridge, Mass., Harvard University
?Young hetaira with rimmed pricked eyes.   Bright red clay
Note Cf. AT 21.   1st cent. B.C.

UT 82   Terracotta mask   Compiègne, Musée Vivenel, V 804
Wimpled hetaira
Note Probably 2nd cent. B.C.   Not unlike DT 25 but perhaps Italian

UT 83   Terracotta mask   Dresden, 1274
H. 0,026 m.
Mask (?42) with small knot of hair on back of head: fat face, sleepy eyes, wreath with flowers and leaves
Ref. Simon 108, 196 n.33; *A.A.*, 1895, **223** n.14
Note Cf. DT 27.   2nd cent. B.C.

UT 84   Terracotta relief   Florence, Mus. Arch. 931
Mask of old nurse
Ref. Bieber, *H.T.*, fig.277; *D.*, no.172; Pickard-Cambridge, *Dith.*, fig.28;
         Simon 130 (caricature, *not* Comedy);   199 n.10a

UT 85   Terracotta mask   Leipzig, Kunstgewerbe Museum, 19.123
Lampadion mask (42)
Ref. Bielefeld, *Wiss. Zeitschr. Greifswald*, 4 (1954), 99, fig.9-10
Note According to Bielefeld the clay is Attic.   Not unlike ET 3.   Early
         Hellenistic

UT 86   Terracotta mask   London, British Museum, W.T. 310
Hetaira with melon hair (39)
Ref. Walters, *Catalogue*, D 99
Note Early Hellenistic

UT 87   Terracotta mask   Madrid 3369
H. 0,09 m.
Melon hair;   remains of wreath.   Red ochre clay;   two suspension holes
Ref. Laumonier, no.854, pl.101, 3
Note Very like IT 59.   Not after 2nd cent. B.C.

UT 88   Terracotta mask   Madrid 4045
H. 0,08 m.
Wreathed, first *pseudokore* (34): sleepy eyes.   Ochre clay;   one hole
Ref. Laumonier, no.855, pl.101 no.1
Note Not after 2nd cent. B.C.

UT 89   Terracotta mask   Madrid 17226
H. 0,065 m.
First *pseudokore* (34): evanescent eyes.   Suspension holes
Ref. Laumonier, no.425, pl.25, 3

UT 90   Terracotta masks side to side   Milan
          H. 0,14 m.
          Herakles mask with bored hair, beard, pupils; girl's mask with striated hair
          and evanescent eyes
          Ref. Sambon, no.287, pl.9
          Note Not quite certain whether mask is male or female.   Late Hellenistic

UT 91   Terracotta mask   Milan
          H. 0,09 m.
          Hetaira: wreath; earrings; full hair; large, outlined eyes; fat face
          Ref. Sambon, pl.12, no.305
          Note Late Hellenistic

UT 92   Terracotta mask   Munich 5402
          H. 0,065 m.
          Hetaira: probably 39 rather than 42
          Note Cf. DT 2, ZT 38.   2nd cent. B.C. or earlier

UT 93   Terracotta mask   Oxford, 1872. 1276
          Hetaira mask (42): sharp lids, marked pupils
          Note Early Hellenistic

UT 94   Terracotta mask   Vienna, Inv. V 2720
          Lampadion (42)
          Note Cf. DT 25.   2nd cent. B.C.

Additions

UT 95   Terracotta statuette   Paris, Louvre Camp. 5010
          H. 0,13 m.
          Seated slave, right arm tugging at cloak over left shoulder, crossed legs;
          peaked speira, raised brows, semicircular trumpet
          Ref. T.K., 424/10
          Note Perhaps Early Hellenistic

UT 96   Terracotta statuette   Paris, Louvre E.D. 2070
          Seated slave: right arm to cloak over left shoulder, double-girt chiton,
          fat: elaborate wreath, raised brows, deep striated trumpet with rounded
          bottom
          Note Cf. MT 35

UT 97   Terracotta mask   Paris, Louvre Camp.4581
          Young Pan: bored pupils.   Rough work
          Note Cf. UT 21 etc., IT 43

UT 98   Terracotta mask   Paris, Cab.Med.

Wimpled hetaira with pierced eyes and small mouth with turned down corners

Note Stylization not unlike Hellenistic masks from Capua

UT 99   Terracotta statuette   Paris, Cab.Med.

Standing slave, with child on left arm;   himation across breast and falling
to knees;   very fat legs.   Mask 22

Note Very like and possibly replica of TT 2

UT 100   Terracotta statuette   a) Paris, Cab.Med. 152 (54)
                                  b) Paris, Louvre (Campana)
                                  c) Karlsruhe

H. 0,12 m.

Standing slave with deep, smooth trumpet;   right hand to mouth;   himation
over shoulder falls decently;   fattish legs.   Mask 22

Ref. *T.K.*, 424/2 takes as Italian.   Cf. above UT 48, 61

UT 101   Terracotta mask   Berlin 6957

H. 0,07 m.

Slave (22): elaborate wreath with fruit and flowers;   hard modelling;   pricked
pupils;   smooth wide trumpet

Ref. Robert, fig.57

Note Perhaps 2nd cent. B.C.

UT 102   Terracotta mask   Berlin 3508

H. 0,045 m.

Slave (22): smooth speira with peak;   uneven brows;   bored eyeballs;   wide,
smooth trumpet

Ref. Robert, fig.94

Note Perhaps 2nd cent. B.C.

UT 103   Terracotta mask   Basel, Private collection   ?Tarentum

H. 0,095 m.

Slave (25): wreathed with ivy wreath;   framed eyes with bored pupils;   deepish
trumpet

Ref. Schefold, *Meisterwerke*, no.387

Note Perhaps late 2nd cent. B.C.

UT 104   Terracotta mask   Basel, Private collection   ?Tarentum

Youth (?15): smooth hair;   ivy wreath;   wide eyes with bored pupils;   Roman
nose

Ref. Schefold, *Meisterwerke*, no.388

Note Perhaps late 2nd cent. B.C.

UT 105   Terracotta mask   Basel, Private collection   ?Tarentum

Bearded man: wreathed; long narrow eyes; corkscrew beard, hair in *sakkos* (?dramatic)

Ref. Schefold, *Meisterwerke*, no.389, suggests a priest

Note Perhaps late 2nd cent. B.C.

UT 106   Terracotta mask   Utrecht University 280   ?Alexandria

H. 0,048 m.

Wreathed *Pornoboskos*: dotted wreath with band across middle; domed forehead; twisted brows; depressed pupils; corkscrew beard

Note Perhaps Hellenistic

II: ROMAN PERIOD

ATHENS

Lead Tokens

AJ 7-13   The old man (10) has the shortish beard also found on old men's masks on
           Roman lamps (cf. IL 6).   The fat-faced slave (9) and the girl (8) and
           youth (12) with pseudo-*onkos*, if rightly interpreted as comic, suggest
           that the date is not before the Imperial period.   The tokens may have
           been theatre tickets: 7 is inscribed the *Theophoroumene* of Menander.

AJ 7   Lead tokens   a)   Athens, National Museum
                             b)   Athens, Agora, IL 1311-13   Agora

          Menander, *Theophoroumene*:   masks of *kore*, slave, youth.   The girl has
          pseudo-*onkos* rather than wreath, the youth has long locks and may be the
          second youth with wavy hair

          Ref.   P.C.F., fig.206/4;   Benndorf, *Beiträge zur Kenntniss des attischen
                Theaters*, 1875, pl.1, no.23;   Postolacca, *Annali*, 1868, 268

          Note Perhaps Roman

AJ 8   Lead token   Athens, N.M.   Athens
          Profile mask of *kore* (33) with pseudo-*onkos*
          Ref. Benndorf, *Beiträge*, 1875, 71, pl.1, no.20;   *P.C.F.*, fig.206/2
          Note Probably comic rather than tragic

AJ 9   Lead token   Athens, N.M.   Athens
          Frontal slave mask with fat face and twisted trumpet with narrow edges
          Ref. Benndorf, no.21

159

AJ 10   Lead token   Athens, N.M.   Athens
         Three-quarter old man's mask (4) with shortish beard
         Ref. Benndorf, no.22; *P.C.F.*, fig.206/3

AJ 11   Lead token   Athens, N.M.   Athens
         Frontal mask of kore (33)
         Ref. Benndorf, no.25

AJ 12   Lead token   Athens, N.M.   Athens
         Profile mask of youth with pseudo-*onkos*
         Ref. Benndorf, no.26

AJ 13   Lead token   Athens, N.M.   Athens
         Frontal mask of Maison
         Ref. Benndorf, no.29

Lamps

AL 2-5   2 is shown by the clay to be an import.   3 is not unlike IL 8 and may not
         be much later.   It shows an early stage in the new type of fat leading
         slave mask (22) with the beard confined to a narrow rim round the edge of
         the trumpet;   the wavy-haired slave (27) of this type appears very clearly
         on AL 4 and 5

AL 2   Terracotta lamp   Athens, Agora T 2300   Athens, Agora   1st cent.B.C./
         (grey clay)   1st A.D.
         H. 0,081 m.
         Bald, straight-haired slave, perhaps (23) rather than (25);   semicircular smooth
         trumpet
         Ref. Cf. Broneer, Type XIX; Howland, Type 49A

AL 3   Lamp: handle above   Athens, N.M.4186   Early 1st
         forehead; spout below chin   cent.A.D.
         Leading slave (22) with uneven brows, finely striated speira, and trumpet with
         narrow striated edge
         Ref. Brueckner, *Skenika*, 36, fig.3;   for type of lamp, cf. Broneer, Type XXII
               (Augustan to Tiberian).   Howland Type 47C.   For mask cf. AS 9

AL 4   Roman lamp   Athens, Agora L 4076   Agora   250/300 A.D.
         Mask of wavy-haired slave (27) with flaming hair, lock of hair by right ear
         Ref. Cf. CL 6 (815), Broneer Type XXVIII

AL 5   Roman lamp   Athens, Agora L 2111   Agora   350 A.D.
         Mask of wavy-haired slave (27)
         Note Cf. also L 944

Sculpture

AS 6-13 Sculptures asserted to be carved in Pentelic marble are included here as well as sculpture found in Athens.   A Pentelic marble disk decorated with a young satyr in low relief and extremely like similar decorative reliefs found in Pompeii was discovered in the Athenian Agora (S 934; H. A. Thompson, *Hesperia*, 18 (1949), 222, pl.44/2) and shows that these decorative works were produced in Athens.   6 and 7 are copies of Early Hellenistic originals (6 is repeated more elaborately by IS 10).   10-12 are probably also copies of earlier originals.   10 is very like an earlier Italian mosaic IM 2 and a gem UJ 34.   (XS 2 may also belong here.)

8 (the grave relief set up by an actor for his son), 9 (possibly from the Council House of the Technitai), 13 (an actor wearing his mask) are valid evidence for contemporary practice.   The masks of 9 and 13 certainly belong to the new type of slave mask; the slave mask of 8 is Late Hellenistic in type.

AS 6 Marble relief   Princeton, Art Museum, 51-1

H. 0,495 m.

Menander with masks: 11, 34, 4.   Pentelic marble

Ref. Bieber, *Festschrift A. Rumpf*, 14, pl.5; *B.H.T.*[2], fig.316; Simon 194 n.59; 'Princeton', fig.29; Jones, *Ancient Art in Princeton*, 45

Note According to Bieber the marble is Pentelic and the relief is a copy of an original of the 3rd cent. B.C., earlier than the Lateran relief (IS 10) and not later than the 1st cent. B.C.   For stylization of old man cf. NS 7

AS 7 Marble relief   Berlin 951

Young poet contemplating mask 3

Ref. Krüger, *A.M.*, 26 (1901), 136, fig.3; Simon 193 n.42c; *Beschr.* 'acquired in Aquileia, Greek marble'.   Hellenistic?

AS 8 Grave relief   Verona, Mus.Lapidario   Athens   50 A.D.

Grave-relief with two masks,(3) with low peaked speira, short corkscrew beard, and (22) with low peaked speira, trumpet with flat narrow edge, in square frame on pillar.   Pentelic marble.   Inscription: *Gaios Silios Bathyllos Azenieus: Dionysas: Sotimas: Seilia*.   Added later *Erotion, Seilios*.   D. is presumed the boy between Silios and Silia

Ref. Conze, *Att. Grabreliefs*, IV, 98, no.2113, pl.463, named after Augustan dancer.   Inscription in original form dated mid-1st cent. A.D. by *I.G.*, III[2], 5302 (*I.G.*, III, 1488).   For square frame, cf. Bieber, *Hell. Sc.*, fig.656 etc.

AS 9 Marble mask   Athens, N.M. 3373   Athens, Kerameikos

H. 0,34 m.

Mask of slave (22): uneven brows, bored pupils, striated peaked speira, fat face

Ref. Bieber, *H.T.*[1], fig.266; *H.T.*[2], fig.810; *P.C.F.*, fig.137; Simon 77, 189 n.37; Brueckner, *Skenika*, 32, pl.2, suggests origin from Council House of Technitai (Wycherley, *Agora*, III, p.21) and dates 1st cent. A.D.

AS 10   Marble mask   London, B.M. 2440 (Hamilton Collection)

Delicate youth (13).   Pentelic marble

Ref. *R.B.*, 32 (1949), fig.1; Simon, 184, n.72, pl.VI,1; *P.C.F.*, fig.116;
        W.L.G.C., pl.4a

Note Probably 1st cent. A.D.   Very like IM 2, UJ 34

AS 11   Marble mask   Ince Blundell 136   Rome, Villa Mattei

H. 0,63 m.

Mask 22: speira with striations, swinging brows with very hard outlines,
depressed pupils, very large striated trumpet.   Pentelic marble

Ref. Ashmole pl.46; Simon, 193 n.49b takes as old man

Note Very like IS 34.   Copy of an Early Hellenistic original

AS 12   Marble   Ince Blundell 133   Rome, Villa Mattei

H. 0,93 m.

Mask 34.   Pentelic marble.   Shut mouth (perhaps then not dramatic)

Ref. Ashmole pl.46 (Hadrianic); Simon, 197, n.40

AS 13   Marble head   Agora Museum S 995   Agora

H. 0,11 m.

Furrowed forehead, swinging brows, deeply sunk eyeholes showing actor's eyes,
fat face; semicircular trumpet mouth showing actor's mouth inside

Note Perhaps 3rd cent. A.D.

Terracottas

AT 26-47   Terracottas from the Athenian Agora mostly well dated.[1] The third century
            examples are good in themselves and show the new slave masks worn with
            new costumes.   The slave masks are of two types: the most complete
            example of the first, which is presumably the leading slave mask (22), is
            the large mask AT 32.   The brows are even, the hair is combed back from
            the forehead, the beard is quite short and appears as a narrow frame to
            the slightly twisted trumpet mouth.   The second, of which AT 31 is a
            very fine example, is presumably the wavy-haired leading slave (27):   the
            brows are uneven, the hair flames up from the forehead in a pseudo-onkos,
            the cheeks are fat, the beard is formed in the same way but has a serrated
            edge instead of a smooth edge (cf. also UT 108-11).   AT 31, 36, 44 have
            quilted sleeves and stockings instead of the plain tights worn before;
            AT 36 wears a long chiton and a small mantle but seems nevertheless to be
            a slave.   These new garments can be parallelled on contemporary Italian
            monuments (IL 50, IT 80, 81).

            The mould AT 37 reproduces with minor variations a scene known from
            contemporary Italian moulds (IT 81) but is alone in having an inscription
            COMEDIA PYLADES; presumably it commemorates the actor Pylades playing
            a Latin comedy.

            1. The numbers given to these in Grandjouan, *Roman Terracottas*, are
               inserted in brackets after the Agora numbers.

AT 46 probably comes from a vase but it seemed most economical to list it under terracottas.   AT 38 and 47 are both freakish: 38 should be compared with the Terence miniatures and one of the Ostia masks (IS 31).

From the Agora

AT 26   Terracotta mask   Athens, Agora T 1406   Athens, Agora, D 4: 1 Late 1st
      H. 0,058 m.   (Grandjouan, 576)   cent.A.D.

Fragment of bald-headed male with wrinkled forehead and swinging brow;   bored eye.   Traces of pink.   *Kolax* (17)

Ref. Robinson, *Agora V, Roman Pottery*, no.G 228, pl.48

AT 27   Terracotta mask   Athens, Agora T 3469   Agora   Late 1st/early 2nd
      H. 0,048 m.   (Grandjouan, 530)   cent.A.D.

Fragment from fat, right cheek of mask: probably 22

AT 28   Terracotta mask   Athens, Agora T 3191   Agora, late Roman   Late 2nd/early
      H. 0,08 m.   (Grandjouan, 561)   fill, S.Stoa   3rd cent.A.D.

Life-size slave mask (22):   raised brow, petal eye, bored pupil, striated hair

Ref. Webster, *Wiener Studien*, 69 (1956), 108

AT 29   Terracotta mask   Athens, Agora T 262   Agora   2nd/3rd cent. A.D.
      H. 0,064 m.   (Grandjouan, 566)

Pierced eyes very wide apart;   semicircular striated beard unframed.   Probably mask 27

AT 30   Terracotta mask   Athens, Agora T 1863   Agora   3rd cent. A.D.
      H. 0,08 m.   (Grandjouan, 574)

Fragmentary mask: cheek, eye, and trumpet (unframed), probably 27

AT 31   Terracotta statuette   Athens, Agora T 3635   Agora   Before 250 A.D.
      (?from vase)   (Grandjouan, 1110)

Seated slave, left hand to left ear.   Yellow flaming hair;   red face;   uneven brows;   white eyes;   trumpet semicircular, unframed, striated;   quilted sleeves and stockings;   crossed legs

Note Mrs. D. B. Thompson says from first generation mould of which T 1231 (AT 39) is second generation

AT 32   Terracotta mask   Athens, Agora T 478   Agora Q 15:1   250 A.D.
      H. 0,27 m.   (Grandjouan, 560)

Mask of slave (22):   striated hair with peak, raised eyebrows, framed eyes, bored pupils, semicircular trumpet mouth with narrow edge striated and framed

Ref. *Hesperia* IV, 338, fig.25;   *P.C.F.*, fig.135;   *W.S.*, 69 (1956), 108; Robinson, *Agora V, Roman Pottery*, no.K 136;   *Agora Picture Book*, no.3, fig.76

AT 33   Terracotta mask   Athens, Agora T 3556   Agora, Well Q 19:1   250 A.D.
         H. 0,083 m.   (Grandjouan, 564)

Leading slave (22): striated trumpet mouth, eyebrow in high relief; petal
eyes, iris inscribed, pupil bored

AT 34   Terracotta head   Athens, Agora T 1447   Agora Deposit,   250/267 A.D.
         H. 0,032 m.   (Grandjouan, 575)   M 17: 1

High forehead; two small furrows; thick raised brows nearly meeting; outlined
eyes; wide snub nose: leading slave (22)
Ref. Robinson, *Agora V: Roman Pottery*, p.101, M 184, pl.48

AT 35   Terracotta masks   Athens, Agora T 1090,   Agora Deposit   250/267 A.D.
         H. 0,095; 0,076 m.   3078 (Grandjouan, 563)   H-I 12:1

Fragmentary masks of fat-faced slaves (22): petal eyes, neat trumpets

AT 36   Terracotta statuette   Athens, Agora T 3074   Agora Deposit   250/267 A.D.
         H. 0,15 m.   (Grandjouan, 505)   H-I 12:1

Body of actor, clothed in himation, long chiton with narrow belt, quilted sleeves,
shoes; left hand pulls at himation, right hand on chest
Ref. *Hesperia* 21 (1952), 110 pl.30b
Note Dumped soon after the Herulian sack 267 A.D.

AT 37   Terracotta mould   Athens, Agora T 2404   Agora Deposit   250/267 A.D.
         H. 0,112 m.   (Grandjouan, 502)   H-I 12:1

Slave with fat face, hair striated backwards from forehead, semicircular trumpet
mouth striated, sleeved long chiton, himation; chin pillared on right hand, left
hand holding wreath; seated at the foot of couch.   Young woman with long hair,
holding a wreath, lying on couch.   COMEDIA PYLADES
Ref. *B.H.T.*[2], fig.796

AT 38   Terracotta mask   Athens, Agora T 3016   Agora, I 12:1   250/267 A.D.
         H. 0,068 m.   (Grandjouan, 571)

Pierced eyes; uneven flaring brows; furrowed forehead and cheeks; very triangular striated trumpet
Note The large trumpet is unusual in contemporary slaves; the triangular shape
        does not suit an old man; the uneven brows are unlikely for a satyr

AT 39   Terracotta mask   Athens, Agora T 1231   Agora   200/300 A.D.
         H. 0,05 m.   (Grandjouan, 506)

Wavy-haired slave (27): flaming hair, uneven brows, fat face; semicircular
narrow striated trumpet.   Red orange on face, blue on hair, white on drapery
and over the eyes

AT 40   Terracotta mask   Athens, Agora T 1638   Agora   3rd cent.A.D.
         H. 0,068 m.   (Grandjouan, 572)

Slave mask (27): raised brows, trumpet mouth, flaming hair broken off

AT 41   Terracotta mask   Athens, Agora T 2091   Agora, Stoa,   3rd cent. A.D.
         H. 0,039 m.   (Grandjouan, 568)   room B

         Slave mask (27): flaming hair, uneven brows, semicircular trumpet

AT 42   Terracotta mask   Athens, Agora T 3232   Agora, South Stoa 3rd/4th cent.A.D.
         H. 0,040 m.   (Grandjouan, 567)

         Slave mask (27): raised brows and trumpet mouth

AT 43   Terracotta mask   Athens, Agora T 1415   Agora   Late Roman
         H. 0,032 m.   (Grandjouan, 573)

         Fragmentary head: flaming hair, furrowed brows, probably *not* knotted; deep
         squinting eyes;   smooth trumpet

AT 44   Terracotta statuette   Athens, Agora T 743   Agora L-M 11-12:1 Late 3rd/early
         H. 0,064 m.   (Grandjouan, 498)   4th cent. A.D.

         Seated slave with quilted sleeves and tights; tunic to knees.   Holding stick?

AT 45   Terracotta head   Athens, Agora T 3424   Agora   3rd/4th cent. A.D.
         H. 0,04 m.   (Grandjouan, 592)

         Fragmentary head, possibly of young man

AT 46   Terracotta mask from   Athens, Agora T 1167   Agora, Cistern   200-250 A.D.
         vase   (Grandjouan, 477)   D 6: 2
         H. 0,047 m.

         Slave mask (22): roll of hair, uneven brows, smooth semicircular trumpet

AT 47   Terracotta mask   Athens, Agora, Pnyx   Pnyx: Assembly
                                T 141   Place, Period III

         Bald head; beard; bored pupils.   Good modelling (25).   Perhaps not dramatic
         Ref. D. B. Thompson, *Hesperia*, Supplt.7 (1943), fig.62, no.77
         Note Perhaps 2nd cent. A.D.

      Other terracottas, probably Attic of Roman period

AT 48   Terracotta mask   Athens, N.M. 5041   ?
         Mask (7): large and flat

AT 49   Terracotta mask   Athens, N.M. 13624   ?
         Large wreathed mask of *Hapalos*: back arranged as theatre mask

AT 50   Terracotta mask   Athens, N.M. 13627   ?
         Large wreathed theatre mask of *oulos*

AT 51   Terracotta statuette   Athens N.M. 14682 (Lambros collection)   ?
         Eros with bald slave mask (25)
         Note Cf. ZT 55

AT 52   Terracotta mask   London, B.M. 1901.5.8.2   3rd cent. A.D.

Pale yellow clay, thin.   Old man (7): hair in tight curls;   swinging brows;
corkscrew curled beard.   Signed ΠΡΕΙΜΟΣ on hair

Ref. Walters, *Catalogue*, D 177

Note Preimos is a third century A.D. lampmaker.   Cf. UT 116

CORINTH

Lead token

CJ 2   Lead disk   Corinth Museum, 1241   Corinth

Youth's head: *agroikos* (14)

Ref. *Corinth* XII, no.929

Note Roman period.   Described as 'inlay' but perhaps a theatre ticket like
AJ 7 etc.

Lamps

CL 2   Terracotta lamp   Corinth, 950   (Italy)   Late 1st cent.A.D.

?Slave mask.   Grey buff clay;   brown glaze

Ref. Broneer, *Corinth*, IV, 2, no.542, pl.26, Type XXVI

CL 3   Terracotta lamp   Corinth 234   Corinth   2nd cent. A.D.

Oulos (12) with mouth closed, filling whole discus.   Red clay unglazed

Ref. Broneer, *Corinth*, IV, 2, no.678, pl.28, Type XXVII

CL 4   Terracotta lamps   Corinth 1110   Corinth   2nd cent. A.D.

Kore with long hair, braided (33);   wavy-haired slave with peaked wig hair, uneven
brows, narrow striated edge to trumpet (22);   mask with striated hair, beardless
(?youth or old woman).   Pale yellow clay, unglazed.   Signed: ΑΡΙΣΤΟΝΕΙΚΟΥ

Ref. Broneer, *Corinth*, IV, 2, no.702, pl.12, Type XXVII, Group IV

Note A lamp from the same mould was found in the Agora at Athens.   Cf. also
XL 2

CL 5   Terracotta lamp   Corinth 339   Corinth   2nd cent. A.D.

Small mask of *agroikos*;   mouth closed.   Pale yellow clay, unglazed

Ref. Broneer, *Corinth*, IV, 2, no.710, pl.29, Type XXVII, Group IV (cf. however
no.1211, which Broneer interprets as negro)

CL 6   Terracotta lamp   Corinth 1085   250 A.D.

Mask 27, with flaming hair, long locks to the left, trumpet with narrow edge
striated.   Grey brown clay;   dark brown glaze

Ref. Broneer, *Corinth*, IV, 2, no.1212, fig.183, Type XXVIII

Note Broneer compares XL 4.   Cf. also AL 4

MAINLAND GREECE (OTHER SITES)

Bronzes

XB 1   Bronze lamps   Belgrade   Pozarevac   1st cent. A.D.

Handle formed of mask with corkscrew curls and triangular hat

Ref. Cermanovic, *Starenyar*, 9-10 (1959), 203.   Cf. YT 13, FB 1

Lamps

XL 1-4   Lamps from Corfu and Delphi.   All have the later type of leading slave mask.   3 has an interesting old man's mask, cf. UL 1.   IL 47 should perhaps have been included here as it was found in the Chersonese;   it is extremely like AL 4, CL 6, XL 4

XL 1   Clay lamp   London, B.M. no.806   1st cent. A.D., early
(triangular handle
with palmette)

Slave mask: peak hair;   wide, twisted trumpet

Ref. Walters, *Catalogue of Greek and Roman Lamps*, 121, fig.146;   Broneer, Type XXI

Note Should probably be excluded as a forgery

XL 2   Clay lamp   London, B.M. no.1230   Greece   2nd cent. A.D.

Three slave masks: single row of striations above forehead, smooth wide trumpet with narrow edges

Ref. Walters 187 fig.268:   close to Corinth 702 (= CL 4), i.e. Broneer, Type XXVII

Note Very much cleaned with acid

XL 3   Clay lamp   London, B.M. no.1231   Greece   125/50 A.D.

Three masks: old man (fat face, trumpet mouth, long beard below);   slave (fat face, speira, side locks);   youth (speira, side locks)

Ref. Walters 187:   Broneer, Type XXVII

Note For the old man, cf. UL 1

XL 4   Terracotta lamp   Delphi   Marmaria   250 A.D.

Slave (27) with long locks to left of head, flame hair, trumpet with narrow striated edge

Ref. *Fouilles de Delphes*, V, 188, no.521, fig.815.   Broneer, Type XXVIII

Note Cf. AL 4 and CL 6

Mosaic

XM 1   The seated figure has been explained as an old man with white hair (Ivanov) and as a girl with a white veil (Toynbee).   The young men look like rival lovers rather than disparate heroes, and fourth century Achaeans are to be preferred to Homeric heroes.   The style of the mosaic is late Roman including the large mouths, but nothing else in the masks or clothing precludes its deriving ultimately from an early Hellenistic original.

XM 1   Mosaic   Oescus   Oescus   4th cent. A.D.

'Menander, *Achaeans*'.   Masks 15, 33, ?13.   Seated *kore*, between soldier and
young man.   Wreathed unmasked figure stands behind (Menander?).   City gate to
left; house-door to right

Ref. Ivanov, *Monuments de l'art en Bulgarie* II (1954);   Toynbee, *J.R.S.*, 45
1955, 204 (interpretation and date);   *G.T.P.*, no.C 57;   Ivanov, *Studia in
honorem D. Decev*, 489;   Weitzmann, *Ancient Book Illumination*, 83;   *B.H.T.*[2],
fig.315

Sculpture

XS 1   Marble mask from frieze   Cambridge, G.R.10.1865   Stratonikeia

Mask 22:   peaked hair;   uneven brows, petal eyes (unfinished),   deep trumpet

Ref. Simon 193 n.48;   Clarke, *Marbles*, no.XIX;   Michaelis, 247, no.10;   Nicoll,
Masks, etc., 62, fig.58

Note Perhaps 1st cent. A.D.   Probably copy of earlier original

XS 2   Marble mask   London, B.M., 2449   ?Greece

First pseudo-kore (34)

Ref. Simon 110, 197 n.43

Note Probably 1st century A.D.   Perhaps Attic like AS 10-12

Terracotta

XT 25   Terracotta antefix   Belgrade

Probably *kore*:   smooth brows, elaborate curly hair over forehead and hanging
locks

Ref. Veličkovič, *Narodni Musej, Belgrade, Antika III*, no.78, pl.37

Note Perhaps 2nd/3rd cent. A.D.

DELOS

Terracotta

DT 29   Terracotta mask   Delos A 3649   Delos, west of   2nd cent. A.D.
        (fragments)   guardian's house

H. 0,09 m.

Wreathed hetaira or youth: bored eyes, smooth brow below wreath.   Very flat

Ref. *Delos* 23, no.1387, cf. *Corinth*, XII, no.436;   *Tarsus*, I, pl.234-6 = ZT 61,
typical late flat Roman mask

CYPRUS

Terracottas

KT 7-10   The bored eyes and hard modelling suggest a Roman date for 7-8.   10 is
            the fat-cheeked slave known from Athens and elsewhere.

KT 7   Terracotta mask   Nicosia, Cyprus, D215   Cyprus

Youth with wreath, slightly raised brows, probably wavy hair, iris and pupil
bored: striated hair behind wreath: perhaps 11

KT 8   Terracotta mask   Nicosia, Cyprus, D216   Cyprus

Youth with smooth brows, wavy hair (?16):   bored iris and pupils, barley-sugar
curls in pseudo-onkos
Ref. G.T.P., no.C 59

KT 9   Terracotta head   Nicosia, Cyprus, D204,1935   Cyprus

Slave (22?):   peaked hair, raised brows, rimmed eyes, depressed pupils, semicircular trumpet.   Possibly a caricature, but the mouth suggests a dramatic
mask
Note Cf. below ZT 58

KT 10   Terracotta mask   Nicosia, Cyprus, D 217   Cyprus

Slave (22):   swing brows, petal eyes, semicircular striated trumpet with flat
edges, fat cheeks.   Break suggests pseudo-onkos
Ref. G.T.P., no.C 6 ;   *Wiener Studien*, 69 (1956), 108 (large, perhaps mould
        for worn mask).   Cf. above AS 9

KOS

Sculpture

YS 1   Marble table support   Kos, no.178   Kos
         H. 0,74 m.

Slave (mask 22):   pupils and iris bored;   hands folded in front of stomach;
sleeved chiton;   himation across chest and round waist (if it is not double-
girt long chiton)
Ref. L. Laurenzi, *Annuario* 33-34 (1955-6), 137 no.178 cf. 179-181
Note Probably not before 2nd cent. A.D.   Cf. below ZS 7

YS 2   Travertine mask   Kos, no.186   Kos
         H. 0,25 m.

Mask of comic slave: bored eyes;   trumpet mouth;   striated speira.   Perhaps
used as fountain
Ref. L. Laurenzi, *Annuario* 33-34 (1955-6), 138, no.186
Note Probably 2nd cent. A.D.

Terracottas

YT 13   Terracotta mask   Heraklion Museum   Knossos (Roman tomb   50/100 A.D.
                                                       under New Sanatorium)

         ?Pan: mouth open;   two horns on onkos

ASIA MINOR

Glass

ZG 1   Roman glass jug   Boston 31.411   Homs (Syria)
         Mask of wavy-haired slave in medallion below handle
         Note Probably 1st cent. A.D.   Cf.NV 3 (clay), UG 2 (glass)

Lamps

ZL 7   Terracotta lamp   Adana Museum   Tarsus, Roman fill   1st cent.A.D.
         Seated slave: very fuzzy hair, locks, trumpet mouth with flat striated edge
         (27).   Seated with hands crossed, sleeves
         Ref. Goldman, *Tarsus*, I, 34, 124, fig.107, no.333, compares Broneer, Type
              XXIII

ZL 8   Terracotta lamp   Ann Arbor, Kelsey   Asia Minor, from
                                 Museum 794   Rhoussopolos Collection
         Maison mask with raised eyebrows and small turned up nose
         Note Late Roman.   Cf. EL 32

ZL 9   Clay lamp   Leningrad   Smyrna   1st cent.A.D.
         Lamp in form of fat wavy-haired slave mask with striated speira, hanging locks,
         bored eyes, flat striated edge to trumpet: 27
         Ref. Waldhauer, *Antiken Tonlampen*, no.517
         Note Perhaps variant of Broneer Type XXIII.   Compare for the mask AL 3, AS 9

ZL 10   Terracotta lamp   London, B.M. 1119   Ephesos   3rd cent.A.D.
         Seated actor, holding a pot on his lap, flying cloak, head frontal (27)
         Ref. Messerschmidt, *R.M.*, 46 (1930), 186; Walters, *Cat.*, 169.   Broneer,
              Type XXVIII

Mosaic

ZM 2-5   Mosaics from Antioch.   The masks of 2 are traditional.   On 4 Comedy is
         dressed as an actor and holds a mask which seems to have a slave mouth and
         beard: if so, the slave was wearing clothing which reached to the feet (cf.
         on AT 36).

ZM 2   Mosaic   Hartford   Antioch, House of   c.200 A.D.
                                                      Mysteries of Isis

Comic masks: f) *Kore*, *Kolax*, ?curly haired youth with wreath, *Kore*, hetaira;
g) slave mask with semicircular trumpet and much hair, haggard mask with trumpet
(?21)

Ref. Levi, *Mosaic Pavements*, 163, pl.102**f, g**;   Friend, *Antioch on the Orontes*,
        III, 178, nos.114-6

Note Traditional masks slightly restylized

ZM 3   Mosaic   Baltimore   Antioch, House of the   c.250 A.D.
                                                      Boat of Psyches, Room 8

Masks: slave with fat face, very wide trumpet, and rising hair;   girl with
elaborate treatment of hair over forehead (34 or 35);   dark youth with speira

Ref. Levi, 186, pl.42a; Friend, III, 183ff., nos.46-54

ZM 4   Mosaic   Princeton 40.435   Antioch   3rd cent. A.D.

Menander; Glykera; Comedy in long chiton and himation over left shoulder,
holding stick, mask of old man or slave (4 or 27, probably 27);   mask of *kore* (33)
below

Ref. 'Princeton' fig.28;   Friend, 63, pl.63, 131;   Levi, 202ff., pl.45 (the
        building dates from the mid-2nd cent.); *B.H.T.*^{2}, fig.321

ZM 5   Mosaic   Antioch, House of the   c.400 A.D.
                                                      Masks

Masks: Maison (25) with very wide trumpet, Kore (33) with braided hair, little
hetaira (39) with fillet

Ref. Levi, 307, pl.122b

Sculpture

ZS 4   Marble   Vienna   Ephesos

Mask of youth (12): striated pseudo-onkos, long corkscrew locks, sloping brows,
bored iris and pupils

Ref. Rumpf, in *Mimus u. Logos* 166, pl.VIIb; *G.T.P.*, no.C 78

Note Probably 2nd cent. A.D. or later

ZS 5   Marble frieze   Vienna 38   Ephesos (Theatre)   Early 3rd cent.A.D.

Masks of 12, 16, 27, 33 between swags

Ref. *Ephesus*, II, 91, placed in third storey of *scaenae frons* (dated p.52 early
        3rd cent. A.D.); *J.d.I.*, 38/39 (1924/5), 275ff.

ZS 6   Marble frieze   Side   Side, theatre   2nd cent. A.D.

Leading slave (22-or)27) with fat cheeks, and young man (?10) with considerable
onkos and hair down to chin level

Ref. *A.J.A.*, 62 (1958), 98; *A.J.A.*, 63 (1959), 80

ZS 7   Marble statuette,   Constantinople 1768   Tralles
        support of table

        H. 0,795 m.

        Standing slave (27): semicircular trumpet with actor's mouth seen; legs crossed, hands clasped level with hips, himation cross-draped

        Ref. Bieber, *H.T.*[1], fig.420; [2] fig.584; Simon 173, 191 n.62

        Note Cf. above YS 1. Probably 3rd cent. A.D.

Terracottas, etc.

ZT 50-62, ZV 6   Terracottas and vase fragment.   50-52. *Seleucia.*   50 is very fine but may not be dramatic (the mouth is not preserved).   51 is extremely rough and like an Italian terracotta mask NT 24.

    Smyrna.   53 and 54 are both large flat masks perhaps for wall decoration. 53 has an elaborate wreath of a type known from other monuments.   ZV 6 in brown yellow glaze is very like ZV 5 in green glaze and should perhaps not be separated from it.

    Tarsus.   55 is made from a plaster mould and therefore derives from a metal original: other examples of Eros with a mask are noted on BT 14.   56 is the slave corresponding to the late Hellenistic old man ZT 39; they might have been placed together.   57 also may be a Roman repetition of a late Hellenistic type.   59-62 are fragments of large flat masks like 53-4 from Smyrna.   The slaves 59-60 have parallels in the Athenian Agora (AT 32, 31). The young men 61 also have parallels from Attica (AT 45, 49-50) and Delos (DT 29).   For the technique cf. ET 63, JT 6-7, UT 160-1

    Seleucia (Tigris)

ZT 50   Whitish terracotta mask   Ann Arbor, Kelsey   Seleucia, from   2nd cent. A.D.
                                        Museum 15918   Trial Trench IV, Level Ia

        Wavy-haired slave (very good).   Not certainly dramatic

        Ref. Van Ingen, *Figurines from Seleucia*, no.1375

        Note For style compare UT 1 23

ZT 51   Terracotta mask   Ann Arbor, Kelsey   Seleucia,   Early 2nd
                                        Museum 16226   Level I (?II)   cent. A.D.

        Slave with bored eyes: twisted plain mouth.   Very rough.   (?27)

        Ref. Van Ingen, no.1381, pl.73, 539

        Note Cf. below NT 24

ZT 52   Terracotta mask   Ann Arbor, Kelsey   Seleucia, Trial   2nd cent. A.D.
                                        Museum 15901   Trench IV, Level Ia
        H. 0,056 m.

        Slave

        Ref. Van Ingen, no.1390

Smyrna

ZT 53   Terracotta mask   Athens, N.M. 5547 (1250)   Smyrna

H. 0,055 m.

Wreathed young *episeistos* or *oulos*: the wreath goes back from the forehead and meets a band across from the ears

Note Not before 1st cent. A.D.

ZT 54   Terracotta mask   Oxford, Ashmolean 1890.150   Smyrna   1st cent.A.D.
                                                                            or later
Corkscrew hair;   raised brows.   Hard red clay;   very flat

Tarsus

ZT 55   Terracotta mask   Adana Museum   Tarsus,   1st cent. A.D.
                                                               Roman fill

Bald slave mask (25) held by winged Eros: knotted brows, eyes done with two pellets, mouth shows inside semicircular twisted trumpet

Ref. Goldman, *Tarsus* I, 300, fig.220, no.98, made from plaster mould

Note Cf. AT 51 for subject

ZT 56   Terracotta statuettes   Adana Museum   Tarsus   1st cent. A.D.

Mask with good head of peaked, striated hair; bored pupils, swinging brows, semicircular trumpet (22)

Ref. Goldman 34, 345, fig.234, nos.259, 261-3.   No.259 comes from Roman fill; the rest are unstratified

Note These may be the slave type which corresponds to the old man (ZT 39) and the Hellenistic moulds may still have been used

ZT 57   Terracotta statuettes   Adana Museum   Tarsus   1st/2nd cent.A.D.

Wreathed slave with wide twisted trumpet (22 or 25), wrapped in cloak, perhaps seated

Ref. Goldman, fig.234 nos.260, 268.   No.268 comes from concrete wall chambers. It is not clear whether the mask is bald or not

ZT 58   Terracotta statuette   Adana Museum   Tarsus   1st/2nd cent.A.D.
                                                               5.20 m. Complex

Maison head (25): outlined eyes, bored pupils, trumpet with striated flat edge

Ref. Goldman, 35, fig.234 no.271

Note The resemblance to KT 9 is probably fortuitous

ZT 59   Terracotta masks   Adana Museum   Tarsus   2nd cent.A.D.
            (fragmentary)   276. Circuit Wall Deposit
                                                      277. 5.90 Complex

Slaves (22): pupil and iris completely pierced; swinging brows, low speira striated back from forehead

Ref. Goldman, fig.234, nos.276-7

Note Cf. AT 32

ZT 60   Terracotta masks   Adana Museum   Tarsus   2nd/3rd cent. A.D.
        (fragmentary)

        Masks of slaves, with wide fat face, flaming hair, flat trumpet with narrow edge
        (striated on 280)

        Ref. Goldman, fig.234-5, nos.280, 281, 300.   Cf. AT 31, 39 etc.

ZT 61   Terracotta masks   Adana Museum   Tarsus   2nd/3rd cent. A.D.
        (fragmentary)   314.Cemetery level

        Youths: pupils and iris completely pierced

        Ref. Goldman, fig.235-6, nos.275, 287, 288, 289, 309, 312, 314, 315

        Note Of these 275 has a low striated speira and even brows (perhaps no.13);
                287 has curls on the forehead and a wreath of fruit and leaves (perhaps
                no.16); of 288 only the wreath remains; 289 wreath and part of brow;
                309 brow separated by thick wreath from hair running back in ridges from
                the forehead (perhaps no.13: cf. above ZT 2); 312, 314, 315 give chin
                and lower part of face of thin-faced youth (perhaps no.11)

ZT 62   Terracotta mask   Adana Museum   Tarsus   2nd/3rd cent. A.D.
        (fragmentary)

        Female (39): pupil and iris completely pierced; hair carefully waved; bow
        of narrow fillet

        Ref. Goldman, fig.235, no.295

    Vase

ZV 6   Brown yellow vitreous   Boston 03.867   Smyrna
        glaze

        Mask of slave (25) with twisted trumpet, in cap?, over altar

        Ref. Cf. ZV 5 above.   Cf. also Robinson, *Agora V*, on no.G 160

        Note Probably 1st cent. A.D.

AFRICA

EGYPT

Bronze

EB 3   Bronze statuette   Berlin 71N   Egypt

        H. 0,20 m.

        Seated old man (4) with narrow beard, knee-length chiton, net stockings

        Ref. Rumpf, in *Mimus u. Logos*, 168 pl.VIIa, interprets as man playing eunuch;
                Robert, fig.103; Neugebauer, *Bronzen*, no.71, dates 'post-Julio-Claudian';
                G.T.P., no.C 76; *B.H.T.*[2], fig.413

Glass

EG 1-11   Cameos;   ornamented glass plaques in mosaic technique;   glass pendant;
           glass masks from vases.   The plaques in mosaic technique (3-8) are convin-
           cingly dated by Zahn in the early Imperial period.   5 has the new leading
           slave mask.   The hetaira masks 6-8 should be compared with contemporary
           paintings (e.g. NP 11).

EG 1   Glass plaque   Schiller Collection   ?Egypt   1st cent. A.D.
        (cameo technique)

        H. 0,034 m., B. 0,018 m.

        Mask of bald old man with rough beard;   crook;   Pan pipe

        Ref. Zahn, *Sammlung Schiller*, no.374

EG 2   Glass plaque   Schiller Collection   ?Egypt   1st cent. A.D.
        (cameo technique)

        H. 0,03 m., B. 0,019 m.

        Full-face mask of slave (25);   profile mask of youth (possibly 12 rather than
        tragic)

        Ref. Zahn, *Sammlung Schiller*, no.375

        Note For the juxtaposition cf. the Clieveden sarcophagus, IS 47

EG 3   Glass plaque   Sarti Collection   Egypt   1st cent. A.D.
        (mosaic technique)

        Mask of *pornoboskos* with red face and ivy wreath

        Ref. P. Sarti, *Catalogo della Collezione*, Rome, 1906, 69, pl.27;   Kisa, *das
                Glas*, II, 344, fig.169; 505

EG 4   Glass plaque   Ray Winfield Smith   Egypt   1st cent. A.D.
        (mosaic technique) Collection

        Mask of *pornoboskos* (half plaque)

        Ref. *Glass from the Ancient World*, Corning Museum, no.98

EG 5   Glass plaque   Princeton, Art Museum,   Egypt   1st cent. A.D.
        (mosaic technique) 52-81

        H. 0,022 m., B., 0,024 m.

        Slave (22) with two rolls of striated hair;   yellow face;   red nose

        Ref. 'Princeton', no.54

EG 6   Glass plaque   Princeton, Art Museum,   Egypt   1st cent. A.D.
        (mosaic technique) 52.83

        H. 0,012 m., B. 0,029 m.

        Hetaira with white face, high red hair with wreath of ivy

        Ref. 'Princeton', no.56

EG 7   Glass plaque   Yale Art Museum   ?   1st cent. A.D.
        (mosaic technique) (Hobart Collection)

        Mask with white face, yellow hair with vine-leaf wreath, red falling locks
        (half-plaque)

        Ref. Eisen, *Glass*, I, 139, pl.27 (cf. Seattle, GS 3.9)

EG 8   Glass plaque   Schiller Collection   Egypt   1st cent. A.D.
         (mosaic technique)
         H. 0,025 m.
         Probably young hetaira, full face (half-plaque)
         Ref. Zahn, *Sammlung Schiller*, no.379

EG 9   Glass pendant   Ray Winfield Smith Collection   Syria   1st cent. A.D.
         Mask of young *episeistos*.   Yellow face
         Ref. *Glass from the Ancient World*, Corning Museum, no.160

EG 10   Glass mask from vase   Amsterdam 111   Alexandria
         Leading slave (22)
         Ref. *Algemeene Gids*, no.1793, suggests date 3rd/4th cent. A.D.

EG 11   Glass mask from vase   Amsterdam 7725   Alexandria
         Wavy-haired slave (27)
         Ref. *Algemeene Gids*, no.1794, suggests date 3rd/4th cent. A.D.

Ivory and Bone

EI 3   Ivory statuette   London, Mustaki Collection   Alexandria   ?1st cent.A.D.
         Seated slave (?27)

EI 4   Ivory mask   Borelli Collection, 396   Unknown
         H. 0,08 m.
         Mask 32
         Ref. Simon 196 n.30

EI 5   Bone theatre ticket   Alexandria Museum   Alexandria
         Menander with mask (16?), pseudo-onkos, hanging locks, mouth shut
         Ref. Herbig, *Röm. Mitt.*, 59 (1944), 82 n.3, 87, fig.4; *B.H.T.*[2], fig.320.
                 Cf. *Pergamon*, I, 2, 293, no.24 (where however the mask cannot be seen).
                 Acc. to Benndorf, *Beiträge*, 1875, of imperial date

Lamps

EL 30-37   32 in style is not unlike ZL 8;   it is very highly coloured like ET 64.
            36 and 37 have the new wavy-haired slave mask.

EL 30   Terracotta lantern   ?   Pergamon
         with masks
         Masks of slave, young man, hetaira
         Ref. Loeschcke, *Bonner Jb*. 18 (1910), p.409, fig.20: cf. pl.35, 3 and 8
         Note Perhaps Late Hellenistic

EL 31   Mask below handle of lamp   Dresden, Sieglin Collection   1st cent. A.D.

         H. 0,06 m.

         Slave (27): flaming hair, bored pupils.   Grey clay

         Ref. Sieglin, II, 3, pl.38/1.   Not before Broneer, Type XXII

EL 32   Terracotta lid of lamp   Fouquet Collection 428   Achmoun

         H. 0,062 m.

         Old man (3), speira, short square beard.   Covered with white paint, hair and
         lips red, ears, eyes, beard are black

         Ref. Perdrizet, pl.86, no.428

         Note Perhaps 3rd cent. A.D.

EL 33   Terracotta lamp   Frankfurt   Fayoum   3rd/4th cent.A.D.

         Kore with straggly hair (33)

         Ref. Kaufmann, *Ägyptische Terrakotten*, fig.130/2; ?*Koroplastik*, no.721, pl.68

EL 34   Clay lamp (KA)   London, B.M. 1104   Egypt

         Three masks with speira and deep striated trumpet

         Ref. Broneer, Type XXV (variant)

         Note Very rough examples of the masks on IL 6

EL 35   Clay lamp   Mainz 6349   Sakkara   Late 1st cent.
                                                                A.D.
         Three small slave masks with peaked hair and narrow edged trumpets

         Ref. Menzel, *Antiken Lampen zu Mainz*, no.296

         Note For mask, cf. on IL 8

EL 36   Clay lamp   Leningrad   Egypt   3rd cent. A.D.

         Lamp in form of slave mask, flaming striated wig hair, striated flat edge to
         trumpet

         Ref. Waldhauer, *Antiken Tonlampen*, no.518

         Note Perhaps variant of Broneer, Type XXVIII

EL 37   Terracotta lantern   London, B.M. 1925.11.20.40   Egypt

         Body of lantern formed by fat wreathed slave mask with semicircular trumpet (27)

Terracottas

ET 62-65   62 has the new slave mask.   63 is a dark red flat mask like the Tarsus
            fragments ZT 59 etc.   (UT 118 may belong here.)   64 is highly coloured;
            it may reproduce a pantomime dancer's mask rather than a comic mask.   65,
            a plaster from Begram, is included here because the parallels quoted for
            these plasters all point towards Alexandria, and this particular plaster is
            partially reproduced on EV 16 and 17.

ET 62   Terracotta statuette   Fouquet Collection 438   Unknown

H. 0,60 m.

Slave (27): elaborately striated hair with long locks; bored pupils; narrow
striated edge to mouth; stippled chiton tied by string at waist; arms folded

Ref. Perdrizet, pl.87, no.438

Note Probably 1st cent. A.D.

ET 63   Terracotta mask   University College London   ?Egypt

Bored pupils; small wreath with vine-leaves; hair with horizontal striations:
Mask 39. Dark red clay

Ref. Cf. ZT 59 etc. Not before 1st cent. A.D.

ET 64   Terracotta mask   Amsterdam, 7379   Hawara, Egypt

H. 0,20 m.

Girl in Phrygian cap: white slip, black eyebrows, etc.   Shut mouth

Ref. *Algemeene Gids*, no.468

Note Formerly Collection von Bissing.   Perhaps not dramatic.   Not before 2nd
cent. A.D.

ET 65   Plaster cast   Kabul   Begram   11st cent. A.D.

Comic poet under tree; Muse with mask of youth

Ref. Kurz, *Nouvelles Recherches à Begram*, 136, no.226

Vases

EV 16-17   The *lagynoi* reproduce a much earlier original, partially known from the 1st
century plaster from Begram; there the central slave mask (which on 16 is
clearly of the new type and on 17 has had the beard increased) is missing;
the Begram plaster has a twin with a poet of tragedy, which seems to derive
from an early Hellenistic original (also reproduced on EV 17).   The same
date may be suggested for the original of the comic poet, which must then
stand in some relation to the Menander relief (AS 6) and the seated statue
of Menander.

EV 16   Terracotta lagynos   Alexandria 9867   Hadra

Young poet with Muse of Comedy with stick and mask of youth; on the ground
slave mask, hair running back from forehead, swinging brows, fat cheeks, wide
twisted trumpet with narrow edges

Ref. *Mon. Piot* 51 (1960) 81 fig.8

Note Same mould as EV 17

EV 17   Terracotta lagynos   Cairo 86635   Akmîm   c.300 A.D.
[= Tragedy EV]

Plastic head with hooked nose.
1) Young poet seated with scroll: Muse of Comedy with stick and mask of youth?:
slave mask and a girl's mask on ground.   Youth has double row of striated
hair on forehead; slave has long hair, hair running back from forehead, wide
mouth with striations below   /see next page

EV 17 (cont.)

Ref. Lilly Ghali-Kahil, *Mon. Piot* 51 (1960), 73, pl.5, dates by style,
vegetation, and twisted columns.   Interprets as Menander

Note Earlier stage in a plaster from Begram (Kurz, *Nouvelles Récherches*,
no.226), which omits central mask of slave (= ET 65)

ELSEWHERE

Lamps

FL 1   Lamp   Tipasa   Tipasa, tomb   1st cent. A.D.

Slave seated on altar(?): (22): smooth speira, wide shallow trumpet

Ref. J. Baradez, *Libyca*, 5 (1957), 233, pl.12, 14, other lamps are Claudian

FL 2   Terracotta lamp   Leiden (store room)   ?N. Africa   ?2nd/3rd cent.
       Two bearded masks   A.D.

Ref. Brandts no.396.   Probably Broneer, Type XXVII.   Cf. below IL 12

FL 3   Terracotta lamp   Leiden (store room)   ?N. Africa   ?2nd/3rd cent.
       Two bearded masks   A.D.

Ref. Brandts no.442.   Probably Broneer, Type XXVII.   Cf. below IL 12

Mosaics

FM 1   Mosaic   Acholla   Acholla, Baths of   115-20 A.D.
                                                        Trajan, room 25

Head with corkscrew hair, smooth brows, wide eyes (probably *curly*)

Ref. G. C. Picard, *Etudes d'Arch. Class.*, 2 (1959) 73, pl.19/2: cf. Villa
of Triumph of Neptune

FM 2   Mosaic mask   Sfax (Tunisia)   Villa of Neptune,   175/200 A.D.
                                                        Boutria

1) Young *episeistos* mask;
2) First *pseudokore* (?) mask with ivy staff

Ref. *Fasti* 9 (1954), no.5214

Note Both have small mouths and may not be dramatic

FM 3   Mosaic   Bône (Algeria)   3rd cent. A.D.

Slave mask 27 with low speira, fat face: kore mask (33) with curly pseudo-onkos
and sloping brows

Ref. Reinach, *R.P.* 228/ 8; Simon 191 n.63

FM 4   Mosaic   Sousse   Ued.Bliboen   4th cent. A.D.

Youth restrains youth from threatening slave.   All apparently wear long chitons;
youth with pseudo-onkos

Ref. Simon no.12; Reinach, *R.P.*, 311/5

Painting

FP 1   Fresco   Sfax (Tunisia)   Villa of Hercules   ?1st cent.A.D.

Young *episeistos* mask with stick behind: mouth shut, perhaps not dramatic

Sculpture

FS 1   Marble mask   Louvre, Salle d'Afrique 1836   Carthage

Mask of *eikonikos* (19)

Ref. Bieber, *H.T.*, fig.537; Rumpf, in *Mimus u. Logos*, 166;   *G.T.P.*, no.C 77

Note Probably 2nd cent. A.D.

FS 2   Marble relief   Sabratha   Sabratha   3rd cent. A.D.

Mask 10

Ref. Simon 183 n.67; *Africa Italiana*, III 28 fig.24

FS 3   Marble relief   Sabratha   Sabratha   3rd cent. A.D.

Mask 16

Ref. Simon 186 n.126; *Africa Italiana*, III, 32, fig.27

SICILY

Mosaics

SM 1   Mosaic masks (Lion   Palermo   Palermo   1st cent. A.D.
        hunt mosaic)

Masks 3, 15 (with swinging brows knotted at the nose), 21, 29, 33, 35 (with *mitra* and therefore perhaps rather 41)

Ref. Simon pl.XI; 67, 186 n.134; 190 n.44; 98 n.5; 193 n.46; 195 n.5;
        112, 117 n.57a; 129, 199 n.7a; Gabrici, *Mon. Ant.*, 27 (1921/2), 181ff.,
        pl.3; cf. *G.T.P.*, no.C 21

Sculpture

SS 1   Marble mask   Syracuse   ?Sicily   2nd cent. A.D.

Wreathed youth (16): bored pupils, smooth brows, wreath with berries, hair heavily undercut

Note Cf. NS 4, 12 below

SS 2   Marble masks   Syracuse, N.M.22457,   Priolo Bagnoli   1st cent. A.D.
                                12232, 6821

Women's masks with parted hair (33): bored iris and pupils

Ref. Cf. for style IS 32 below

Terracotta

ST 29   Terracotta mask   Syracuse   Serra Orlando Aidone
         ?Hetaira (38)
         Note Probably 2nd cent. A.D.

SOUTH ITALY

Sculpture

TS 1   Marble masks in relief   Brindisi   Brundisium   1st cent. A.D.
        Slave mask and kore mask: peaked speira, deepish slightly twisted trumpet
        Ref. Degrassi, *Fasti* XII, no.5268, fig.121

Terracottas

TT 31-33   31: The framed eyes and bored iris and pupil are not earlier than
           Augustan.   33: This small mask is very like those on the Campana
           reliefs (IT 72 etc.).

TT 31   Terracotta disk   Boston 87.399   S. Italy
         Slave mask (27): bored iris and pupils, striated hair and beard, peaked
         speira, semicircular twisted trumpet with narrow edge; framed eyes
         Ref. 'Princeton' fig.40; Bieber, *H.T.*^{1}, fig.263; ^{2}, fig.388; Jones
         compares AT 32, ZT 60

TT 32   Terracotta mask   London, B.M., D 60   Ruvo
         Wavy-haired slave (27): peaked speira, semicircular trumpet.   Small, white
         Ref. Walters, *Cat.*, 308
         Note Possibly Late Hellenistic.   Very like IL 14

TT 33   Terracotta mask   Oxford, 1922.128   S. Italy
         (?from lamp)
         Leading slave (22): depressed pupils, rough hair, peaked, wide twisted
         trumpet
         Note Cf. terracotta reliefs IT 72.   Probably 1st cent. A.D.

CAMPANIA

In this section the arrangement within each of the main sections (bronzes,
jewellery, mosaics, painting, stone sculpture, terracottas, vases) is primarily
local, 1. houses in Pompeii, 2. Pompeii, general, 3. houses in Herculaneum,
4. Herculaneum, general, 5. other Campanian sites in alphabetical order.

Bronzes

NB 4-9   4-8.   The masks at the handles of bronze vases continue a Hellenistic
           tradition.   9.   The bronze masks held by the pair of Erotes must be comic
           (cf. above on BT 14);   they are interesting because the corkscrew hair over
           the forehead is formed into a low onkos which shows very clearly in profile.

NB 4   Bronze jug   Pompeii   Pompeii, I,vi,3,   1st cent.B.C./
                                                     no.1606   A.D.

        Mask at handle of youth, wreathed

NB 5   Bronze jug   Pompeii   Pompeii, I,vi,3,   1st cent.
                                                     no.1833   B.C./A.D.

        Mask at handle of old man (?4)

NB 6   Bronze jug   Pompeii   Pompeii, I,vi,3,   1st cent.
                                                     no.1853   B.C./A.D.

        Mask at handle of slave

        Ref. Maiuri, *Guide*, 67.   The shop of Verus

NB 7   Bronze jug   Pompeii, Antiquarium 1847   Pompeii   1st cent.B.C./A.D.

        Mask of Lycomedian at handle

NB 8   Bronze amphora   Pompeii, Antiquarium   Pompeii   1st cent.B.C./A.D.
                              1910/4

        Masks on handles of *panchrestos* and kore

NB 9   Bronze mask (pair)   Naples 5028, 5030   Herculaneum,   1st cent. **A.D.**
                                                     Villa Suburbana

        Mask (12?) held by bronze Eros: corkscrew hair, sloping brows

        Ref.   *Guida*, no.866, 876;   Reinach, *R.S.*, 283, 540

Silver cups

NJ 1   Silver cup   Naples   Pompeii, Casa del   1st cent. A.D.
                                                     Menandro,I,x,4

        Mask of tragic and comic *panchrestos* on shelf

        Ref. Maiuri, *Casa del Menandro*, pls.39-40, skyphos, nos.9 and 10

NJ 2   Silver cup   Louvre   Boscoreale   1st cent. A.D.

        Skeleton of Menander with mask of Agroikos (14)

        Ref.   Schefold, *Bildnisse* 167;   *Mon. Piot.* 5 (1899), 58;   *Festschrift B.
                 Schweitzer*, 261, pl.57;   *G.T.P.*, no.C 24

        Note On date see below on NP 49.   The mask may be an allusion to Menander's
                Hypobolimaios or *Agroikos*

Mosaics

NM 1-6   1 and 2 are dated by mosaic technique and by the writing of the signatures
to the very late 2nd century B.C. The painting in Stabiae (NP 54) perhaps
presupposes an earlier original common with 2. In any case the style of
the figures and the kantharos held by the old woman on 1 are claimed for
the early 3rd century B.C., and the two young men of 2 are repeated in two
terracotta statuettes from Myrina (MT 1 and 15). Both mosaics therefore
repeat early Hellenistic originals.

4-6. The practice of a floral border to pictures is attested for the 2nd
century B.C. by a papyrus epigram (*J.J.P.*, 5 (1951),237). Probably the
thick garlands in which these masks are set could not be dated much earlier.
The date of the borders is not affected by the date of the picture in the
middle (the papyrus epigram refers to a picture of Apelles). The slave
masks on 6 look more modern with their wide twisted trumpets than those on
4 and 5. The leading old men on 4 and 5 have shortish beards. On 4 the
young man's mask at the bottom left-hand corner has speira, raised brows,
hollow cheeks (cf. DT 5), and the flat underpart of the chin is shown.

NM 1   Dioskourides mosaic   Naples 9987   Pompeii, House of   Late 2nd
                                                     Cicero   cent. B.C.
H. 0,42 m.

Women at breakfast (Masks: 29, 35, 39)

Ref. Pfuhl, fig.685; Rumpf, *J.H.S.*, 67 (1947), 16; *M.u.Z.*, 153, 167; Bieber,
H.T.[1], fig.242; [2], fig.347; *D.*, no.136; Simon, no.10; Pernice, VI,
169ff.; Curtius, *Wandmaleri*, 336ff.; Beazley, *E.V.P.*, 235; Pickard-
Cambridge, *Theatre*, fig.86; *P.C.F.*, fig.95; *G.T.P.*, no.C 19

Note From original of early 3rd cent. B.C.

NM 2   Dioskourides mosaic   Naples 9985   Pompeii, House of   Late 2nd
                                                     Cicero   cent. B.C.
H. 0,437 m.

Revellers (Masks: 10, 13, 39)

Ref. Pfuhl, fig.684; Bieber, *H.T.*[1], fig.239; [2], fig.346; *D.*, no.135;
Simon no.8; Pickard-Cambridge, *Theatre*, fig.85; *G.T.P.*, no.C 20;
Richter, *Greek Art*, fig.398 (see also references for NM 1).

Note From original of 3rd cent. B.C.

NM 3   Mosaic masks   Pompeii   Pompeii,I,vii,1   1st cent.A.D.

Masks of slave with striated speira and deepish trumpet with narrow white edge,
two old men (one with short corkscrew beard), young man (?)

Ref. Pernice, VI, 95, pl.40; Schefold, *Wände*, 29

Note For slave mask cf. NP 6

NM 4   Mosaic masks (tiger   Naples, M.N.9991   Pompeii, Casa del   2nd/1st cent.
       rider mosaic)   Fauno VI,12 (Triclinium) B.C.

Masks 3, 4, 10, 17, 21, 22, 33, 39: slave masks with semicircular trumpet with
narrow edge; haggard youth; old man with shortish beard

Ref. Simon 183 n.63; 190 n.43e; 194 n.60; Blake, *Mem. Am. Acad.*, 7 (1930),137;
Pernice, VI, pl.59; Rizzo, *Pittura*, pl.82; *Antike* 1937, fig.14; Krien,
J.O.A.I., 42 (1956), 114, fig.57; Schefold, *Wände*, 128 (1st style); Rumpf,
M.u.Z., 166 dates mosaic late 2nd to 1st cent. B.C.; *B.H.T.*[2], fig.565

NM 5   Mosaic masks (Dove mosaic) Naples MN.114281   Pompeii VIII,ii,34   2nd/1st cent.
        Masks ?3, 4, 10, 11, 21, 22, 33, 39.   The leading slave mask has nicked   B.C.
        brows and deepish twisted trumpet with striated edge

        Ref.   Simon 93; 183 n.61; 184 n.82b; 190 n.43c; 190 n.45; 194 n.60;
               Anderson 25762, 25795; Blake, *Mem. Acad. Rome*, 17 (1930), 129; *Antike,*
               1937 pl.4; Pernice, *Hell. Kunst in Pompeii*, VI, pl.64; Rumpf, *M.u.Z.,*
               166, pl.56/1; *G.T.P.*, no.C 21; Schefold, *Wände*, 217

        Note According to Pernice the border is 1st cent. B.C.

NM 6   Mosaic (philosophers   Naples 12545   Torre Annunziata   1st cent.B.C.
        or seven sages)

        Masks: *papposilenos*; 11; young satyr; 27; young satyr; 39; old satyr; 21.
        The youth has haggard cheeks; the slaves wide trumpets; one has an uneven brow

        Ref.   Schefold, *Bildnisse*, 154/1; Blake, *Mem. Acad. Am. Rome*, 7 (1930), 144
               (late Republican); Simon, 112; 184 n.83, 190 n.43d; Alinari 12199; cf.
               G.T.P., no.C 21

Painting

NP 1-54 There is no significant variation in their date which may be regarded as 1-69
         A.D., mostly later rather than earlier.   As NP 6 is known in two copies (the
         other is NP 46), and NP 54 (in Stabiae) reproduces the same original as NM 2,
         earlier Greek originals must be expected for the pictures of comic scenes (6,
         8, 9, 13, 14, 21-8, 38, 45-6), but this need not necessarily be true of the
         masks poised on or in decorative architecture (3, 7, 12, 15, 16, 30, 51, 55)
         or enclosed in small panels (2, 10?, 11, 17, 18, 32, 34-7, 47-8, 53) or held
         by Muses or the like (1, 19, 20, 39) or arranged in groups (4, 5, 33, 41-2, 44):
         in each case any positive indication must be noted.

    1. Houses in Pompeii

NP 1-28 Some correspondences which suggest early Hellenistic originals are indicated
         here:

         4. The sharp corners of the trumpet of the slave beard can be seen on some
         Hellenistic terracottas (MT 26, 27, XT 23).   It also occurs on 13, 22.

         6. The slave is dressed like MT 27, his stance recalls MT 30.   (DT 20 may
         also have some resemblance.)   The youth is dressed like MT 17; so also are
         the youths of 22 and 23.   The slave mask (particularly on the other copy
         NP 46) suggests a 2nd century original.

         8. The youth is dressed like MT 19 and his stance is not unlike.

         13. The soldier slave is like a terracotta from Cyrenaica in the British
         Museum (C 837, *T.K.*, 427/2; *P.C.F.*, fig.138), which is not dramatic but gives
         an early Hellenistic date for the dress.   The other slave has the same attitude
         as a bronze in Paris (cf. Poulsen, *loc.cit.*) which however like the terracotta
         is not dramatic (the mouth is normal).

         23. Cf. above on 6.   The very fat slaves of 23-5, 27 recall the earliest
         Myrina group, but the pseudo-onkos of the youth perhaps forbids a date before
         the late 2nd century.

25. The attitude of the slave is not unlike MT 26.

27. The attitude of the slave recalls MT 5. The scene is repeated on UJ 9.

28. The figures are extremely faint: they are placed in front of a third style architectural background, which has no connection with the stage.

NP 1   Painting   Pompeii, Villa Imperiale,   Pompeii   1st cent.A.D.
                            Main Room

Bearded wreathed poet; girl with *pedum* and comic mask of old man with speira and long beard; seated Muse

Ref. Maiuri, *Roman Painting*, 109; Schefold, *Wände*, 290; Rumpf, *A.J.A.* 60 (1956), 77

NP 2   Painted masks   Pompeii, Villa Imperiale,Porticus   Pompeii   1st cent.A.D.

Masks of *panchrestos*, kore; second *episeistos* in panels

Ref. Maiuri, *Guide*, p.96; Schefold, *Wände*, 291

NP 3   Painted mask   Naples 9847   Pompeii,Villa of Diomede 1st cent.B.C.

Old *episeistos* of comedy in architecture

Ref. Schefold, *Wände*, 353

Note From same room as Naples 8594, Curtius, fig.74-6. Second style

NP 4   Painting   Pompeii   Pompeii I,ii,6,   Early 1st
                                                       peristyle,west wall   cent. A.D.

Masks: 2nd pseudokore (35), old slave with square trumpet (21), wreathed

Ref. Robert, *A.Z.*, 34 (1878), pl.IV; *P.C.F.*, 210, fig.151; Robert, fig.69;
        R.P., 319/3; Simon 197 n.57 takes as kore; *G.T.P.*, no.C 44; Schefold,
        Wände, 9

NP 5   Painting   Pompeii   Pompeii I,ii,6,peristyle, 1st cent.A.D.
                                                       south wall

Masks: youth (10), girl (33), slave (22), old man (7), wife (31), old man (3)

Ref. Simon 193 n.44, 194 n.73, 197 n.63; *R.P.*, 319/6; Robert, fig.97, 18, 70;
        A.Z., 34 (1878), pl.5/2; Schefold, *Wände*, 9; *G.T.P.*, no.C 44

NP 6   Painting   Pompeii   Pompeii,I,vi,11, Atrium,   1st cent.A.D.
        H. 0,51 m.   east wall

Old slave (21), woman (42), and youth (10): the slave mask has a semicircular twisted trumpet with narrow flat edges

Ref. Bieber, *H.T.*[1], fig.524; *G.T.P.*, no.C 41; Simon no.2; *Roman Painting*
        (Skira), 95; Schefold, *Wände*, 25

Note Copy of same original as NP 46

NP 7   Painted masks   Pompeii   Pompeii, I,vi,11, Atrium   1st cent.A.D.
                                                       east wall

Masks of *hapalos*, *panchrestos*, and *kore* grouped round one column, and of *episeistos* old man in blue *pilos* on another

Ref. *N.Sc.*, 1929, 404f.; Maiuri, *Guide*, p.66; Schefold, *Wände*, 25; *G.T.P.*,
        no.C 40

NP 8   Painting   Pompeii   Pompeii I,vi,11, Atrium,   1st cent. A.D.
                                                  West wall

H. 0,52 m.

Parasite (18) visits cook (25) (wide mouth with slave beard)

Ref. Simon no.3; *N.Sc.*, 1929, pl.22; *G.T.P.*, no.C 43; Schefold, *Wände*, 25

NP 9   Painting   Pompeii   Pompeii I,vi,11, Atrium,   1st cent. A.D.
                                                  West wall

Old man (7), with long beard

Ref. Simon no.4; *N.Sc.*, 1929, 407, fig.31; *G.T.P.*, no.C 42; Schefold,
        Wände, 25

NP 10   Painted mask   Pompeii   Pompeii I,vi,11, Cubiculum   1st cent. A.D.

Mask of youth, wreathed

Ref. Maiuri, *Guide*, p.66

NP 11   Painted masks   Pompeii   Pompeii I,x,4, Casa del   1st cent. A.D.
                                                  Menandro, Atrium

Kore and youth with wreath: both with pseudo-onkos but less high than onkos
of tragic pair

Ref. Maiuri, *Casa del Menandro*, pl.III, fig.9; Schefold, *Wände*, 39; Beyen,
        Antiquity and Survival, 2 (1958), 356, pl.4

NP 12   Painted mask   Pompeii   Pompeii, House of the   1st cent. A.D.
                                                  Hermaphrodite,VI,vii,18

Panchrestos with wreath: contorted brows, corkscrew hair from onkos and
corkscrew locks

Ref. Curtius, fig.123; Schefold, *Wände*, 100

NP 13   Lost painting   Pompeii   Pompeii, Casa del Grande   1st cent. A.D.
                                                  Fontana, VI,viii,22

Soldier-slave (27) with wide trumpet, and leading slave (22) with square trumpet

Ref. Robert, fig.9; Bieber, *H.T.*[1], fig.237, [2], fig.371; *D.*, no.134; *R.P.*,
        313/1; Simon no.14; *P.C.F.*, fig.98; *G.T.P.*, no.C 25; Rumpf in *Mimos
        und Logos*, 164; Bieber, *A.J.A.*, 60 (1956), 172; Schefold, *Wände*, 107;
        F. Poulsen, *From the Ny Carlsberg Glyptotek*, III (1942), 155

NP 14   Wall painting   Bonn E 168   Pompeii, VI,ix,6,   1st cent. A.D.
                                                  Casa dei Dioscuri

Old man (3) leaving a woman (31), also slave (27)

Ref. Bieber, *H.T.*[1], fig.229; [2], fig.327; Simon no.7; *P.C.F.*, fig.101;
        G.T.P., no.C 28; *R.P.*, 310/6; Richardson, *Mem. Am. Ac. Rome*, 23 (1955),
        153, pl.51,2; Schefold, *Wände*, 119

NP 15   Wall painting   Pompeii?   Pompeii, Casa del   1st cent. A.D.
                                                  Laberintho,VI,xi,70

S atyr mask, kore mask, **pseudokore** mask in architecture

Ref. Beyen, *Wanddekoration*, figs.94, 95, 126; Little, *A.J.A.*, 60 (1956), 31,
        fig.24; Schefold, *Wände*, 125

NP 16   Painted masks   Pompeii   Pompeii, House of Vettii,VI,xv,1   1st cent.A.D.

Mask of youth beside basket; wavy dark hair; smooth brows; small mouth; vine wreath (?16)

Ref. Maiuri, *Guide*, 44; Curtius, 142; Brogi, 1124

NP 17   Painted masks   Pompeii   Pompeii, Casa degli Amorini   1st cent.A.D.
                                             Dorati, VI,xvi,7

Frontal mask of old *episeistos* (or *papposilenos*)

Ref. Schefold, *Wände*, 155-6

NP 18   Painted masks   Pompeii   Pompeii, House of Ara Maxima,   1st cent.A.D.
                                             VI, xvi,15

Kore mask (with white face) and pseudokore mask (with red face)

Ref. Maiuri, *Guide*, p.49; Schefold, *Wände*, 156f.

NP 19   Wall painting   Pompeii   Pompeii, VII,ix,4-12   1st cent.A.D.

Mask (3) in lap of Muse; crook in her right hand

Ref. Simon 193 n.43; Reinach, *R.P.*, 154/3; Helbig 886; Schefold, *Wände*, 197
        Cf. CS 1

NP 20   Wall painting   Pompeii   Pompeii, Casa del Diadumeno,IX,i,20 1st cent.A.D.

Muse with stick, slave-mask (cap-hair, swinging brows, twisted trumpet with narrow edge) and mask of youth (cap hair, smooth brows)

Ref. Schefold, *Wände*, 237; Neg. Inst. Rom. 53, 596

NP 21   Painting   Pompeii   Pompeii, Casa del Centenario,Atrium 1st cent.A.D.

Woman (33); slave by altar with bird (21); slave in hat (21)

Ref. Simon no.15; Dieterich, *Pulcinella*, pl.3; *R.P.*, 311/4; Robert, fig.39;
        G.T.P., no.C 34; *B.H.T.*[2], fig.771

NP 22   Wall painting   Pompeii   Pompeii, Casa del Centenario,   1st cent.A.D.
                                             Atrium, East wall

Old slave (21) with square trumpet, and boy (13) with torch (two unmasked figures)

Ref. Robert, fig.54; Simon no.16; *P.C.F.*, fig.100; *G.T.P.*, no.C 33; *R.P.*,
        311/3; Schefold, *Wände*, 273; Weitzmann, *Ancient Book Illumination*, 84;
        B.H.T.[2], fig.770

NP 23   Painting   Pompeii   Pompeii, Casa del Centenario,   1st cent.A.D.
                                             Triclinium

Young man with pseudo-onkos (10) and slave (21)

Ref. Simon no.17; Dieterich, *Pulcinella*, fig.1; *R.P.*, 312/3; Bieber, *H.T.*[1],
        fig.519; [2], fig.765; *G.T.P.*, no.C 35

NP 24   Wall painting   Pompeii   Pompeii, Casa del Centenario,   1st cent.A.D.
                                             Triclinium, IX,viii,3

Old man (4), interrogating slave (27)

Ref. Robert, fig.86; Simon no.18; Schefold, *Wände*, 279; *G.T.P.*, no.C 36;
        R.P., 312/1

NP 25   Painting   Pompeii   Pompeii, Casa del   1st cent.A.D.
                                                    Centenario, triclinium

Slave, *lena* and woman (Masks: 27, 29, 39)

Ref. Robert, fig.88; Simon no.19; *G.T.P.*, no.C 37; *R.P.*, 312/2

NP 26   Painting   Pompeii   Pompeii, Casa del   1st cent.A.D.
                                                    Centenario, triclinium

Old woman soliloquizing

Ref. Simon no.20; Reinach, *R.P.*, 312/4; *G.T.P.*, no.C 38

NP 27   Painting   Pompeii   Pompeii, IX, viii, 3, Casa   1st cent.A.D.
                                                    del Centenario, triclinium

Old man and slave (Masks: 3, 21)

Ref. Robert, fig.53; Simon no.21; *P.C.F.*, fig.99; *G.T.P.*, no.C 39; Schefold,
         Wände, 279; *R.P.*, 312/5

NP 28   Wall paintings   Pompeii   Pompeii, IX, ix, 7-8, House   1st cent.A.D.
                                                    of Sulpicius Rufus

Actors in front of architectural setting

Ref. Rostovtzeff, *R.M.*, 26 (1911), fig.26-7; Beyen, *Wanddekoration*, I pl.46,
         fig.131-2; Neg. D.A. Inst. Rom. 54.707; Schefold, *Wände*, 285

Note The figures are extremely faint: a) may be old man flying out at slave;
         b) probably slave

2. Pompeii (no definite find-spot)

NP 29-39   These are arranged in Museum order.

29. The general type for this and 37 is given by ZT 2 and the other examples
quoted there.   36 probably belongs to the same type.

34-6 probably come from the same house (cf. 47-8 below).   The movable steps
must either belong to the early Greek stage (i.e. before the action took
place above the *proskenion*) or to the Roman stage; the latter is unlikely
because the steps in the Roman theatre would have been permanent.   An early
Hellenistic original is therefore likely for these pictures, and the mask of
the old man on 47 may be compared with e.g. FT 1.

38. The wavy-haired slave has a longish beard like MT 2 and the original
should be early Hellenistic

NP 29   Painted mask   Boston 25.97   Pompeii   1st cent. A.D.

Frontal young *episeistos* (16) with reddish hair and yellow wreath decked with
green vine leaves

NP 30   Painted mask   Naples 9031   ?Pompeii   1st cent. A.D.

Mask of youth (15) in architecture: wild hair, swollen raised brows, large
nose

Ref. Schefold, *Wände*, 334

NP 31   Painting   Naples 9050   ?Pompeii   1st cent. A.D.

Mask (3) held by Dionysus, while young actor in long chiton, fringed himation,
and shoes is being dressed

Ref. Simon 193 n.50; Reinach, *R.P.*, 314/3; *A.Z.*, 1855, 145, pl.82/1; Schefold,
Wände, 335

NP 32   Painting   Naples, N.M. 9760   Pompeii   1st cent. A.D.

Kore (33) with white face and brown hair, smooth brows; *pinax* in garden fragment

Ref. Schefold, *Wände*, 352

NP 33   Painting   Naples, N.M. 9791   ?Pompeii   1st cent. A.D.

Three comic masks, possibly 16, 14, 33

Ref. Schefold, *Wände*, 352

NP 34   Painting   Naples 9804   Pompeii   1st cent. B.C.

Movable steps with mask 11 (?)

Ref. *R.P.*, 318/8

NP 35   Painting   Naples 9805   Pompeii   1st cent. B.C.

Movable stairs with mask 35 (?)

Ref. Bieber, *H.T.*^{1}, fig.447a; ^{2}, fig.762; *R.P.*, 320/8

NP 36   Painting   Naples 9806   Pompeii   1st cent. B.C.

Movable stairs with mask 13 with wreath

Ref. Bieber, *H.T.*^{1}, fig.447b, ^{2}, fig.761; *R.P.*, 320/8

NP 37   Painted mask   Naples 9833   Pompeii   1st cent. A.D.

Wreathed fattish young head with basket and thyrsos in background: probably 13

Ref. *R.P.*, 318/11; Helbig 1742; Schefold, *Wände*, 353

NP 38   Wall painting   Palermo   ?Pompeii   1st cent. A.D.

Woman (38) and marketing slave (27)

Ref. Bieber, *H.T.*^{1}, fig.243; ^{2}, fig.383; *D.*, no.131; Simon no.6; *P.C.F.*,
fig.96; *G.T.P.*, no.C 29; *Antike Kunst*, 3 (1960), 33, n.37

NP 39   Painting   Paris, Louvre P.10   Pompeii   1st cent. A.D.

Muse with *pedum* and mask of old slave or old man

Ref. *Mon. Piot*, 51 (1960), 85 fig.13; Roscher M.L. s.v. Musen, fig.10a;
B.H.T.^{2}, fig.334

Note The mask is probably an old man with a short beard, cf. IL 6 etc.

3. Houses in Herculaneum

NP 40-48 On 45 the slave with the flute player has a wide twisted trumpet; the
figure is not unlike IS 41, 30. This may be the new type of fat leading
slave.

NP 40   Painted mask   Herculaneum   Herculaneum, Insula III,15   1st cent.A.D.
Wreathed youth (red) and wreathed youth (white)
Ref. Maiuri, *Guide*, p.30

NP 41   Painted masks   Herculaneum   Herculaneum, Insula IV,1   1st cent.A.D.
Hetairidion, kore, *panchrestos*, 2nd *episeistos* youth with wreath and seeming
onkos
Ref. Maiuri, *Guide*, p.27

NP 42   Painted masks   Herculaneum   Herculaneum, Insula V,1   1st cent.A.D.
Old man with wreath; invisible; young man with wreath; slave.   These have
a marked pseudo-onkos
Ref. Maiuri, *Guide*, p.41

NP 43   Painted masks   Herculaneum   Herculaneum, Insula VI,11   1st cent.A.D.
Two small masks of comic slaves

4. Herculaneum, no find-spot

NP 44   Wall Painting   Naples   Herculaneum   1st cent. A.D.
Mask 35(?), and on a low platform mask of youth and slave
Ref. Simon 195 n.12; Reinach, *R.P.*, 318/7; Helbig 1746

NP 45   Wall Painting   Naples 9035   Herculaneum   1st cent. A.D.
Old slave (21), young slave (22), and flute player (39).   Young slave has very
wide twisted trumpet
Ref. Bieber, *H.T.*[1], fig.228; [2], fig.328; *D.*, no.133; Simon no.5; *R.P.*,
        314/5; *G.T.P.*no.C 26; Richardson, *Mem. Am. Ac. Rome*, 23 (1955), 155,
        pl.52,2; Schefold, *Wände*, 334

NP 46   Wall painting   Naples 9037   Herculaneum   1st cent. A.D.
Old slave (21), woman (42) and youth (10)
Ref. Robert, fig.72; Bieber, *H.T.*[1], fig.238; [2], fig.395; *D.*, no.132; Simon
        no.1; *P.C.F.*, fig.97; *R.P.*, 315/4; *G.T.P.*, no.C 30; Schefold, *Wände*,
        335
Note Copy of same original as NP 6

NP 47   Wall painting   Naples 9838   Herculaneum   1st cent. B.C.
Movable staircase: mask 3
Ref. Bieber, *H.T.*[1], fig.448; [2], fig.763; *R.P.*, 318/10

NP 48   Painting   Naples 9850   Herculaneum   1st cent. B.C.
Mask of kore with veil over high hairdressing, on movable staircase
Ref. *B.H.T.*[2], fig.760; *R.P.*, 318/9
Note Is she perhaps the girl in Menander's *Theophoroumene*?

5. Other sites in Campania

NP 49-54   49-50. It has recently been argued that the paintings date from later than
the change of ownership in 12 A.D.   49 is only relevant for the scenery;
Rumpf has argued that it is a copy of an original of the 2nd century B.C.
The white-haired slave in 50 has a wide twisted trumpet.

51. A fine mask with deep trumpet, bald head and shock of hair over ears.
It is possible that the white round the trumpet and on the hair is high-
lighting rather than the colour of the hair.

52 is a very fine *panchrestos* mask.

On 54 cf. above on NM 2.

55 is a very fine mask of the first *episeistos* with wavy hair.

NP 49   Wall painting   New York   Boscoreale   1st cent.B.C./

        Comic scenery with masks of old and young satyrs and   1st A.D.
papposilenos

Ref. Bieber, *H.T.*[1], fig.345/6; [2], fig.472/3; Pickard-Cambridge, *Theatre*,
fig.90; Rumpf, *J.H.S.*, 67 (1947), 18; Beyen, *Wanddekoration*, figs.56-66;
Lehmann, *Roman Paintings from Boscoreale*, 90 ff., pls.26-28; Little,
A.J.A., 60 (1956), 27; *G.T.P.*, no.C 23; Rumpf, *M.u.Z.*, 148, 158, pl.54,
57 (copy of original painted 170-70 B.C.); Tanassia, *Arch. Class.*, 11
(1959), 208, dates paintings to change of owner in 12 A.D.

NP 50   Painted masks   Mariémont   Boscoreale   1st cent.B.C./
                                                     1st A.D.

Kore, *panchrestos*, slave (with white hair, wide twisted trumpet), pseudokore
in pairs; in architecture

Ref. Curtius, fig.56-7; Beyen, fig.23 and 23b; Lehmann, fig.18; G. Faider-
Feytmans, *Antiquités de Mariémont*, R 56, pl.54; Beyen, *Antiquity and
Survival*, II (1958), 364, fig.1

NP 51   Wall painting   New York   Boscotrecase   Early 1st cent.
                                                          A.D.

Architecture with hanging mask of Maison (25): semicircular trumpet with
white outline, shock of white hair over ears

Ref. C. Alexander, *Metr. Mus. Studies*, I, 178

NP 52   Wall painting from   Naples   Naples   1st cent.A.D.
        chamber tomb

Mask 10?: small speira and raised brows with hooked inner end

Ref. Simon 183 n.60; *Mon. Ant.*, 31 (1926), 401, fig.14, 387, fig.8; *A.A.*,
1928, 175/6, fig.35

NP 53   Painting   Minori, Salerno   Salerno   1st cent.A.D.

Mask of wreathed young *episeistos*, small on wall divided by floral bands

Ref. *Fasti*, XI, no.4717, pl.39

Note Cf. NP 11 above

NP 54   Painting   Naples 9034   Stabiae   1st cent. A.D.
H. 0,21 m.

Revellers (copy of same original as NM 2)

Ref. Simon no.9; *R.P.*, 313/3 (see also references for NM 2)

NP 55   Painting   Stabiae   Stabiae, Edificio   1st cent. A.D.
                                                   Porticato

Mask (15) with dark wavy hair, swinging brows with hooked inner ends, in
architecture

Ref. Elia, *Pittore di Stabia*, p.31

Sculpture

NS 1-31   Sculpture in stone arranged under 1) houses in Pompeii, NS 1-8.   The
Casa degli Amorini Dorati (2-8) had a bust of Menander (*N.Sc.*, 1907, 549 ff.,
fig.31) and the owner may therefore have had some special interest in Greek
comedy.   2. Pompeii with no definite find spot, NS 9-27.   3. Other Campanian
sites, NS 28-31.   Most of these are traditional and many derive from Early
Hellenistic originals.   The only ones which may throw light on contemporary
practice are 25 and 31.

The type of *old man* (Pollux no.3) on NS 1 is very similar to 28 below;   the
type is known from the third century B.C., e.g. AV 16, CS 1.   The beard on
NS 3, 17, is shorter but this may be due to their position in the relief;   the
short beard is however also clear on NS 25, where it is clearly distinguished
from the wavy-haired old man (Pollux no.4).   The wavy-haired mask appears
also on the reliefs 7 and 22 and as a substantive mask in 9 and 26:   in 9 the
ends of the beard are stylized in very short corkscrews below the trumpet (cf.
for this IS 12, if this is to be interpreted as the wavy-haired old man;   also
IS 3, 16);   the beard of 26 recalls IL 6.

Slave masks: the wavy-haired leader (Pollux no.27) can probably be identified on NS 2 and 22 with a sharply pointed trumpet of traditional shape, on
25 with a shallowish twisted trumpet and a fat face, and on 31 with a pseudo-
onkos and a trumpet with narrow edges: the last two are the late Hellenistic
and the Roman type respectively.

The leading slave (Pollux no.22) probably appears on NS 3 with peaked hair
and semicircular trumpet, on NS 8 wreathed and with a wider flatter trumpet,
on NS 17 and NS 19 with a shallow semicircular trumpet.

Young men's masks: the young mask on 3 is unclear but may be the *panchrestos*
(Pollux no.10), who is also identified by Simon in 18.   Simon identifies 4,
which is wreathed, as the second *episeistos* (Pollux no.16) and takes 12 with
it (but 12 with its narrow eyes is better taken as Pollux no.13);   29 probably
also belongs here.   The examples without wreath are not so clear.   7 and 25
both have wavy hair undoubtedly;   5, 11, 17, 22, 30 have a peaked speira, which
would make them the *hapalos* (Pollux no.13) or the *melas* (Pollux no.11) rather
than the second *episeistos*;   Simon however takes 5 as the *hapalos* but 11 as
the *episeistos*.

16.   This mask is the same as 28 and IS 20.   It could be interpreted as the
young man with curly hair (Pollux no.12);   but as it is also associated with
tragic masks (*G.T.P.* 124 f.), it may rather be the young Dionysos.

1. Houses in Pompeii

NS 1   Marble mask   Pompeii, Casa della seconda   69-79 A.D.
                               Fontana, VI, ix, 23-4

Old man with corkscrew beard (3)

Ref. Stein, *Et. Arch. Class.*, 2 (1959), 99, pl.24,5

NS 2   Marble relief   Pompeii, VI, xvi, 7, Casa degli   1st cent. A.D.
                               Am. Dor., peristyle, S. wall

Wreathed slave mask 27 on rocky ground with torch.   Big trumpet striated but
not very deep, pointed

Ref. Simon 191 n.60b; *N.Sc.*, 1907, 558, fig.8; *G.T.P.*, no.C 45a

NS 3   Marble relief   Pompeii, Casa degli Am. Dor.,   1st cent. A.D.
                               peristyle, S. wall

Masks 22, ?10, 3 in high relief.   The youth's mask is very unclear;   the old
man has a not very long square beard;   the slave has peaked hair and a big
striated semicircular trumpet

Ref. *N.Sc.*, 1907, 560 fig.10; *G.T.P.*, no.C 45b

NS 4   Marble mask   Pompeii, Casa degli Am. Dor.,   1st cent. A.D.
                               peristyle, between columns

Mask 16?:   long face, elaborate wreath, long hair

Ref. *N.Sc.*, 1907, 583, fig.32; *G.T.P.*, no.C 46a

NS 5   Marble mask   Pompeii, Casa degli Am. Dor.,   1st cent. A.D.
                               peristyle, between columns

Mask of youth (13 or 16):   very long nose and face, slightly bored eyes, striated
speira and locks

Ref. Simon 184 n.72; *N.Sc.*, 1907, 588 fig.37; Maiuri, *Guide*, p.49; *G.T.P.*,
no.C 46b

NS 6   Marble mask   Pompeii, Casa degli Am. Dor.,   1st cent. A.D.
                               peristyle, between columns

Mask 33:   parted waved hair, cheerful;   small nose

Ref. Simon 197 n.62; *N.Sc.*, 1907, 589 fig.38; *G.T.P.*, no.C 46c

NS 7   Marble relief on low   Pompeii, Casa degli Am. Dor.   1st cent. A.D.
        pilaster

Masks 4, 16, 41:   the old man has a longish, straggly beard

Ref. Simon 184 n.73; 197 n.55; *N.Sc.*, 1907, 580/1, fig.22; *G.T.P.*, no.C 47a

NS 8   Marble relief on low   Pompeii, Casa degli Am. Dor.   1st cent. A.D.
        pilaster

Mask 22;   4;   41 before curtain.   The slave mask has a wide flattish striated
trumpet, rather less pointed than NS **3** and 7, and an elaborate wreath

Ref. Simon 198 n.73; *N.Sc.*, 1907, 583 fig.26; *G.T.P.*, no.C 47b

2. Pompeii (no definite findspot indicated)

NS 9   Marble mask   Dresden 224   Pompeii   1st cent. A.D.

Mask of man (4): peaked speira with hair coming down in front of ears, trumpet mouth with shortish corkscrew beard

Ref. Bieber, *H.T.*[1], fig.254; [2], fig.330; Simon 92, 194 n.57

NS 10   Marble relief   Naples   Pompeii   1st cent. A.D.

Beardless man contemplating mask 13(?)

Ref. *Mus. Borb.* XIII, pl.21; *A.M.*, 26 (1901), 133, fig.2; Simon 184 n.77

NS 11   Marble mask   Naples 6608   Pompeii   ?1st cent. A.D.

Mask of youth (13 or 11): peaked speira and hanging locks

Ref. Simon 186 n.123a; Alinari 19057

NS 12   Marble mask   Naples 6609   Pompeii   ?1st cent. A.D.

Mask 13: elaborate wreath, hanging locks, no speira

Ref. Simon 186 n.123c; pl.V.1; Alinari 19057

NS 13   Marble mask   Naples 6612   Italy   1st cent. A.D.

H. 0,067 m.

Mask of wife's maid: 43

Ref. Bieber, *H.T.*[1], fig.281; [2], fig.356; *D.*, no.175; Simon 109, 119, 197 n.41; Robert, fig.63; *P.C.F.*, fig.152

NS 14   Marble mask   Naples 6614   ?   1st cent. A.D.

Mask (43?): hair tied over the forehead

Ref. Simon 197 n.41

NS 15   Marble mask   Naples 6616   Italy   1st cent. A.D.

H. 0,17 m.

Mask of courtesan with mitra, long nose, small bow above scarf: 41

Ref. Bieber, *H.T.*[1], fig.286; [2], fig.362; Simon 113, 124, 197 n.68; *P.C.F.*, fig.154

NS 16   Marble mask   Naples 6618   Pompeii   ?1st cent. A.D.

Mask of youth: pseudo-onkos with corkscrew curls, hanging corkscrew locks

Ref. Simon 186 n.123b; *P.C.F.*, fig.59; Alinari 19057

NS 17   Marble relief   Naples 6619   Pompeii   1st cent. A.D.

H. 0,26 m.

Masks of old man (3), slave (22), young man (13), and young satyr. (Reverse: Papposilenos and young satyr.)

Ref. Bieber, *H.T.*[1], fig.259; [2], fig.563; *D.*, no.138; Simon 66, 88, 186 n.127; *P.C.F.*, fig.159

NS 18   Marble mask   Naples 6623   1st cent. A.D.

Mask 10: wreathed

Ref. Simon 183 n.62a; Alinari 19057

NS 19   Marble mask   Naples 6624   Pompeii   1st cent. A.D.

Mask 22: speira with peak, shallowish rounded trumpet

NS 20   Marble mask   Naples 6625   Italy   1st cent. A.D.

Mask of hetaira: 39: bored pupils, long nose, fillet tied in a very small bow above forehead

Ref. Bieber, *H.T.*[1], fig.280; [2], fig.361; *D.*, no.174; Simon 113 n.67, 121, 123; *P.C.F.*, fig.153

NS 21   Marble mask   Naples 6628   Pompeii   1st cent. A.D.

Mask 16?: wild hair flaming up from forehead. (More probably a young satyr like the mask in the background of NS 17)

NS 22   Marble relief   Naples 6623   Pompeii   1st cent. A.D.

Masks 4, 13(?), 27, fourth mask lost: temple and curtain. (Two other heads on the reverse, perhaps tragic)

Ref. Simon 184 n.76, 194 n.59; Schreiber, *Hell. Rel.* pl.99; Robert, fig.102; *B.H.T.*[2], fig.562

NS 23   Marble disk   Naples 6634   Pompeii   1st cent. A.D.

Slave (22) with peaked speira, shallowish rounded trumpet with corkscrew curls, and papposilenos. (Reverse, two satyrs)

Ref. Krien, *J.D.O.A.I.*, 42 (1956), 108f., fig.47; *B.H.T.*[2], fig.566

NS 24   Marble relief   Naples 6685   ?Pompeii   ?1st cent. A.D.

Muse of comedy with mask of old *episeistos* under tree

Ref. Cf. relief in Rome, Conservatori, Pickard-Cambridge, *Theatre*, fig.62

NS 25   Marble relief   Naples 6687   Pompeii   1st cent. A.D.

Mild old man, angry old man, flute girl, young man, slave (Masks 4, 3, 16, 27)

Ref. Robert, fig.85; Bieber, *H.T.*[1], fig.225; [2], fig.324; *D.*, no.130; Pickard-Cambridge, *Theatre*, fig.77; *P.C.F.*, fig.94; Simon, 66, 80, 88; *G.T.P.*, no.C 48; *W.A.M.*, n.109

NS 26   Marble statue   Pompeii, Museum   S.Italy   1st cent. A.D.
                                1047/4

Eros with mask of old man (4): bored pupils, striated hair and shortish beard

Note For the mask cf. IL 6

N S 27   Marble relief   Pompeii, Horreum   Pompeii   1st cent. A.D.

Masks of *panchrestos* and *hetairidion* alternating

3. Herculaneum and other sites in Campania

NS 28   Marble masks   Herculaneum, Insula V,7   Herculaneum   1st cent. A.D.
Two old men (probably no.3) flanking wreathed youth with onkos

Ref. Maiuri, *Guide*, p.44, pl.xx; Stern, *Ét. Arch.*, 2 (1959), 99, pl.24/5;
cf. Schefold, *R.M.*, 60-61 (1953), 122; *G.T.P.*, no.C 32

NS 29   Marble mask   Milan, Museo Teatrale 38   ?Capua   1st cent. A.D.
Mask (probably 16): bored pupils; vine leaves in hair; very careful locks

Ref. Belloni, *Dioniso*, XIV, 157; Albizzati no.18; Sambon, no.583, pl.10

NS 30   Marble mask   Milan, Museo Teatrale 437   Capua
H. 0,16 m.

Youth (13): striated hair, bored pupils, smooth brows

Ref. Sambon 585, pl.10

NS 31   Marble relief   Milan, Museo Teatrale   Capua   Not before 1st cent.
H. 0,71 m.   A.D.

Comic Muse with crook and slave mask (27) with hollow eyes, wrinkled brow, broad
smooth trumpet, onkos

Ref. Simone, no.69; Sambon, no.588 (perhaps from theatre at Capua)

Terracottas

NT 22-48   Terracottas are arranged in alphabetical order of sites.   26 should probably
be excluded because the mouth is shut: it may belong to the general class
noted on FB 1.

27-48. Pompeii. 27-28 are statues rather more than half life size: their
masks and costumes are traditional.   29-48. The majority of these are
architectural.   They are arranged in the order of the Pollux mask list. The
stylization is individual but the types appear to be traditional: the semicircular slave beards suggest a second century origin.   Only 30 and 33 may
be contemporary.   Corkscrew locks behind the ears are almost universal:
their absence on 41 probably justifies distinguishing this mask as the leading
slave from 42 as the wavy-haired slave (it is very like IB 3).   The young
men and the women are also clear; the only question is whether, as Simon
thinks, 46 can be separated from 47 and 48.   The old men are for various
reasons more difficult.   31, 32, 34 clearly belong together and may, as Simon
says, be the curly-haired old man (Pollux no.7); 33 has a short, square beard
and a very different stylization of the hair, although the hair could perfectly
well be described as curly.   29 has much more side hair than the others and
the hair on his head is left smooth; I do not feel certain whether he is the
wavy-haired old man (Pollux no.4).   30 has a short curly beard and may be
compared with the old man who appears on some Roman lamps (cf. on IL 6).

NT 22   Terracotta mask   Capua   Capua   1st cent. A.D.
H. 0,19 m.

Mask of wavy-haired slave (27): very deep trumpet

Ref. *N.Sc.*, 6 (1952) 312, fig.5.   Stylization very like UT 56 etc.   Context
1st cent. A.D.   Cf. Rohden-Winnefeld, fig.7.

NT 23   Terracotta antefix   London, B.M. D 706   Capua   1st cent. A.D.
H. 0,15 m.

Mask of wavy-haired slave (27), wreathed: striated hair, eyes pierced, semi-circular striated trumpet coming to point

Ref. Walters, *Cat.*, 421; Rohden-Winnefeld, 13, fig.8

NT 24   Terracotta mask   Madrid 3375   ?Capua
Slave: twisted trumpet beard; bored pupils (?27)

Ref. Laumonier, no.861, Salamanca collection, pl.101, 4

Note Compare the stylization with ZT 51 of the 2nd cent. A.D., but there can be no connection

NT 25   Terracotta antefix   London, B.M., D 700   Cumae   1st cent. A.D.
H. 0,152 m.

Mask of wavy-haired slave (27): pupils deeply cut; wig hair, striated, no peak; semicircular, twisted, striated trumpet

Ref. Walters, *Cat.*, 420

Note Should be considered with NT 13 above

NT 26   Terracotta mask   Miseno   ?Misenum   1st/2nd cent. A.D.
H. 0,18 m.

Mask of youth (16), with corkscrew curls and wreath, bored pupils, shut mouth

Ref. *N.Sc.*, 1928, 193 fig.6; Mingazzini dates early 2nd cent.

NT 27   Terracotta statue   Naples, MN 22249   Pompeii   1st cent. A.D.
H. 1,15 m.

Actor wearing mask 10: peaked speira, raised eyebrows, sleeves, chiton, himation, sandals

Ref. *B.H.T.*[2], fig.548; Simon 56, 183 n.66; pl.VII/I; Levi, 202, no.871; *G.T.P.*, no.C 27. For attitude cf. YT 11

NT 28   Terracotta statue   Naples 22248   Pompeii   1st cent. A.D.
H. 1,11 m.

Maiden (33), blue chiton, red himation with fringes, sleeves, short hair

Ref. *B.H.T.*[1], fig.409; [2], fig.548; Levi, no.872; Simon, 197 n.56; Pl.VII/II; *G.T.P.*, no.C 27

NT 29   Terracotta mask   Pompeii 937   Pompeii   1st cent. A.D.
Mask (4), with smooth peaked speira, corkscrew locks, and large corkscrew beard

Ref. Simon 194 n.59, pl.X/I. The identification is doubtful

NT 30   Terracotta mask   Pompeii   Pompeii   ?1st cent. A.D.
Old man with rough hair, short wavy beard (?4)

Ref. Simon 83, 192 n.13; 88, 193 n.38; pl.X/1 top row, left

Note Simon says from same mould as NT 14 but that is clearly bald. This may be the same mask as IL 37

NT 31   Terracotta antefix   Pompeii 925   Pompeii   60/70 A.D.
         H. 0,18 m.

         Lykomedeios (7): curly hair, curly beard
         Ref. Robert, fig.101; Simon 194 n.66, pl.X/1, bottom row, 2nd from left;
                 G.T.P., no.C 18; Rohden, 12 ff., pl.15,2

NT 32   Terracotta water spout   Pompeii   Pompeii   1st cent. A.D.
         Mask 7: very fierce, with corkscrew curls
         Ref. Simon 194 n.68; Rohden 24, pl.15,1

NT 33   Terracotta mask   Pompeii 915   Pompeii   ?1st cent. A.D.
         Mask 7: hair striated back from forehead, short beard in corkscrew curls
         Ref. Simon 194 n.69, pl.X/1, bottom right.   The identification is uncertain
         Note For the hair cf. the left hand slave on IS 53

NT 34   Terracotta mask   Pompeii 900   Pompeii   1st cent. A.D.
         Mask 7: remains of head covering, beard smoothed as water spout
         Ref. Simon 194 n.70, pl.X/1, middle row, second from right.   Identification
                 uncertain

NT 35   Terracotta mask   Naples 116713   Pompeii   ?1st cent. A.D.
         Young mask with vine leaves (13)

NT 36   Terracotta mask   Pompeii 784   Pompeii   1st cent. A.D.
         Mask 11: peaked striated speira with locks hanging behind ears, smooth brows
         Ref. Simon 186 n.128, pl.X/1, middle row, right (taken as no.16); Licht,
                 Sittengeschichte, I, 139,2

NT 37   Terracotta mask   Naples MN.5378   Pompeii   1st cent. A.D.
         Mask 11: peaked, striated hair with longish locks hanging behind ears
         Ref. Simon 195 n.2; Rohden, pl.XIV,2
         Note Simon probably rightly takes as 16 rather than feminine because the hair
                 does not cover the ears and there is no lock in front of the ears

NT 38   Terracotta altar   Pompeii, Antiquarium Pompeii   1st cent. A.D.
                                  1548/4

         Mask of wreathed young *episeistos* (16)

NT 39   Terra cotta mask   Naples 116712   Pompeii   1st cent. A.D.
         Kolax (17)

NT 40   Terracotta mask   Leningrad 413   Pompeii   1st cent. A.D.
         H. 0,13 m.

         Mask 22 on *sima* with palmette background: peaked speira, striated, unframed
         trumpet rather pointed
         Ref. Simon 190 n.41a; Rohden, pl.IX,1

NT 41   Terracotta masks on   Pompeii   Pompeii   1st cent. A.D.
         waterspouts

         Slave with striated speira slightly peaked, swinging brows, semicircular
         striated trumpet unframed (perhaps 22)

         Ref. Simon, pl.X,1, top row, middle pair

NT 42   Terracotta mask on   Pompeii 933   Pompeii   1st cent. A.D.
         waterspout

         Slave mask 27: large wreath with streamers, corkscrew locks, raised brows,
         semicircular trumpet

         Ref. Simon 191 n.60b, pl.X,1, top row, right; Rohden, 33, fig.23

         Note Compare IB 3

NT 43   Terracotta mask   a) Leningrad 412   Pompeii   1st cent. A.D.
                                 b) Pompeii 749

         H. 0,15 (a)

         Mask (30): petal eyes, bored pupils, corkscrew locks

         Ref. Simon 199 n.3a, pl.X,3; n.3b, pl.X,1, middle row, left

NT 44   Terracotta mask   a) Pompeii 928, b) 812   Pompeii   1st cent. A.D.

         Mask (30): wreathed

         Ref. Simon 199 n.4a, pl.X,1, middle row, second from left; n.4b

NT 45   Terracotta   Madrid 3268   Pompeii, Odeum   1st cent. A.D.

         H. 0,125 m.

         Old woman's head, wreathed

         Ref. Laumonier, no.569, pl.48,6

NT 46   Terracotta roof tile   Leningrad 414   Pompeii   1st cent. A.D.

         H. 0,155 m.

         Mask 32: wavy hair from parting, corkscrew curls behind at the bottom

         Ref. Simon 107, 196 n.29; Rohden, pl.XIV,1.   Simon compares IS 35

NT 47   Terracotta mask   Pompeii 332   Pompeii   1st cent. A.D.

         Mask (33): smooth hair, earrings, corkscrew curls behind at bottom

         Ref. Simon 197 n.53, pl.X (bottom row)

NT 48   Terracotta mask   Pompeii (Isis Temple)   Pompeii   1st cent. A.D.

         H. 0,15 m.

         Mask (33): smooth hair; corkscrew locks at bottom

         Ref. Simon 197 n.59; Rohden, fig.30, p.13

Vases

NV 2   Terracotta *askos*   Pompeii, Antiquarium 1545/4   Pompeii

         Slave mask as *askos*

         Note Perhaps Late Hellenistic

NV 3   Clay jug with mask   Ann Arbor, Kelsey   possibly Cumae
        at handle   Museum 2839

        Slave mask (27): mouth closed

        Ref. *C.V.* Michigan, pl. 39/2

        Note Shape suggests a date in 1st cent. A.D.

CENTRAL AND NORTHERN ITALY

Bronzes

IB 1   Bronze mask on disk   Imola   S. Maria in Regola, Imola

        Slave with narrow fillet (27): raised brows; upward cast eyes with bored
        pupils

        Ref. Mancini, *Imola*, 185 n.4; pl. 26/11

        Note Perhaps 1st cent. A.D.

IB 2   Bronze statuette   Imola

        Seated slave (?)

        Ref. Mancini, *Imola*, pl. 26/6

        Note Perhaps 1st cent. A.D.

IB 3   Bronze disk   Naples 4994   Italy

        Wreathed slave (27): wreath with berries, corkscrew locks, semicircular
        twisted trumpet with smooth inside

        Note Not unlike NT 42. Probably 1st cent. A.D.

IB 4   Bronze statuette   Rome, Terme 66065   ?Italy

        Slave (25) with strigil, i.e. pretending to be an athlete

        Ref. Jucker, *der Gestus des aposkopein*, 106, fig. 44-5

        Note Probably 1st cent. A.D.

Lamps

IL 3-51 The lamps are arranged in order of Broneer types. The first two are
        Hellenistic and earlier examples of the types will be found under Hellenistic
        lamps.

           In this section are included all lamps that can reasonably be supposed to
        have been made in Italy wherever they were found. Examples of these types
        which have been found elsewhere and may have been made elsewhere will be
        found under the following headings:

                Type xxi: XL 1, EL 23-4, UL 1-5
                     xxii: AL 3, ZL 9, EL 31, FL 1
                     xxiii: ZL 7
                     xxv: EL 34, 35
                     xxvi: CL 2
                     xxvii: CL 3-5, XL 2-3, FL 2-3
                     xxviii: AL 4, CL 6, XL 4, ZL 10, EL 36

Here scenes and masks are discussed in the order in which they first occur in the list and later examples are considered *with* the earlier examples.

5 is a three-quarter slave mask and may perhaps derive from an original in painting (cf. UL 1).

6 and 7 are the same mask.   The short square corkscrew beard is too long for a slave beard, although in 7 and later examples it is shown inside the deep trumpet mouth.   This seems therefore to be an old man's mask and the same mask in marble is held by an Eros from Pompeii (NS 26), where the smooth brows also suggest an old man rather than a slave (cf. also NP 39, NT 30, IS 53, IT 63, JS 1).   The same mask is seen on later lamps both alone (9, 25, 38) and united with a bust (24, 37, 44): three appear on the disk of EL 34, perhaps also on IL 52 (left).

8, in spite of the corkscrew locks of three examples, has peaked hair and a framed trumpet beard, which associates it with AL 3 rather than with the later AT 31 etc.   It is probably this mask which appears on some later lamps e.g. 22, 26 and perhaps 49 and 52 (right).   FL 35 is a very weak example.   US 1 is probably the same mask.

10 (like UL 1 and IS 41) is a slave mask to which an old man's beard has been added.   It is probably a provincial copy of a Roman lamp, and a much better version of the mask is found on a lamp of type xxv, IL 20.   It is clearly distinguished by wavy hair and flowing beard from the mask discussed on 6 and 7.

11 is an elaborate wavy-haired slave mask with striated hair, long corkscrew locks, and a wide twisted trumpet.   The type is very common on contemporary and slightly later lamps (19, 29).

12 has two rather indistinct masks, which are much more clearly seen on the fragmentary 13 and on lamps of later types (27, 39).   The masks have a double row of light striations and shortish locks on either side of the face.   It is tempting to regard this as an earlier stage of the leading slave mask which is found in type xxvi, IL 28, and strongly contrasted both with 11, which is the newer type of wavy-haired slave mask, and with 14 which is the older type of wavy-haired slave mask looking back to the first century B.C.   (cf. above UL 4a contrasted with UL 3.)

30-32 are unique slave masks.   Probably 30 is a variant of the type represented by 28, 31 of the type represented by 29, while 32 is a wreathed example of 29.

33-6 are beardless, and difficult to interpret.   33 is perhaps the young man with pseudo-onkos and 34 a variant of the same mask.   (52 may have a weak example of the same.)   35 with the emphatic central knot of hair is perhaps the second pseudokore.   36 has the locks spreading more freely from the head than 33 and may therefore be the kore.

42 and 43 have both been taken as representing tragic rather than comic scenes; but the actors would have worn boots with heightened soles if they had been tragic.   The actor on 42 seems to wear shoes and perhaps quilted tights show above (cf. 50).   His mask is unclear; and though a youth is more likely, a slave cannot be quite excluded and the gait suggests the running slave (cf. AT 6 etc.).   The youth and woman with swords on 43 seem to have made a suicide pact and the title *Synapothneskontes* of Alexis, Diphilos, and Philemon might be relevant.

45-7 have the fat slave mask with flaming hair which is well known from contemporary Greek lamps (AL 4, CL 6, XL 4).   48 is a very late example.   51 is a fully modelled plastic lamp illustrating the same mask.

50 shows the long chiton noted above on AT 31 and 36.   The slave is undoubted. The other figure has been interpreted as a woman, which the parted hair suggests;   but the quilted tights which show below the chiton fix the figure as male and the pillared chin, denoting thought in comedy, suggests a man scheming rather than a woman.   The head must be a variant for one of the very young men, and Phaedria in the *Phormio* aedicule (IP 2) is so stylized.

Type XI

IL 3   Clay lamp   Leningrad ST. 268   2nd cent. B.C.

Mask (with striated hair and largeish trumpet mouth) on spout: probably slave

Ref.   Waldhauer, *Antiken Tonlampen*, no.19

Note   For mask cf. above ZL 1

Type XII

IL 4   Clay lamp   Leningrad   2nd cent. B.C.

Lamp in form of old man's mask with raised brows, speira, and longish beard: spout below beard

Ref.   Waldhauer, *Antiken Tonlampen*, no.500

Note   Perhaps variant of Type XII.   For style cf. UL 2

Type XXI

IL 5   Terracotta lamp   Nijmegen   Nijmegen   Early 1st cent.A.D.

Three-quarter mask of slave with fat face and trumpet mouth with flat edge

Ref.   Evelein, *Romeinsche Lampen*, pl.5/31

Note   For ¾ mask cf. UL 1

IL 6   Terracotta lamp handle   Rome, Wollmann Collection 2110

Bust of actor: mantle over shoulder, short-sleeved chiton;   striated wig hair; raised brows;   short square corkscrew beard

Ref.   Messerschmidt, *R.M.*, 47 (1930), 185 pl.65a (says mask 3)

Note   Very well modelled, perhaps handle of Broneer, Type XXI

IL 7   Terracotta lamp, with 2   Milan   Early 1st cent.A.D.
nozzles and mask in centre
disk

Mask of old man: corkscrew locks;   deepish trumpet with curly hair inside; bored pupils.   Inscription on handle: ANNY-NOVM FAV-STVM FEL-ICEM MI-HI. R.E.

Ref.   Sambon, pl.4, no.49.   Cf. for inscr. British Museum, Walters no.873 from Pozzuoli

IL 8   Lamps   a) Bryn Mawr L 29   1st cent. A.D.
       H. 0,12 m.   b) Munich;   c) Vienna 756
                              d) Musée Lavigerie

Slave mask 22 forms body of lamp: corkscrew hair on either side of beard, peaked striated hair, framed trumpet with flat edges   /see next page

IL 8 (cont.)

> *Ref.* b) and c) Simon 191 n.60c; *A.A.*, 1929, 23, no.61, fig.22 (Munich):
> stamped (C)OMUNIS (both lamps are from the same mould).   d) Martin,
> *Musées de l'Algérie et de la Tunisie, Musée Lavigerie*, Supplt.II, no.3

> *Note* Doubts have been expressed about the genuineness of a, b, c; d, which
> was found in Bordj-Djedid, lacks the corkscrew curls and has one brow
> raised, one even

Type XXIII

IL 9   Clay lamp   London, B.M. no.811   ?   1st cent. A.D.
         Mask with wavy hair and deep trumpet
         Note For mask cf. IL 6

IL 10   Clay lamp (HOS.CR)   London, B.M. no.737   Vaison, France   1st cent. A.D.
         Mask with long hair flying out sideways, small trumpet, narrow pointed beard
         below
         Note Variant Broneer Type XXIII.   Perhaps provincial rendering of mask 4?

IL 11   Clay lamps   London, B.M. a) no.739   a) ?Rome   1st cent. A.D.
         (C. STROBILUS)   b) no.790   b) Pozzuoli
                                           c) no.888   c) Cologne
         Wavy-haired slave
         Note Masks same type as IL 19, 29

IL 12   Clay lamp   London, B.M. no.791   Pozzuoli   1st cent. A.D.
         Two slave masks on disk
         Note Small masks indistinct.   Cf. IL 13, 27, 39; FL 2, 3

Fragments which may belong to type XXIII

IL 13   Terracotta lamp   Compiègne, Musée Vivenel, V 807   1st cent. A.D.
         2 masks of slaves: double row of striations, wide trumpet with narrow smooth
         edges

IL 14   Terracotta lamp   a) Cambridge GR.91.1937   Italy   ?1st cent. A.D.
                               b) Compiègne, Musée Vivenel,
                                  V 829
                               c) Harvard University
         Mask of slave: wavy hair; semicircular trumpet with smooth narrow edges (27)
         Note Mask looks back to DT 19 etc.

IL 15   Terracotta lamp   London, B.M. D 68, 69, 70, 71,   ?1st cent. A.D.
         (fragment)   72, 73, 79
         Wavy-haired slave mask (22): semicircular trumpet, wig hair
         Ref. Walters, *Cat.*, 309, Towneley Collection

IL 16   Terracotta lamp (fragment)   London, B.M. D 80   ?1st cent. A.D.
         H. 0,0335 m.
         Leading slave mask (22)
         Ref. Walters, *Cat.*, 310, Towneley Collection

IL 17   Terracotta lamp?   London, B.M. D 74   ?1st cent. A.D.
          (fragment)
          H. 0,022 m.
          Maison mask (25)
          Ref. Walters, *Cat.*, 309, Towneley Collection

IL 18   Terracotta lamp   London, B.M. D 376   ?1st cent. A.D.
          (fragment)
          H. 0,0305 m.
          Mask of curly youth (12): mouth shut, probably not dramatic
          Ref. Walters, *Cat.*, 367, Towneley Collection

   Type XXIV

IL 19   Clay lamp   Mainz 10878   Late 1st cent.
                                                                       A.D.
          Wavy-haired slave with hanging locks cross-divided, twisted trumpet with
          narrow smooth edges
          Ref. Menzel, *Antiken Lampen zu Mainz*, no.252, fig.34/2.   For mask cf. IL 11

   Type XXV

IL 20   Clay lamp(C.CORN.URSI) London, B.M. no.1085   1st/2nd cent.A.D.
          Old man with wavy hair and long flowing beard (4)

IL 21   Terracotta lamp   Agen (Lot et Garonne)   Agen   1st cent. A.D.
          Bust of actor with hands folded in front of body (22)
          Ref. *Gallia* 17 (1959) 399, fig.35, 1
          Note Found with Julio-Claudian objects.   Perhaps Broneer, Type XXV

IL 22   Roman lamp   Bryn Mawr L 30   1st cent. A.D.
          Slave mask (22) in middle of disk with scrolls surrounding: peaked hair down to
          chin, wide trumpet with narrow edge
          Note Perhaps Broneer, Type XXV.   For mask cf. IL 8

IL 23   Clay lamp (green glaze)   London, B.M. no.1037   1st/2nd cent.A.D.
          Slave mask (indistinct) in surrounding wreath

   Type XXVI

IL 24   Terracotta lamp   a) Rome, Wollmann Collection 355   c.100 A.D.
          (a)FORTIS)   b) Coimbra
          Bust of old man (4): bored pupils, speira, deep trumpet striated inside
          Ref.   a) Messerschmidt, *R.M.*, 45 (1930), 188, pl.65c takes as slave
                   b) Oleiro, *Catálogo*, Coimbra, 1952, no.27
          Note For mask cf. on IL 6

IL 25   Terracotta lamp   Machado de Castro   Conimbriga   Late 1st cent.
                                                                       A.D.
          Full-face mask with wavy hair, deep trumpet with striations inside
          Ref. Oleiro, *Catálogo de Lucernas Romanas*, Coimbra 1952, no.5
          Note For mask cf. IL 6

IL 26   Clay lamps   a) Dunedin, Otago Museum E 36.280   1st cent. A.D.
         a) CAMPILI   b) Mainz 24139
         b) FORTIS

         Slave mask on disk: striated wig hair with peak; even brows; trumpet with
         flat edges

         Ref. b) Menzel, no.367

         Note For mask cf. IL 8

IL 27   Clay lamp (PULCHRI)   Mainz 0.30860   1st/2nd cent. A.D.

         Two small masks with striated hair below ears: trumpet with narrow edges

         Ref. Menzel, no.372

         Note Cf. IL 12 and 13

IL 28   Clay lamps (a,b, FORTIS   a) Rome, Wollmann Collection   1st cent. A.D.
         c) CASSI, d) EUCARPI)   b) London, B.M. no.887
                                    c) London, B.M. no.906
                                    d) Mainz 29380

         Small slave mask: double layer of hair, only lower striated, wide trumpet
         with smooth, narrow edges

         Ref. a) Messerschmidt, *R.M.*, 45 (1930), 188, pl.65e
                 b) Walters, 135, fig.178,   c) Walters, 138, fig.181,   d) Menzel, no.361

         Note For mask cf. on IL 12

IL 29   Clay lamps (a, STROBILI   a) Warsaw, no.126954   1st cent. A.D.
         b, IEGIDI   b) London, B.M. no.889
         c, VIBIUS   c) London, B.M. no.898
         d, VIATOR)   d) Mainz 24138, e) Mainz 16291
                                    f) Leningrad 506   f) Bulgaria

         Slave mask: hair over forehead with double layer of striations running
         towards forehead; corkscrew locks on either side; smooth twisted trumpet with
         narrow edges

         Ref. a) Bernhard, no.445; b) Walters, pl.27; c) Walters, 137, fig.179;
                 d) Menzel, no.403; e) Menzel, no.404; f) Waldhauer, no.454

         Note For mask cf. on IL 11

IL 30   Clay lamp (STATI)   Mainz 34016   1st/2nd cent. A.D.

         Slave mask with ridged hair, wide trumpet with narrow edges

         Ref. Menzel, no.369

IL 31   Clay lamp (VITE)   Mainz 0.26065   1st/2nd cent. A.D.

         Wavy-haired slave with wig hair down to chin level; fuzzy narrow edge to speira

         Ref. Menzel, no.391

IL 32   Clay lamp   London, B.M. no.908   1st/2nd cent. A.D.

         Wavy-haired, fat slave with wreath above head

         Note Aberrant mouth to spout

IL 33   Clay lamps (a,EUCARPI,   a) London, B.M. no.905   a) London   1st cent.A.D.
         b, COMMUNIS   b) Warsaw, 139610
         c, FORTIS)   c) Besançon 884-1-30

Beardless mask with corkscrew hair on *onkos* and side hair in two levels;
smooth brows: probably youth

Ref. a) Walters, 138, fig.180;   b) Bernhard, no.447;   c) Lerat, no.144

IL 34   Clay lamp (EUCARPI)   Mainz 12062   1st/2nd cent. A.D.

Mask with hair down to ears, high speira, very narrow trumpet mouth: perhaps
youth

Ref. Menzel, *Antike Lampen zu Mainz*, no.362

IL 35   Terracotta lamp   Nijmegen   Nijmegen   Late 1st cent. A.D.
         (CAPITO F.)

Full-face mask of woman with knob of hair central, and long locks: perhaps
2nd pseudokore

Ref. Evelein, *Romeinsche Lampen*, 34, pl.7, II/14

IL 36   Terracotta lamp   Nijmegen   Nijmegen   Late 1st cent. A.D.

Full-face beardless mask with hanging locks.   Locks hang further apart than
B.M. 905 (IL 33).   This may be the kore (Pollux, no.33)

Ref. Evelein, *Romeinsche Lampen*, 38, pl.8, V/7

Type XXVII

IL 37   Clay lamps   London, B.M., a) no.986   2nd cent. A.D.
         (a, L. OPPI RES,   b) no.987
         b, L. MON. THRE.)

Bust of comic actor: speira with long locks, deep trumpet striated inside,
sleeves, tunic.

Ref. Walters, 149

Note b) is a weak copy of a).   Cf. IL 6

IL 38   Terracotta lamp (C.OPP.RES) Harvard University   2nd cent. A.D.

Mask (?4): striated hair with long locks, deep striated trumpet

Ref. D. G. Mitten, *H.S.C.P.*, 64 (1959), 248f., no.25

Note Cf. for mask IL 6

IL 39   Clay lamp   Syracuse   Syracuse

Two slave masks with speira and twisted trumpet

Ref. N.Sc., 1954, 320, fig.15/6

IL 40   Clay lamp   Civitavecchia   Civitavecchia

Three masks: two bearded, one beardless

Ref. N.Sc., 1940, 191

IL 41   Clay lamp (L.FABRIC MASC.) London, B.M. 1958.2.15.7

Three masks of wavy-haired slaves (27)

Type XXVIII

IL 42　Terracotta lamp　(MARMIUS) Rome, Wollmann Collection　　3rd cent. A.D.
　　　　　　　　　　　426

　　Mask 15: **actor** with wig hair striding forward and speaking:　long himation
　　over arm, with perhaps shoes and quilted stockings

　　Ref. Messerschmidt, *R.M.* 45 (1930), 186 pl.65b compares also lamp in Cologne
　　by Caecilius Saevus (Niessen no.1917)

IL 43　Terracotta lamp　　　　　　Ostia　　　　　　Ostia　　　　3rd cent. A.D.

　　Woman lying on couch with sword;　man with long hair and sword sitting at her
　　feet.　(?*Synapothneskontes*)

　　Ref. Bieber, *D.*, no.53;　*H.T.*[1], fig.518;　[2], fig.797;　*Skenika*, p.21, pl.Ib;
　　Squarciapino, *Arch. Class.*, 6 (1954), p.84 n.1

IL 44　Clay lamp　　　　　　　　Rome, Wollmann Collection 1495　　3rd cent. A.D.

　　Bust of bearded man with bored pupils, speira, deep trumpet striated inside.
　　Weak impression

　　Ref. Messerschmidt, *R.M.* 45 (1930), 188 pl.65d

　　Note For mask cf. IL 6

IL 45　Clay lamp　　　　　　　　Syracuse　　　　　　Syracuse

　　Wavy-haired slave with trumpet with narrow edge and extra locks

　　Ref. *N.Sc.*, 1954, 321, fig.16/12

IL 46　Terracotta lamp　　　　　　Biscari　　　　　　　2nd/3rd cent.A.D.

　　Slave mask on disk with double row of striations to forehead hair

　　Ref. Libertini, *Museo di Biscari*, pl.123, no.1294

IL 47　Terracotta lamp　　　　　　Leningrad　　　　Chersonese　　250 A.D.
　　　　　　　　　　　　　　　　Inv. 1897/32

　　Slave with flaming hair, long side locks, wide striated trumpet with narrow
　　edges

　　Ref. Waldhauer, *Antiken Tonlampen*, pl.47, 494

　　Note Found with coins of 2nd and 4th cent. A.D.

Type XXXI

IL 48　Clay lamp　　　　　　　　London, B.M. no.1355　　　4th/5th cent.A.D.

　　Slave mask with erect hair, corkscrew locks, bored eyes, wide trumpet with flat
　　smooth edges

　　Ref. Walters, 203, fig.306

Unusual lamps

IL 49　Terracotta lamp (5 wicks)　Pettau 135　　　Pettau　　3rd/4th cent.A.D.

　　Mask of slave:　peaked speira, wide shallow trumpet slightly twisted (indistinct)

　　Ref. Ivanyi, *Pannonischen Lampen*, no.830, pl.33/2

　　Note Similar piece found with coin of Valentinian

IL 50   Clay lamp (plastic)   Rome, Museo delle Terme   2nd/3rd cent.A.D.
                                 Inv. 62462

Slave and youth from Roman Comedy: 27, 16?.   Slave mask with hair striated
back from forehead and flat striated trumpet, youth with wavy, parted hair.
Slave with left hand pulling short mantle, right hand to breast, long chiton,
quilted stockings;   youth wreathed, chin pillared on right hand, quilted
sleeves and stockings

Ref. Bieber, *H.T.*[1], fig.424; [2], fig.582; Simon 80, 17**3**, 212 n.16;
        Messerschmidt, *R.M.*, 45 (1930), 182, dates early 2nd cent., but all
        the analogies for costume are later

IL 51   Clay lamp   Nijmegen   Nijmegen   2nd cent. A.D.

Lamp in form of Mask 27: flaming hair; raised brows; wide striated speira

Ref. Evelein, *Romeinsche Lampen*, 59, pl.16

Note Cf. IL 45

IL 52   Clay lamp   London, B.M. no.474   Pozzuoli   Late 1st/early 2nd
         (triangular with grooved handle)   cent. A.D.

Old man's mask, slave mask, mask of youth.   (Very indistinct: slave has
peak hair with striations running towards forehead;   old man has short beard;
youth mask is perhaps like IL 33)

Ref. Walters, pl.14

Note Perhaps cf. Broneer Type XXVIII

M osaics

IM 1-9   3. Deep slightly pointed trumpet perhaps suggests early Hellenistic
         original.   Dr. Simon suggests that the slave has discovered a child.

         4. These are traditional masks.   Dr. Simon identifies the left bottom
         mask as the *kolax* rather than the curly-haired youth suggested by Dr. Krien.
         The left top mask is the wreathed young *episeistos*.   The mask at the
         bottom on the right is very strange: it seems to me possible that it is
         an old woman and it is so taken by Dr. Krien.

         5. Traditional.   The old man's mask is very fine.   The two youths are
         chiefly differentiated by the furrowed forehead of the one above.

         6. Probably traditional but the slave mask is late rather than early
         Hellenistic.

         7. Both masks have a considerable pseudo-*onkos*.

         8. This is the new slave mask with petal eyes and wide twisted trumpet.

         9. The pseudo-*onkos* is very clear on the youth and the slave.   In both
         it is combined with long locks.   The slave should be compared with the
         flaming-haired slaves known from Athenian terracottas etc., e.g. AT 31,
         cf. also AS 9.   The youth may be compared with US 1.

IM 1   Mosaic masks   Priverno   Privernum   1st cent. B.C.

Mosaic border with masks among fruit

Ref. Jacopi, *Fasti* XII, no.2894

208

IM 2   Mosaic   Imola   1st cent. B.C.

Mask 13, with wreath, even black brows, set in garland between bearded satyr
and young satyr with wild hair

Ref.   Simon 186 n.121 (takes as 16); *N.Sc.* 1897, 55, fig.4, 5; Blake, *Mem.*
         Am. Acad., 7 (1930), 145; Mancini, *Imola*, 190, no.76, pls.2, 22/1-2,
         and cover

Note   Very like AS 10, UJ 34

IM 3   Mosaic   Naples M.N. Inv.6146   Late 1st cent.B.C.

H. 0,22 m., B. 0,21 m.

Leading slave and female servant on left: mask 22 with fat face and deep trumpet

Ref.   Bieber, *H.T.*[1], fig.262; [2], fig.401; Simon no.11, pl.III; 24, 152, 173
         (perhaps discovery of a child); Pernice, VI, 172, pl.72/1

Note   Slave mask perhaps Early Hellenistic in type

IM 4   Mosaic masks   Rome, Terme 1039 (1238, 1013)   Tusculum ?1st cent.A.D.

Masks 13, 17 (left) and 29, 39 (right)

Ref.   Simon 182 n.32; pl.II,2; Paribeni, p.300; Helbig, II[3], no.1480; *Maske*
         und Kothurn, 1 (1955), 82; *J.O.A.I.*, 42 (1956), 106, fig.49, 58; *R.P.,*
         3 20/9

Note   Traditional masks

IM 5   Mosaics   Rome, Vatican,   Hadrian's villa,   Early 2nd cent.
                                  Cab. Masch.   Tivoli   A.D.

a) Masks 3, 10, 11, 33: grouped 33 left above, 10 and 3 right above, 11 below;
b) Mask 33; c) Mask 34

Ref.   Simon 184 n.71, 82a; Nogara, *Mosaici*, pl.28; *R.P.*, 318/6, 319/1-2;
         B.H.T.[2], fig.808

IM 6   Mosaic   Rome, Capitoline   Rome, Thermae   2nd cent. A.D.
                                                      Decianae

Masks of slave with ivy and berry wreath, fat face, semicircular twisted trumpet,
and flute-player (22, 39)

Ref.   Bieber, *H.T.*[1], fig.270; [2], fig.329; *D.*, no.137; Stuart Jones, 154, pl.35;
         Simon 114; *R.P.*, 320/3; *P.C.F.*, fig.158; Rumpf, *M.u.Z.*, 183 (Hadrianic)

IM 7   Mosaic masks   Rome, Terme 171   Rome, Aventine   2nd cent. A.D.

Border of Nile mosaic: wreathed mask of second *episeistos* (12) and mask of kore
(33), pseudo-onkos

Ref.   Helbig II, no.1267; Paribeni, no.324; Lienhard, *Gaz. Arch.*, 6 (1880),
         170f., pl.25

IM 8   Mosaic mask   Lost   Centocelle   3rd cent. A.D.

H. 0,41 m.

Mask 22: elaborate wreath; framed eyes; wide, smooth, twisted trumpet; fat
face

Ref.   Simon 190 n.43a, pl.III/2; Blake, *Mem. Am. Acad.*, 17 (1940), 102

Note   Cf. AT 35

IM 9   Herakleitos Mosaic   Rome, Lateran   ?   3rd cent. A.D.

Masks ?16, 38, 27: youth and slave with flaming hair; slave with semicircular trumpet with flat edges

Ref. *B.H.T.*[1], fig.542; [2], fig.802; Rumpf, in *Mimus u. Logos*, 165; Simon
        80, 191 n.64, 110, 123; Helbig [3], 1231; Nogara, *Mosaici*, 3ff; Blake,
        Mem. Am. Acad., 8 (1930), 131; Krien, *Maske u. Kothurn*, 1 (1955), 81f.;
        R.P., 320/14

Painting

IP 2   Robert in his discussion of the Terence illuminations traced the masks back
        to Hellenistic originals but did not note where the miniaturist was inspired
        by later versions of these originals.   The Vatican manuscript (Latinus 3868
        = C) seems to have preserved the tradition most faithfully, but even there
        the masks in the *aediculae* at the beginning of the plays do not always agree
        with those worn by the same characters in the pictures, and in the pictures
        free men and slaves are more certainly distinguished by costume than by mask:
        slaves never wear a large himation, although they sometimes have a small
        scarf-like himation.   Slaves more often wear a long chiton than a short
        chiton (though the practice is inconsistent within individual plays), and
        this precludes a date earlier than the third century A.D. for the original
        (see Introduction).

        Slave masks may be distinguished as younger or older by dark or white
        hair, but they are not otherwise distinguished from each other; the trumpet
        mouth with narrow flattened edges is universal; the pseudo-onkos is some-
        times clear (e.g. *Andria*, fol.15v.), a stylization which first appears in the
        second century and is very common in the third (e.g. IM 9).

        Old men's masks are often indistinguishable from slaves' masks, but
        sometimes they are given beards below a normal mouth or below a slave trumpet.
        In the *Andria aedicula* leading old man with short beard below slave mouth
        (Simo), Lycomedeian with full beard (Crito), and wavy-haired old man with
        pointed beard (Chremes) are clearly distinguished.   The last is a third
        century mask (cf. AT 38, IS 31) and appears again for Menedemus in the
        Heautontimoroumenos, Hegio in the *Adelphoe*, Chremes in the *Phormio*.   Sannio
        in the *Adelphoe* and Dorio in the *Phormio* are completely unlike the Hellenistic
        pornoboskos: they are bald with dark hair and a slave mouth with no beard
        below it.

        The young men are mostly like the young man of the Lateran mosaic (IM 9),
        with elaborate hair high over the forehead (for this pseudo-onkos see e.g.
        Adelphoe, fol.59v.).   Older is sometimes distinguished from younger by
        raised brows and furrows on either side of the mouth (e.g. *Andria aedicula*).
        Phaedria in the *Phormio* has parted hair like the youth on the Terme lamp
        (IL 50).   The soldier in the *Eunuch* (e.g. fol.33v.) has short wavy hair
        and a cylindrical cap identified as the *pileus Pannonicus* of the fourth
        century A.D. (Jones and Morey, 44f.); it may be a restylization of the
        Macedonian *causia*.   Chairea, when dressed as the eunuch, wears a Phrygian
        cap, striped chiton and stockings.

        The parasites in the *Eunuch* and *Phormio* have slave mouths and in one
        picture (*Phormio*, fol.81v.) Phormio is clearly bearded.   The beard is
        probably a misunderstanding by an artist who knew that the slave mouth implied
        a beard.   The only certain parallels for beardless youths with these large

mouths are the soldier and the lover of the Oescus mosaic (XM 1) and some heads on sarcophagi (e.g. IS 48), which might otherwise be interpreted as slaves. Like the leno, the parasite is dressed as a free man but looks like a slave: the stylization of the mouth is certainly later than the Vatican bust (IS 42).

Among the women old women, hetairai, and wives are clearly distinguished; the only surprises are the *lampadion* mask of Antiphila in the *Heautontimoroumenos* and the bun of hair on the top of the head for the wives of the *Hecyra* and *Phormio*: this may be a misunderstood veil.

IP 1   Painting   Rome, Terme   Villa Farnesina   1st cent. A.D.

a) Seated poet with mask: probably a slave wreathed and with biggish twisted trumpet;

b) Still life with masks: ?2, 17, 16 (wreathed) - no.1231 (*Guide*, p.142)

Ref. *Mon.* 12 (1884), pl.22/2; *R.P.*, 329/2; Morey, *Sardis*, V/1 (1924), 64 fig.126; Kurz, *Begram*, 136; Bieber, *H.T.*[1], fig.427

IP 2   Terence MSS.   Rome, Vatican, Vat.Lat.3868   9th cent. A.D.

Scrinia and individual pictures

Ref. Jachmann, *Gesch. des Terenztextes*, 12f.; Robert, *Masken*, p.87ff.; Jones and Morey, *Miniatures*; Bieber, *D.*, 170ff.; *H.T.*[1], fig.525ff.; [2], fig.559-61; Schefold, *Bildnisse*, 170; Byvanck, *Mededeelingen Rome*, 1934, 51ff.; *Mnemosyne*, 1939, 115ff.; Bieber, *P.A.P.S.*, 103 (1959), 383; Jucker, *Aposkopein*, 106; Bethe, *Buch u. Bild*, 61ff.; Weitzmann, *Ancient Book Illumination*, 85

Sculpture

IS 2-60   As find spot is often unknown these are divided into 1. Reliefs, 2. Masks, herms and other sculptures in the round, 3. Sarcophagi. This gives a rough chronological order as many of the reliefs can be dated in the 1st cent. A.D., some of the sculpture in the round in the second, and the sarcophagi later. Within each section the objects are arranged in alphabetical order of museums.

Reliefs

2-18.   2, 6 and 7 are included in spite of the shut mouths because of the interest of comic masks occurring on tombstones.   8 is an altar, and if rightly called an altar of Ceres, the masks may allude to the plays at the Cerealia.

3, 4, 5, 9, 13-18 belong to the same class as the reliefs from Campania (NS 2, 17, etc.) and should therefore date from the first century A.D.   The drill-work on 3 suggests a later date.   The wavy-haired slave mask on 4 has a big pointed trumpet as on NS 22 etc.; so also 9, 14 and 17.   10 is a later and more elaborate version of AS 6.   (The same trio of masks appears on 18, if the profile mask in the centre is rightly interpreted as the female mask with the hair tied in a knot above the forehead).

13 is identified by Simon as the *kolax* (Pollux no.17); but, although other-wise like, it does not have the receding hair, which is very clear on 14, and may be rightly identified by Krien with the *oulos* (Pollux no.12).   The old man is presumably a *pornoboskos* (Pollux no.8).

IS 2   Round altar tombstone   Breccia   Breccia   1-50 A.D.

Hetaira mask with wimple (lips closed)

Ref. Montanari, *Rivista dell' Istituto*, 8 (1959), 131, fig.48

IS 3   Marble relief   Cassel 88   Italy   2nd cent. A.D.

H. 0,28 m.

Mask of *episeistos geron* (4) with corkscrew beard, and *diamitros hetaira* (41): drill used for beard

Ref. Simon 193 n.42d; acc. to Bieber, Italian marble (*Sk. in Kassel*, 45, pl.28)

IS 4   Marble disk   Cologne Theater Museum   ?Rome   ?1st cent. A.D.

Mask 17 and 27 with wreath, swinging brows, deep pointed trumpet

Ref. Simon 182 n.31c; pl. IV/1

IS 5   Marble relief   Copenhagen NC 384   ?1st cent. A.D.

Mask 3 and 13 (with wreath slanted across speira)

Ref. Simon 184 n.75a; Poulsen, *Billedtavler*, pl.25 (acquired in Rome); Welcker, *A.D.*, II, 122

Note Small and archaising

IS 6   Round altar tombstone   Este 1513   Este   1-50 A.D.

Kore and older woman (lips closed)

Ref. Montanari, *Rivista dell' Istituto*, 8 (1959), 131, fig.51-2

IS 7   Round altar tombstone   Este 1516   Este   1-50 A.D.

Kore mask with short hair (lips closed)

Ref. Montanari, *Rivista dell' Istituto*, 8 (1959), 131, fig.47

IS 8   Marble altar   London, B.M. 2492   Italy   1st cent. A.D.

H. 0,46 m.

Frontal masks set in garlands: kore (33), hetaira (41), ?slave (27) or more probably satyr

Ref. B.M. *Catalogue of Sculpture*, III

IS 9   Marble relief   London, B.M. 2448   ?

H. 0,235 m.

Masks 22, 39?: slave with wreath, swinging uneven brows, eyes not inscribed or bored, striated pointed trumpet curving out from mouth; the other with large eyes, smooth brows, fillet round head

Ref. Simon 198 n.71, takes as mask Pollux no.41

IS 10   Marble relief   Rome, Lateran 487   1st cent. A.D.

Menander with masks of youth, young woman, old man (11?, 4, 34)

Ref. Bieber, *H.T.*[1], fig.223; [2], fig.317; *D.*, no.129; Robert, fig.96; *Festschrift A. Rumpf*, 14; *Hellenistic Sculpture*, 51ff.; Simon 59, 184 n.84, 92, 119; *P.C.F.*, fig.93; *G.T.P.*, no.C 49; *W.A.M.*, n.115; Schefold, *Bildnisse*, 164, 216

Note A more elaborate version of AS 6

IS 11   Marble frieze   Rome, Lateran 722   Late 1st cent.A.D.

Marble relief of fruit with frieze above of comic *kore* masks with bored pupils and pseudo-onkos

Ref. Moschioni Phot. 8274; Strong, *Roman Sc.*, 123 Flavian

IS 12   Marble relief   Milan, Museo Teatrale   ?Italy   1st cent. A.D.

H. 0,15 m.

Old man's mask (3 rather than 4): wreath, bored pupils, corkscrew beard; stick and cloak in background

Ref. Sambon, no.586, pl.12; Simone, no.70; Pace, *Dioniso*, 10 (1947), 274, n.29

Note Cf. NS 9

IS 13   Marble relief   Rome, Vatican,   ?Rome   ?1st cent. A.D.
                                Cab. d. Masch. 440

H. 0,17 m.

Mask 17: bored pupils, raised brows, curly hair, corkscrew locks; facing woman (?) and bald old man (8)

Ref. Simon 51, 182 n.31a; Robert, 15 and 73; Krien, *J.O.A.I.*, 42 (1956), 104, 106, fig.50 identifies the youth as Pollux no.12

IS 14   Marble relief   Rome, Vatican, Mus.   Ostia   1st cent. A.D.
                                Chiaramonti 106

Masks of old man (4), slave (27), young man (13?), *kolax* (17)

Ref. Bieber, *H.T.*[1], fig.258; [2], fig.564; *D.*, no.139; Simon 51, 92, 182, n.31b; *P.C.F.*, fig.160; Robert, 14

IS 15   Marble relief   Rome, Villa Albani 613   Italy

Mask 16: roll hair; locks in two tiers of corkscrew

Ref. Simon 186 n.125; *E.A.*, 4040

IS 16   Marble relief   Rome, Terme   Nemi (Theatre) 1st cent.A.D.

Mask 4 against curtain, trumpet mouth with depending corkscrew curls

Ref. Simon 193 n.42a; *N.Sc.*, 1931, 270 fig.30

IS 17   Marble mask   Toronto, Royal Ontario Museum 59131-10-1 ?1st cent. A.D.

Wavy-haired slave: mask 27: bored eyes, raised brows, deep striated trumpet

Note For the hair cf. IS 39

IS 18   Marble relief   Vienna, Inv.119   ?Italy   ?1st/2nd cent. A.D.

Mask 4, 13, ?34 (Simon says 42)

Ref. Simon 184 n.74; 194 n.59; 197 n.42a; *B.S.A.*, 10 (1903-4), 145 fig.2; Nilsson, *Act. Inst. Ath. Suec.*, 5 (1957), 34; Schreiber, *Hell. Rel.*, pl.98

Note Back has two tragic masks: *melas* and *panchrestos*

Sculpture in the round

IS 19-45 **19.** This *kolax* like IS 13 seems to have too much hair, but this is not so obvious on the very similar double-herm 27. The slaves on both have a deep trumpet (cf. on 4). On the other hand 42, identified by Krien as the *oulos*, has receding hair and must be the *kolax*.

20 is the same mask as NS 16 and 28.

21. The treatment of the hair in tiny corkscrew curls over the head (as on 13 etc. above and 42 below) is unique for a slave. It is probably the 'curly' slave (Pollux no.24). The petal eyes recall AT 28 etc.

22. The mask is the late fat-faced slave with flaming hair like AT 39. IS 43 is the same.

23 is very like AS 12 and raises the question of Attic originals for these masks (cf. also on 34).

24, 29 are the fat-faced wreathed young *episeistos* deriving from ZT 2.

25 and **34** reproduce the same original as AS 11, with which 34 is almost identical. It is probably an Early Hellenistic slave with deep rounded trumpet rather than an old man. 38 belongs to the same general class.

27 is traditional.

30 (with its twin 41) has affinities with NP 45 (seated slave).

31 a) is the new fat slave mask, b) has a pointed beard and smooth brows and may therefore be an old man (cf. AT 38).

37 is a very fine slave mask of the new type and should be compared with the later AT 32. As it comes from a tomb, it may be relevant for contemporary production.

45 is a very good old man's mask (Pollux no.3).

IS 19   Marble herm   Berlin 214   ?Rome   ?1st cent. A.D.
Mask 17 and 27: bored pupils.   *Kolax* with much hair;   slave with deep trumpet
Ref. Simon 182 n.30b; pl.IV/2
Note According to *Beschreibung* acquired in Rome

IS 20   Marble mask   Bologna   Italy   1st cent. A.D.
Wreathed youth with onkos, perhaps Dionysos (16)
Note Cf. on NS 16

IS 21   Marble bust   Robinson Collection   Tusculum theatre   Not before 1st
H. 0,42 m.   cent. A.D.
Curly-haired slave (24): uneven eyebrows, petal eyes, bored pupils
Ref. D. M. Robinson, *A.J.A.*, 59 (1955), 28, pl.20, fig.42-5

IS 22   Marble mask   Cobham Hall, Kent, no.VII,54   Italy   2nd cent. A.D.
Two Erotes holding slave mask with flaming hair
Ref. C. C. Vermeule, *A.J.A.*, 59 (1955), pl.42, fig.11

IS 23   Marble mask   Copenhagen NC 377   Rome, Sallust's villa   2nd cent.A.D.
         H. 0,84 m.   Inv. 616   or later

         Mask 42: band round hair; possibly tied; long locks; depressed eyes

         Ref. Simon 197 n.38; Poulsen, *Billedtavler* pl.25

IS 24   Marble mask   Copenhagen NC 378   Rome, Sallust's villa   ?2nd cent.A.D.
         H. 0,62 m.   Inv. 616   or later

         Mask 16: wreathed; long locks, but brows smooth; depressed pupils

         Ref. Simon 186 n.131, takes as mask 15; *Billedtavler*, pl.25

         Note Very like 29

IS 25   Marble mask   Copenhagen NC 380   Rome, Sallust's villa   2nd cent.A.D.
         H. 0,62 m.   Inv. 616   or later

         Mask 3 or 22: striated speira; swinging brows; short waved beard round mouth

         Ref. Simon 193 n.49c; *Billedtavler*, pl.25

         Note Poulsen takes as satyr, but in his catalogue 'old man of comedy', as Simon.
                 Perhaps slave (22) with large trumpet, copy of early Hellenistic original

IS 26   Marble mask   Copenhagen NC 381   Italy   2nd cent.A.D. or
         H. 0,26 m.   Inv. 1164   later

         Mask 34(?): woman with hair knotted over forehead; small band; other hair
         combed back; shut mouth

         Ref. Simon 196 n.35; *Billedtavler*, pl.25

IS 27   Marble herm   Copenhagen NC 386   ?Rome   1st cent. A.D.
         H. 0,21 m.

         Mask 17 and 27 with deepish striated trumpet with round edge

         Ref. Simon 182 n.30a; *Billedtavler*, pl.25

         Note Acquired in Rome

IS 28   Marble mask   Ince Blundell 130   Rome, Villa Negroni   2nd cent.A.D.
         H. 0,78 m.

         Mask 33: even brows; small locks in front of ears, large locks behind;
         bored iris and pupils

         Ref. Ashmole pl.46

         Note Architectural sculpture.   Companion to no.131 (IS 29)

IS 29   Marble masks   Ince Blundell 131   Rome, Villa Negroni   2nd cent.A.D.
         H. 0,73 m.

         Mask 16: even brows, falling locks, elaborate wreath, bored pupils and irises

         Ref. Ashmole pl.46

         Note Companion to no.130 (IS 28); architectural sculpture

IS 30   Marble statuette   London, B.M. 1767   Rome

H. 0,62 m.

Seated wreathed slave: legs crossed, himation over left shoulder, wide twisted
trumpet with narrow edges; mask 27.   (Same type as IS 41)

Ref. Bieber, *H.T.*[1], fig.232; [2], fig.558; *D.*, no.152; Simon 191 n.59b

Note For the attitude cf. IT 65

IS 31   Marble masks   Ostia (theatre)   3rd cent. A.D.

a) Mask 27: bored pupils; pseudo-onkos, hanging locks; trumpet with narrow
   striated eged; raised brows;

b) Mask 4: bored pupils; waved, striated hair; pointed beard; even brows

Ref. Rumpf, in *Mimus u. Logos*, 165; Bieber, *H.T.*[1], fig.539; [2], fig.805;
       Calza, *Guide*, 102; Simon 80 (slave); Krien, *Maske u. Kothurn*, 1 (1955),
       80

IS 32   Marble mask   Ostia 91   Ostia   2nd cent. A.D.

Wreathed youth (16): bored pupils and iris, drilled wreath

Note Probably the same type as NS 4

IS 33   Marble mask   Ostia 94   Ostia

Youth (11 or 13): bored iris and pupils; peaked striated hair

IS 34   Marble mask   Rome, Terme, Chiostro   S.Italy   ?2nd cent. A.D.
                             Michelangelo

Old man or slave: striated speira; swinging brows; short, waved beard round
mouth

Ref. Simon 193 n.49a takes as old man

Note IS 25 and AS 11 reproduce the same Hellenistic type

IS 35   Marble mask   Rome, Terme, Chiostro   Tivoli,   2nd cent. A.D.
                             Michelangelo   Hadrian's villa

Mask 32

Ref. Simon 107, 196 n.28, pl.XII/1; Paribeni, 126, no.202 (possibly for
       fountain); Anderson, no.4562; *G.T.P.*, no.C 50; Krien, *Maske u. Kothurn*,
       1 (1955), 83, pl.1,3

IS 36   Marble mask   Rome, Terme   Tivoli,Hadrian's villa   2nd cent.A.D.

Girl with corkscrew locks over forehead, wavy locks behind ear, narrow *stephane*;
smooth brows, bored eyes. Probably *hetairidion*

Ref. Anderson 4561

IS 37   Marble mask   Rome, Terme 58204   Rome, tomb of Calpurnii   1st cent.A.D.

Mask of slave (22): fine striations of hair and beard; beard framed; eyes
framed; knotted brows; pupils bored

Ref. Bieber, *H.T.*[1], fig.264; [2], fig.393; *D.*, no.167; Plattner and Ashby,
       Topographical Dictionary, 477; Simon 77, 190 n.39

IS 38   Marble mask   Rome, Vatican,   ?   ?2nd cent. A.D. or
                                Cortile del Belvedere   later

H. 0,75 m.

Mask 22:   furrowed brows, sunk pupils, large striated trumpet

Ref.   Simon 190 n.40;   Amelung II, 165 nr.66;   Robert, fig.2, compares sarco-
         phagus in Clieveden (IS 47)

IS 39   Marble mask   Rome, Vatican,   ?   ?2nd cent. A.D.
                                Cortile del Belvedere

H. 0,65 m.

Mask 11:   speira with flaming hair, sunk pupils

Ref.   Simon 184 n.81;   Amelung, II, no.102A;   Robert, fig.3

Note   For the hair cf. IS 17

IS 40   Marble bust   Rome, Vatican,   Tivoli   2nd cent. A.D.
                                Gall.dei Busti 313

H. 0,61 m.

Mask of hetaira (40)

Ref.   Robert, pl.I;   Bieber, *H.T.*[1], fig.284;   [2], fig.365;   *D.*, no.177;   Simon
         111, 197 n.52, 125;   *P.C.F.*, fig.156;   *G.T.P.*, no.C 51;   Krien, *J.O.A.I.*,
         42 (1956), 112, fig.56

IS 41   Marble statuette   Vatican, Gall. degli Candelabri 191

H. 0,635 m.

Seated slave: mask 27: wreath;   legs crossed, tights;   himation over left
shoulder;   left hand in lap;   right hand on altar.   (Same type as IS 30)

Ref.   Bieber, *D.*, no.151;   *H.T.*[1], fig.231;   [2], fig.556-7;   Simon 191 n.59a;
         Amelung-Lippold, III, 2, 322

IS 42   Marble bust   Rome, Vatican, Gall. Geogr. no.890   ?

H. 0,52 m.

Mask of *kolax* (17):   hair in spiral curls, twisted locks.   White marble

Ref.   Amelung-Lippold, III, 2, p.478, no.47 (Late 2nd cent. A.D. from early
         Hellenistic original);   Krien, *Maske u. Kothurn*, 1 (1955), 82, takes
         as 12;   Bieber, *H.T.*[1], fig.541;   [2], fig.809

Note   Perhaps cf. IS 59

IS 43   Marble mask   Rome, Vatican,   Italy
                                Mus. Chiar. 75

H. 0,21 m.

Slave mask (27):   wreathed, with wide twisted trumpet, swinging brows, bored
eyes

Ref.   Simon 191 n.60a;   Amelung, I, pl.38

IS 44   Marble mask   Rome, Vatican,   Italy
                                Sala degli Animali

Mask 11

Ref.   Simon 184 n.86;   Amelung, II, 400, no.643

Note   Cf. IS 53

IS 45   Marble mask   Vienna, Inv.27   Italy   ?1st cent. A.D.

Mask (3): speira, raised brows, beard with corkscrew locks, petal eyes

Ref. Simon 194 n.58; Sacken, pl.13, p.31; Sacken-Kenner, no.31; Rumpf in
    Mimus u. Logos, 170 n.22, takes as 4

Sarcophagi

IS 46-60   (This represents only a very small selection of the total.)

46, 52, 55.   These are the new fat slave masks.

48, 51, 54.   These masks are very unclear except for the ribbed hair
and fat face: it is just possible that they are slaves with a very narrow
edge to the trumpet, but 54 has even brows and is better taken as a youth
(11).   Youths' mouths are so stylized on XM 1, and parasites in IP 2 have
slave mouths.

49.   The Muse holds the mask of a wavy-haired old man with a narrow beard
growing from a trumpet mouth as on some Roman lamps e.g. IL 1, 10.

50 is a piece of great interest because the figures on each side of the
door are so extremely like the actors on either side of the portrait of
Terence in the Vatican Terence MS. (IP 2).

53 shows a curious mixture of traditional and modern elements.

59 shows a comic actor in funeral games.

60 has a wavy-haired slave between a young man and young woman with pseudo-
onkos.

IS 46   Muse sarcophagus   Berlin 844   Rome, Via Appia   2nd cent. A.D.

Lid: youth writing between two Muses, slave mask with pseudo-onkos.   Body:
Thalia with fat mask (?old woman) in left hand; fat slave mask with pseudo-onkos
on pillar

Ref. *A.Z.,* 1843 pl.6; *A.M.,* 26 (1901), 131

Note For grouping of Thalia cf. Copenhagen, NC 779

IS 47   Garland sarcophagus   Clieveden   ?

Slave mask with striated speira and semicircular striated trumpet (22), and
profile youth with pseudo-onkos (12 or 16 rather than tragic)

Ref. Toynbee, *Hadrianic sculpture,* 209, pl.xlv.3, late 2nd to early 3rd cent.
    A.D.   Robert, fig.4, compares slave mask with IS 38

Note Compare EG 2 for the two masks

IS 48   Strigil sarcophagus   Copenhagen, NC 779, Inv.853   Italy   3rd/4th cent.A.D.

Muse of comedy with masks of youth? (16) and ?wrinkled old woman (29). (Possibly
both are slaves with very narrow trumpet)

Ref. Poulsen, *Billedtavler,* pl.67, 779

IS 49   Sarcophagus   Copenhagen, NC 782   Italy   Late 2nd/early 3rd
                                                                    cent. A.D.

Two male comic masks on corners of lid: perhaps wreathed 12 or 16.   Reclining
Muse holds mask of old man (4)

Ref. *Billedtavler,* pl.67, 782

IS 50   Column sarcophagus   Ince Blundell 232   Rome   250/300 A.D.

Between the columns: flute-player and actors on either side of door. Actors in long chitons, girded very low, and small himatia. Both old and bald masks. At each end a comic mask on a table, perhaps 33 and 22. On the lid eight large masks among which 33 and probably 4, 22 and 27 can be distinguished

Ref. Ashmole, pl.50

Note For mask at end cf. ZM 4

IS 51   Column sarcophagus   London, B.M. 2305   3rd cent. A.D.

Muse of Comedy with mask

Ref. *Cat.*, III, 316; *A.J.A.*, 25 (1921), 228, fig.7; Rodenwaldt, *J.d.I.*,51 (1936), 101

IS 52   Muse sarcophagus   Paris, Louvre 475 (378)   Rome, road to Ostia

Mask 22 (?) with fat face, twisted trumpet, and extra locks behind held by Muse, wearing sandals and holding *pedum*

Ref. *Guide*, pl.liii

IS 53   Garland sarcophagus   Rome, Terme 441   Rome (Tomb of   100/150 A.D.
                                                        Calpurnii)

Masks 4, 3, 27, 11

Ref. Toynbee, *Hadrianic Sculpture*, 205, pl.xliii,2 (cf. Altmann fig.28 (Villa Pamfili)); Krien, *Maske u. Kothurn*, 1 (1955), 86; Byvanck, *B.V.A.B.*, 35 (1960), 91; Robert, fig.1

IS 54   Column sarcophagus   Rome, Terme 80711, Villa Mattei   3rd cent. A.D.

Muse of Comedy, with mask (probably youth, no.11)

Ref. Reinach, *R.R.*, III, 301; *A.J.A.*, 25 (1921), 228, fig.4; Aurigemma, pl.8

IS 55   Garland sarcophagus   Rome, Terme no.121,657   Rome,Via Imperiale   2nd cent.
                                                                    A.D.

Slave masks with peaked speira of flaming hair, locks in front of ears, very narrow striated trumpet

Ref. Krien, *Maske u. Kothurn*, I (1955), pl.1,4

IS 56   Marble sarcophagus   Rome, Terme 112444   Via Praenestina   ?2nd cent.A.D.

Akroteria: wreathed curly youth (12) and wavy-haired youth (15). The mouths are stylized like slave mouths but this treatment is not uncommon in late masks

Ref. Aurigemma, pl.7

IS 57   Marble sarcophagus   Rome, Terme 125353   Via Praenestina   250 A.D.

Thalia with comic mask and *pedum*

IS 58   Marble sarcophagus   Vienna 171   ?Italy   ?3rd cent. A.D.

Muse of comedy with mask (16). End plate: poet looking at mask (27)

IS 59   Marble relief   Rome, Villa Doria Pamfili   3rd cent. A.D.

Youth with wavy hair and pseudo-onkos, smooth brows (16), in chiton and large himation, tights, and boots (?), holding torch (?)

Ref. Bieber, *D.*, no.55; *H.T.*[1], fig.532; [2], fig.788; *E.A.*, viii, 40; *C.I.L.*, VI 8239. Perhaps cf. IS 42

IS 60   Marble sarcophagus   Rome, Capitoline Museum   2nd cent. A.D.

    Mask of curly-haired boy (12), way-haired slave (27), kore (33)

    Ref. Stuart-Jones, 38 (Atrio), no.36a, pl.8

    Note Cf. slave mask on sarcophagus of poet, British Museum 2313

Terracottas

IT 65-81   65 is dated late Republican to early Augustan by its likeness to the Numitorius relief. The old man in the centre apparently intervenes between the old man on the right and the slave seated on the altar. The attitude of the slave is repeated almost exactly by IS 30, 41; it is not clear that the mask is the same, it certainly has a wide trumpet but the face does not look so fat. The slave wears a short chiton and perhaps tights.

66-74 are Julio-Claudian architectural reliefs. 66 may be the short-bearded old man noted on IL 6-7. The pseudo-onkos is very clear on 68. 69 and 70 come from the same mould. 71-3 come from the same mould. They are clearly in the same tradition as IT 46-8, 58, but the hair is smooth and combed backwards from the forehead with no trace of speira, like the left-hand slave mask on IS 53. 74 is the new type of fat-faced slave.

80-81 are cake moulds (another interpretation is proposed by Squarciapino, *loc. cit.*); they are fixed by external dating as contemporary with AT 37, which reproduces the same scene as IT 81 but with the addition of the inscription COMEDIA PYLADES. The figures wear the new costume seen on contemporary Athenian terracottas and on a contemporary Roman lamp IL 50: long chiton for slaves and small mantle, quilted tights for slaves, young man, and quilted sleeves for women.

IT 65   Reconstruction of   Rome etc.   Late 1st cent. B.C.
    terracotta relief

    Scene from Comedy: slave on altar (27), old man standing central (3), old man running up with stick (4)

    Ref. Bieber, *H.T.*[1], fig.425; [2], fig.587; Pickard-Cambridge, *Theatre*, 219, fig.78/9; Simon 173; *G.T.P.*, no.C 22; Sieveking, *Loeb Br. Tk. u. Vasen*, pl.34/2; Rohden Winnefeld, 52, 143f.; Beyen, *Wanddekoration*, 98 fig.25; Rizzo, *J.O.A.I.*, 8 (1905), 210, fig.49. Cf. also Rohden-Winnefeld, fig.9, slave wringing his hands in front of door

IT 66   Terracotta antefix   Copenhagen, Inv.1722   Italy   1st cent. B.C./A.D.
    H. 0,117 m.

    Old man with striated hair, bushy uneven brows, bored pupils, fullish short beard

    Ref. Breitenstein, no.946 compares Rohden-Winnefeld, p.15, Campana pl.99

    Note Cf. on IL 6-7

IT 67   Terracotta relief   Ostia   Ostia   1st cent. A.D.

    Mask 16: three-quarter face, twisted wreath, pupils bored

    Ref. Simon 186 n.128a; *N.Sc.*, 1910, 95 fig.1

IT 68   Terracotta relief   Vienna 8   1st cent. A.D.

    Two unbearded masks: 16 and 12 (with onkos and descending corkscrew curls), garlands

    Ref. Sacken-Kenner, 250, no.8; Rohden-Winnefeld, 32 fig.65

IT 69   Terracotta relief   Wurzburg   1st cent. A.D.
         Mask 16
         Ref. Simon 186 n.122

IT 70   Terracotta mask on Sima   Paris, Cab.Med.5817   1st cent. A.D.
         Mask 39 with cithara and mask 16
         Ref. Simon 197 n.64; v. Rohden-Winnefeld, pl.CXIV,1

IT 71   Terracotta reliefs   London, B.M., D 658, Italy   1st cent. A.D.
                                659, 660; 1926-3-24-121
         H.: D 660: 0,131 m.
         Masks of wavy-haired slaves (27) in arched frame: striated peaked hair descen-
         ding to ears, raised brows, pupils incised, wide twisted trumpet
         Ref. Walters, *Cat.*, 414; Rohden-Winnefeld, 234-5
         Note Post-Augustan but Augustan original. Contrast the earlier IT 46 etc.
                 and compare IS 53 (left-hand slave)

IT 72   Terracotta relief   Milan, Museo Teatrale, 294 Italy   1st cent. A.D.
         H. 0,12 m.
         Slaves (22): corkscrew hair, swung brows, bored pupils, broad twisted trumpet,
         smooth inside
         Ref. Sambon, pl.8, no.294; v. Rohden-Winnefeld, 234

IT 73   Terracotta relief   Vienna 1829, 1830   Italy   1st cent. A.D.
         Slaves (22)
         Ref. Mus neg.I, 1029

IT 74   Terracotta reliefs   Rome, a) Lateran   a) Ostia   1st cent. A.D.
                                b) Terme
         Slave mask 27: elaborate wreath, wavy hair, fat face, trumpet with flat,
         narrow edge
         Ref. Simon 191 n.60a; v. Rohden-Winnefeld, 80 fig.159, and 295 fig.511, dates
                 a) Augustan and b) second half of 1st cent. A.D.

IT 75   Terracotta mask   London, B.M., D 76   Italy
         H. 0,033 m.
         Wavy-haired slave (27). Small, white
         Ref. Walters, *Cat.*, 309
         Note Perhaps 1st cent. A.D.   Very like IL 14

IT 76   Terracotta mask   London, B.M., D 77   Italy   ?1st cent. A.D.
         H. 0,024 m.
         Wavy-haired slave (27). Small, white
         Ref. Walters, *Cat.*, 310

IT 77   Terracotta mask   Milan   Italy
         Peaked speira; nicked brows; framed eyes with bored pupils and iris; wide,
         twisted trumpet with narrow striated edge, corkscrew locks
         Note Not before 1st cent. A.D.

IT 78   Terracotta masks   Rome   ?Rome   1st/2nd cent. A.D.

Mask of youth (?16), mask of girl (?33): flattish, large bored pupils and irises

Ref.   *N.Sc.*, 1907, 468 fig.42

IT 79   Terracotta mask   Rome   Baths of Caracalla   2nd/3rd cent.A.D.

Mask 13

Ref.   Simon 184 n.78; Ficoroni, pl.66B

IT 80   Cake mould   Ostia   Ostia   After 200 A.D.

H. 0,17 m.

Man (16) kneeling to woman (38), and servant (?27): note quilted sleeves; slave with long chiton and short mantle

Ref.   Bieber, *H.T.*[1], fig.515; [2], fig.793; *D.*, no.52; *Skenika*, 3ff.; Pasqui, *N.Sc.*, 1906, 357ff.; *P.C.F.*, fig.65; Simon 49, 182 n.28; Squarciapino, *Arch. Class.*, 6 (1954), 82f.

Note   Found with lamps signed FLORENT and C. IUN.BIT.

IT 81   Terracotta moulds   a) Ostia   a) Ostia   3rd cent. A.D.
                               b) London,B.M.,E70   b) Unknown
                               c) Paestum   c) Paestum

H. 0,12 m.

Slave and woman on couch: slave with wavy hair and wide twisted trumpet and woman with waved hair down to chin level

Ref.   a) Bieber, *H.T.*[1], fig.516; [2] fig.794; Pasqui, *N.Sc.*, 1906, 369, fig.111;
        b) Bieber, *H.T.*[1], fig.517; [2] fig.795;
        c) Squarciapino, *Arch. Class.*, 5 (1954), 82f., pl.18, fig.2

Note   The same scene is given by AT 37, which is inscribed COMEDIA PYLADES

Vases

IV 8-17   *Arretine ware:*

The slaves with deep trumpets (8-10) are traditional (the ancestry may run back through Italian Megarian bowls to Greek Megarian bowls). 15 is included here as probably being an import in Athens.

IV 8   Arretine ware (Rasinius)   Arezzo   Arezzo   1st cent. B.C./A.D.

Mask 22 with deepish trumpet

Ref.   Stenico, *Ceramica Arretina*, I, no.110

Note   Traditional mask

IV 9   Arretine ware (Rasinius)   Arezzo   Arezzo   1st cent.B.C./A.D.

Mask 22, wreathed, with deepish trumpet

Ref.   Stenico, *Ceramica Arretina*, I, no.244

IV 10   Arretine ware (Rasinius)   Arezzo   Arezzo   1st cent.B.C./A.D.

Mask 25 with twisted trumpet

Ref.   Stenico, *Ceramica Arretina*, I, no.107

IV 11   Terracotta matrix   Arezzo   Arezzo   1st cent. A.D.
         Mask of *panchrestos* (10)
         Ref. Stenico, *Arch. Class.*, 6 (1954), 64, no.62

IV 12   Terracotta matrix   Arezzo 3255   Arezzo   1st cent. A.D.
         Mask of young *episeistos* (16)
         Ref. Stenico, *Arch. Class.*, 6 (1954), 64, no.54

IV 13   Terracotta matrix   Arezzo 6230   Arezzo   1st cent. A.D.
         Mask of slave, wreathed (25): very wide, twisted trumpet
         Ref. Stenico, *Arch. Class.*, 6 (1954), 64, no.53

IV 14   Terracotta matrix   Arezzo 3254   Arezzo   1st cent. A.D.
         Mask of wimpled hetaira (41)
         Ref. Stenico, *Arch. Class.*, 6 (1954), 64, no.55

IV 15   Arretine plate fragment   Athens, Agora   Agora Deposit,   0/50 A.D.
                                    Museum, P 9851   D 4: 1
         Mask with plumpish face, smooth brows and long striated hair, probably kore
         Ref. Robinson, *Agora V: Roman Pottery*, p.26, pl.5, no.G.36, neg.1xi-41

IV 16   Arretine fragment   Oxford, no No.   Cirencester   1st cent. A.D.
         Female mask (profile):   35

IV 17   Arretine fragment   Oxford, 1929.192   Nursling,   1st cent. A.D.
                                                         Southampton
         Masks hanging from rim: one of them pseudokore (35)

THE WEST

Bronzes

JB 1   Bronze head   Wiesbaden   Wiesbaden   ?1st cent. A.D.
         Mask 15(?): mouth *not* open
         Ref. Simon 186 n.133b; Ferri, *Arte Romana*, fig.184b
         Note Perhaps not dramatic

Mosaic

JM 3   Mosaic   Aix-en-Provence   Aix   4th cent. A.D.
         Three women
         Ref. Simon no.13; Millin, *Atlas*, II, 238, pl.33; Wieseler, pl.XII,15

JM 4   Mosaic   Lisbon   Torre del Palma   3rd cent.A.D.
         Thalia with kore mask
         Ref. *R.A.*, 50 (1957), 84, fig.2

Sculpture

JS 1-4   1. The mask is perhaps an old man's mask with a deep striated trumpet (cf. on IL 6-7), but the surface is badly weathered.　It is presumably not traditional but a contemporary mask as worn by Hermolaos.

    2. The high diadem, the lock in front of the ear, the partially concealed ear suggest that this is a girl (?Pollux no.41): UB 36 is not unlike.　The relief is of the same type as the simpler mask reliefs from Pompeii.

    3. Only the identification of the central masks can be regarded as certain. The old man has a long flowing beard, the slave has a ridged speira and a very wide twisted trumpet.　The possible relevance of this funerary monument to contemporary performance has to be considered.

JS 1   Marble altar   Malta, Roman Villa Museum   Malta   100/200 A.D.

Mask of old man: inscription of P. Aelios Hermolaos of Pergamon, komodos and lyristes, 25 years old.　The mask has the hair striated backwards from the forehead and a trumpet striated inside with rounded outline

Ref. E. Coleiro, *J.H.S.*, 77 (1957), 312; for titles cf. Rehm, *Didyma*, I, no.183

Note For the mask cf. on IL 6-7

JS 2   Marble relief   Reus (Spain), Museo Municipal   Tarragona   1st cent.A.D.

H. 0,29 m., B. 0,24 m.

Mask with diadem: hair striated over crown, lock in front of ear, corkscrew locks; poised on rock: pillar with pine cone

Ref. Borras, *Revista del Centro de Lectura, Reus* 4 (1954), 3

Note For mask perhaps cf. AJ 7

JS 3   Marble relief   St.Rémy (Memorial of Julii)   St.Rémy   1st cent. B.C.

Over main relief of S.E. side masks 33, 4, 27, 11, in swags

Ref. Simon 184 n.88; *A.D.*, I,7 and pl.16; Espérandieu, I, 95, no.114; Winter, *K.i.B.*, 163/2, 404/1; *C.I.L.*, XII, 1012; Hübner, *J.d.I.*, 3 (1888), 10 f. takes these masks like those of the other sides to be satyrs (the other sides show clearly satyrs, beardless and bearded, bald and hairy).

JS 4   Marble relief   Toulouse   Toulouse   1st/2nd cent. A.D.

Mask 14 suspended from a frieze: very long corkscrew hair, face possibly damaged

Ref. Simon 195 n.8 (wrongly takes as woman): Espérandieu, II, no.866

Terracottas

JT 4   Terracotta statuette   Marseille, Musée Borély, Froehner 2741   Arles

H. 0,15 m.

Comic slave (27), standing with arms across breast, chiton probably double girt falling to knees; wavy hair, wide twisted trumpet

Note Perhaps 2nd cent. A.D. or later.　Cf. FT 3

JT 5   Terracotta statuette   Marseille, Musée   Arles
                              Borély, Froehner 2742

H. 0,153 m.

Actor taking female part: high headdress, left hand holding veil, right hand holding himation

Note 2nd cent. A.D. or later.   Cf UT 114

JT 6   Terracotta mask   Utrecht 5625   Holland
      (fragment)

Fragments of elaborate hetaira mask

Ref. J.J.C. Van Hoorn-Groneman, *B.V.A.B.*, 35 (1960), 75f. (comparing fragments from Nijmegen and Cologne)

Note Not before 2nd cent. A.D.   Cf. ZT 62

JT 7   Terracotta mask   Utrecht 5640   Holland
      (fragment)

Fragment of male mask with helmet decorated with cock and medallion

Ref. J.J.C. Van Hoorn-Groneman, *B.V.A.B.*, 35 (1960), 75f. (comparing fragments in Nijmegen and Bonn)

Note Not before 2nd cent. A.D.

Vases

JV 1   Central Gaulish pottery   100-190 A.D.

Masks of satyrs, hetairai etc.

Ref. Stanfield and Simpson, *Central Gaulish potters*, figs.13, 19, 41, pls.17, 56, 62, 67, 75, 80, 98, 101, 108, 139, 159

Note These masks are traditional and derive from Arretine ware

UNKNOWN ORIGIN

Bronzes

UB 10-38   The difficulty of dating bronzes makes it impossible to derive much information from them.

10-23. Statuettes. 10 may have the long chiton of later slaves. 11 has a mask not unlike IL 26 but the edge of the trumpet does not seem to be flat. The stance is nearly repeated by 16, which may be dated by its criss-cross tights (cf. AT 31 etc.). 14 has the wide mouth known from the newer type of slave. 17 is very like 11, but the large himation and the long pointed beard suggests an old man rather than a slave: 20 however does not show any beard below the trumpet, but is otherwise almost identical with 17.

Statuettes (in order of museums)

UB 10   Statuette from bronze vase   Baltimore 54.1469

Slave (25) seated on altar: cloak across shoulders, long chiton (?)

Ref. *B.H.T.*[2], fig.555; 'Princeton' fig.36

Note For attitude cf. no.15 below, and IV 3

UB 11   Bronze   Boston 98.677

H. 0,105 m.

Slave declaiming (27): short chiton belted, mantle over right shoulder, right arm raised, peaked wig hair, semicircular trumpet

Ref. Bieber, *H.T.*[1], fig.418; [2] fig.580; 'Princeton' fig.52

Note Bieber suggests Italian origin

UB 12   Bronze statuette   Dresden 23

Slave (25), bald, shock of hair over ears, wide twisted trumpet, standing with hands in front of body

Ref. Simon 188 n.8b; Reinach, *R.S.*, III, 157/2

UB 13   Bronze statuette   Leyden

Mask 22: hands clasped in front of body; chiton to knees; striated speira and very wide trumpet with narrow flat striated edge

Ref. Simon 190 n.50b; Reinach, *R.S.*, II, 558/2

UB 14   Bronze statuette   Madrid, Mus.Arq. 2970

H. 0,08 m.

Standing slave with peaked speira, flat wide trumpet mouth, chiton down to knee; hands clasped

Ref. Madrid neg. 8087; Thouvenot, pl.6, no.41; Hübner, no.457

UB 15   Bronze statuette   Milan

H. 0,64 m.

Wreathed slave (?25) seated on altar, head bowed, hands clasped; legs crossed, big fold between legs

Ref. Sambon pl.16, no.330

Note For attitude cf. no.10 above

UB 16   Bronze statuette   Munich, Market

Comic actor: mask 22: stance and clothes as UB 11, deep striated trumpet, criss-crossed tights

Ref. Bieber, *H.T.*[1], fig.202; [2], fig.581

UB 17   Bronze statuette   New York, Metropolitan Museum 17.230.29

H. 0,114 m.

Old man (4) with right hand engaged in himation: head with hair very like UB 11, but pointed beard

Ref. Bieber, *H.T.*[1], fig.414; [2], fig.554b; Simon p.93, 194 n.62; Bieber, *P.A.P.S.*, 103 (1959), 381

Note Simon doubts genuineness

UB 18   Bronze statuette   Palermo

H. 0,061 m.

Mask 22: dancing slave

Ref. Simon 190 n.48

UB 19   Bronze statuette   Palermo   Sicily

H. 0,049 m.

Maison (25)

Ref. Simon 188 n.8a

UB 20   Bronze   Paris, Cab.Med. 979

H. 0,073 m.

Old man: mask 4, or slave (27): scratching his chin; wrapped in large
himation; left hand forward holding (stick); eyes bored; twisted trumpet
mouth, but no beard under it

Ref. Babelon 979

Note Very like UB 17

UB 21   Bronze   Paris, Cab.Med. 981

Slave seated on altar (22): deep trumpet with flat edge, short chiton, hands
tied behind back

Ref. Babelon 981

Note Bad Roman work

UB 22   Bronze statuette   Unknown

Mask 22

Ref. Simon 190 n.49; Ficoroni, pl.XIX, 2

UB 23   Bronze statuette   Unknown

Mask 22

Ref. Simon 190 n.50a; Ficoroni pl.XXVII, 3

Masks

UB 24-38   25 belongs to the type noted on FB 1, perhaps pantomime dancers. 27 is not
unlike Pompeian painted masks.   28 recalls early Hellenistic masks and the
group may go back to that date, cf. on BT 14.

28 is not unlike the late Hellenistic slaves from Delos, e.g. DT 19.

32 is the late fat-faced slave and much less friendly than the normal Maison
mask.

36 is a very elaborate hetaira mask: cf. above on JS 2.

a) Young Men

UB 24   Bronze mask   Paris, Petit Palais, Dutuit Collection

H. 0,026 m.

Mask 10

Ref. Froehner no.49, pl.47; Simon 183 n.64

UB 25   Bronze mask   Paris, Cab.Med. 992   ?1st cent.A.D.

H. 0,083 m.

Young man (10), wearing *causia* (?), hair curled over forehead, corkscrew locks
in three tiers, shut mouth

Ref. Babelon 992

UB 26   Bronze mask   Copenhagen, Thorwaldsen Museum,   1st cent.A.D.
                                         Room 36;   3, 102

          Curly-haired youth (12)

UB 27   Bronze mask   Vienna 4725   ?Italy

          Mask of youth (16): bored pupils, sloping brows, striated hair across forehead,
          hanging curls, mouth slightly open

          Note Perhaps 1st cent. A.D.

UB 28   Bronze statuette   Vienna 379

          Eros with lover's mask (16): cap hair, contorted brows

          Ref. Sacken-Kenner, no.1170; Sacken, pl.32,4; Reinach, *R.S.*, II, 433,7

          Note Perhaps from an Early Hellenistic original

   b) Slaves

UB 29   Bronze mask   Copenhagen, Thorwaldsen Museum,
                                         Room 36;   3, 94

          Wreathed slave (22)

UB 30   Bronze mask   Vienna 564
          H. 0,054 m.

          Slave (22): peaked striated wig, deepish wide trumpet with striated edge

          Ref. Sacken-Kenner, no.1350; Sacken, pl.47/3

UB 31   Bronze mask   Copenhagen, Thorwaldsen Museum,
                                         Room 36;   3, 95

          Maison mask (25)

UB 32   Bronze mask   Vienna 4726
          H. 0,052 m.

          Slave (25): sunk pupils, swung brows, fat face, wide twisted trumpet, shock
          over ears

UB 33   Bronze mask on weight   Paris, Cab.Med. 1000

          Slave (27?): shock of hair, wide twisted trumpet; perhaps bald

          Ref. Babelon 1000

UB 34   Bronze mask   Paris, Petit Palais, Dutuit Collection
          H. 0,032 m.

          Slave mask 27

          Ref. Simon 191 n.60; Fröhner, pl.46

   c) Women

UB 35   Bronze mask   Paris, Cab.Med. 998

          Hetaira (?38): mouth shut

          Ref. Babelon 998

UB 36   Bronze mask   Paris, Cab.Med. 994

Wimpled hetaira (41):   bored pupils, locks over middle of forehead, hanging
corkscrew locks

Ref. Babelon 994; *P.C.F.*, fig.155

UB 37   Bronze mask   Paris, Cab.Med. 997

Wimpled hetaira (?41):   mouth shut

Ref. Babelon 997

UB 38   Bronze mask   Vienna

Mask (42) with wreath: handkerchief round hair;   long side locks

Ref. Simon 120, 197 n.39;   Sacken, pl.XXX, 5

Glass

UG 1   Glass mask   Copenhagen, Thorwaldsen Museum,
                                            Room 36;   12, 120

Slave mask (22)

UG 2   Glass mask, handle plate   Schiller Collection   1st cent. A.D.
        of jug

H. 0,023 m.

Young *episeistos* (16):   fillet round hair, slightly swollen brow

Ref. Zahn, *Sammlung Schiller*, no.361

Precious Objects

Silver cups

UJ 2   Silver cup   Berlin   Hildesheim   1st cent. A.D.

Masks: perhaps 1, 4; Tragic: Heracles, *Mesokouros* without onkos;   old woman
slave

Ref. Robert, fig.36; Pernice-Winter, *der Hildesheimer Silberfund*, pl.XV-XVI;
        Simon 189 n.17;   192 n.10;   194 n.61

Note The old man (4) has a long beard below a slave mouth

UJ 3   Silver cup   Berlin   Hildesheim   1st cent. A.D.

Mask 16 (twice), 1, 22 (twice), 12 (like Naples marble masks), and tragic
kourimos

Ref. Pernice-Winter, pl.XIII and XIV (Vollgraff/Roos in *Mon. Piot.*, xlvi, 39
        date a similar cup 2nd cent. B.C.)

Gems

UJ 4-55   No attempt has been made to date these in view of the very cautious remarks of
           Miss Richter, *Metropolitan Museum, Catalogue of Engraved Gems*, pp.36, 62.   The
           coverage is virtually restricted to the British Museum, the Metropolitan Museum,
           the Thorwaldsen collection in Copenhagen, and the material in Furtwängler's
           Antiken Gemmen.   They are divided into scenes, groups of masks, masks.

1. Scenes (4-19)

4-5 are poets.   4 has an old bald poet with the mask of a youth on his knee
and two actors, apparently in *long* chitons with masks pushed back on the top
of their heads.

6 is an actor taking a slave part wearing a short chiton and carrying a bald
slave mask.

7, 8, 9, 10.   Actors taking the part of old men.   These are very like the
figures on Pompeian wall paintings, particularly the pair of old man and
slave on 9 which should be compared with NP 27.

11-19.   Actors taking the part of slaves.   All wear short chitons: 14, 15,
17 and 18 are fat, and double girt like the early Myrina slaves.   The running
slave (18) and the slave seated on the altar (13) occur through the whole
history of comedy.   Dancing slaves (11, 14) recall DM 2 (early 2nd century B.C.).
19 has the late type of trumpet with narrow flat incised edge.

UJ 4   Engraved gem   London, B.M. 2183

Seated poet with mask;   two actors with masks pushed back;   three other masks.
Probably comic, but masks cannot be distinguished

Ref. Walters, *Cat.*, (1926), pl.27;   Kurz, *Bégram*, 134 says that *A.G.* 30, 44 with
          the same subject is a forgery

UJ 5   Gem, carnelian   London, B.M. 2194

Old poet with stick and mask of comic youth

Ref. Walters, pl.27

UJ 6   Gem, black paste   London, B.M. 1092

Actor with mask: chiton to knees, chlamys, stick (rather than palm branch) in
right hand, bald mask with shock of hair and wide trumpet (25?)

Ref. Walters, pl.16

Note Said to be Early Roman (3rd cent.)   Cf. *A.G.* 28/51

UJ 7   Gem

Old man in chiton and long himation with stick, turned to the right

Ref. Lippold, *Gemmen*, pl.60/1;   *A.G.*, 41, 48.   Cf. Richter, no.457, which
          certainly has mask 4

UJ 8   Gem

Old man in chiton and long himation with stick and long full beard, turned to
the left;   woman's mask on column

Ref. Lippold, pl.60/3;   *A.G.*, 41, 50.   Cf. Beazley, *Lewes House Gems*, no.108,
          pl 7, which certainly has mask 3

UJ 9   Carneol   Berlin 6512

Bearded old man with stick;   slave (with semicircular trumpet) with right hand
to chin, other hand under right elbow

Ref. Lippold, *Gemmen*, pl.60/2 (cf. 4);   *A.G.*, 29, 33

Note Perhaps 1st cent. B.C.   Extremely like NP 27

UJ 10   Gem   Berlin 6514

Bearded actor in long himation with stick, moving to the left

Ref. *A.G.*, 29/34

UJ 11   Gem

Two slaves, one sitting with lyre, one dancing

Ref. Lippold, pl.60/8

Note Cf. for slave seated with lyre *A.G.* 28/50

UJ 12   Carneol   Arndt Collection

Two slaves fighting for or surprised at a ham: short chitons, himatia, wreaths, semicircular trumpets

Ref. Lippold, pl.60/9; *A.G.*, 29, 27

Note Hellenistic or early Roman

UJ 13   Gem, amethyst   London, B.M. 2184

Slave seated on altar, legs crossed, arms folded, fat face; speira, head bowed, probably wide twisted trumpet

Ref. Walters, pl.27; cf. Fossing, no.261

Note Cf. bronzes in Baltimore (UB 10) and Milan (UB 15)

UJ 14   Gem, brown paste   Copenhagen, Thorwaldsen Museum

Comic actor, bearded, big-bellied, chiton with double girding and a short mantle which covers both arms, dancing to left; head turned back, left leg swung across

Ref. Fossing no.262 pl.IV, 'Roman Republic'.   Cf. *A.G.* 28, 40 and 42 (both have speira and wide trumpet)

Note Recalls subject of DM 2

UJ 15   Gem, brown paste   Copenhagen, Thorwaldsen Museum

Comic actor, big-bellied, short chiton with girdle and on back short mantle covering left arm, moving to right, holding crooked staff in right hand. Head invisible

Ref. Fossing no.263, pl.IV, 'Roman Republic'

UJ 16   Gem   Berlin 1229

Actor (in *causia*?) as slave standing with chin propped on hand; fattish face and wide twisted trumpet

Ref. *A.G.*, 28/39

UJ 17   Gem   Weimar, Goethe Collection

Wreathed slave, fat face, semicircular trumpet, short chiton, with amphora in right hand, lantern in left hand

Ref. *A.G.*, 28/43 = 62/6

UJ 18   Gem   Berlin 1248

Running slave, short chiton, peaked speira with semicircular trumpet

Ref. *A.G.*, 28/49

UJ 19   Carneol   Vescovali

Bust of slave: striated hair;   bored pupils;   wide, twisted trumpet with flat
incision on narrow band

Ref. Lippold, pl.60/11

2. Masks

a) Groups of masks

UJ 20-25   22 should derive from an original of the first half of the 3rd century B.C.
(see Introduction).   24 with the late slave mask cannot b e earlier than the
1st century B.C.   25 has a woman's mask parallelled on NP 38, probably the
full-grown hetaira, no.38.

UJ 20   Gem

Group of old man, young *episeistos*

Ref. Lippold, pl.61/12

UJ 21   Gem, pale brown paste   Copenhagen, Thorwaldsen Museu m

Combination of old man's mask (3) with corkscrew beard and speira, and youth's
mask (or young hetaira):   on 1265 the young head has an ivy wreath

Ref. Fossing, nos.1261 and 1264, pl.XV

Note Graeco-Roman.   Cf. Berlin 5310-5311

UJ 22   Gem   Berlin 6548

Mask of youth with striated speira and smooth brows (13) superposed on mask of
hetaira with melon hair and corkscrew curls

Ref. A.G. 26/76

UJ 23   Gem

Group of slave, hetaira, *episeistos* masks

Ref. Lippold, pl.61/10

Note Hellenistic (or later)

UJ 24   Gem a) carnelian,   Copenhagen, Thorwaldsen Museum
              b) yellow paste

Combination of wreathed slave, fat face, very wide striated trumpet with narrow
flat edge, and girl's mask (?)

Ref. Fossing, nos.1265 and 1266, pl.XV

Note Graeco-Roman

UJ 25   Sardonyx   Marlborough Collection

Group of four masks: bald slave (with shock of hair over ears, striated semicircular trumpet), and hetaira (with hair in a roll round the head and small,
corkscrew curls below), repeated about HELENA

Ref. Lippold, pl.61/16;   A.G., 65/17

Note Probably 1st cent. B.C.   The woman's mask is probably the same as the mask
        on NP 38

b) Masks

UJ 26-55   *Old men.*   26 is a survival of Middle Comedy mask A.   27, 30 with slave
trumpet mouth above the beard are unlikely to be earlier than the first
century A.D. (cf. UL 1).   28, 29 are also late with their shortish beard.
31 may not be dramatic as its mouth is shut.

Young men.   All of these may go back ultimately to an early Hellenistic
original but their immediate affinities are with reliefs and sculpture of
the first century A.D.

Slaves.   27-39. The originals of these leading slaves with semicircular
twisted trumpet are unlikely to be earlier than the first half of the second
century B.C.   40-43. The originals of these leading slaves with wide
twisted trumpet are unlikely to be earlier than the second half of the
second century B.C.   44-47. The originals of these leading slaves with
flat-edged trumpets are unlikely to be earlier than the latest first century
B.C.   49 with deep pointed trumpet goes back to an early Hellenistic
original.

Women.   50 has a more pronounced onkos than any Hellenistic masks.   51-52
derive from originals of at least the early third century B.C.   51 with fat
face and wreath may be the 'full-grown' hetaira no.38.   53-54 are a rather
later youthful hetaira mask, cf. ZM 1 etc.

Old men

UJ 26   Gem, carnelian   Copenhagen, Thorwaldsen Museum
Comic mask, to front, with hair over forehead and ears, very deep trumpet
Ref. Fossing no.1253 pl.XV
Note Graeco-Roman.   (Middle Comedy tradition, Mask A)

UJ 27   Gem
Three-quarter mask: striated hair and speira;   trumpet with striations on
narrow band;   short flowing beard below: old man (3)
Ref. Lippold, pl.61/5; *A.G.* 41/9
Note Cf. UL 1.   Not before 1st century A.D.

UJ 28   Gem, hyacinth   Copenhagen, Thorwaldsen Museum
Comic mask, to front, with hair ending in a roll over the forehead and shortish
full beard arranged in parallel curls (3)
Ref. Fossing no.1251, pl.XV
Note Graeco-Roman

UJ 29   Gem, yellow paste   Copenhagen, Thorwaldsen Museum
Comic mask, half to right, smooth hair, with a shortish beard in regular
parallel curls;   the eyes pierced through (3)
Ref. Fossing no.1252, pl.XV
Note Graeco-Roman

UJ 30   Gem, cameo   Copenhagen, Thorwaldsen Museum

Comic mask, to front, bald, trumpet mouth, with beard composed as a row of parallel curls; *pornoboskos* (8)

Ref. Fossing no.1994, pl.XXIV.   Cf. Lippold, pl.61/6

Note Graeco-Roman

UJ 31   Gem, carnelian   New York, Metropolitan Museum **41.160.877**

Mask of old man with flowing beard (4), brows raised, speira and hair striated, mouth shut

Ref. Richter, no.578

Young men

UJ 32   Gem

Mask of youth with striated speira, furrowed forehead, raised brows, and short nose (10)

Ref. *A.G.*, pl.26/66;   Cf. Lippold, pl.61/8;   Simon 184 n.69

UJ 33   Gem   Berlin 1969

Mask of youth with striated speira, slightly raised brows, straight nose (11)

Ref. *A.G.*, 26/68

UJ 34   Gem, garnet   New York, Metropolitan Museum 81.6.39

Full-face mask of *hapalos* (13): bored eyes, striated speira, falling wreath. The actor's mouth shows through the mask

Ref. Richter, no.579.   Cf. *A.G.*, 26/62

Note For type cf. AS 10, IM 2

UJ 35   Gem, amethyst   New York, Metropolitan Museum 41.160.529

Profile mask of *Kolax* (17): curly hair, corkscrew locks behind ears

Ref. Richter, no.580.   Cf. *A.G.*, 33/47

UJ 36   Gem

Frontal mask of unbearded Pan with longish hair and bored pupils

Ref. Lippold, pl.61/9;   *A.G.*, 41/15

Note Not before 1st cent. A.D.

Slaves

i) Leading slaves with semicircular trumpet

UJ 37   Gem, nicolo   London, B.M. 2220

Full-faced slave mask with wig hair, small nose, semicircular smooth trumpet (22)

Ref. Walters pl.27

Note Cf. Naples frontal glass masks TG 1-2

UJ 38   Gem, sard   Copenhagen, Thorwaldsen Museum

Comic slave-mask to front; over the forehead peaked speira, fat face, semi-circular trumpet (22)

Ref. Fossing no.296, pl.IV, compares Berlin 6556. 'Roman Republic'

UJ 39   Gem, cameo   Copenhagen, Thorwaldsen Museum

Comic mask of slave, to front: striated speira and hair; semicircular twisted trumpet (22)

Ref. Fossing no.1995, pl.XXIV

ii) Leading slaves with wide twisted trumpet

UJ 40   Gem, carnelian   London, B.M. 1588

Three-quarter slave mask with ivy wreath, fat face, wide twisted trumpet; probably a smooth speira, rather than bald

Ref. Walters pl.21, formerly Carlisle Collection

UJ 41   Gem, black paste   Copenhagen, Thorwaldsen Museum

Comic mask with rather long hair straight over forehead, half-turned to left: slave with wide twisted trumpet

Ref. Fossing no.294, pl.IV. 'Roman Republic'

UJ 42   Gem, carnelian   Copenhagen, Thorwaldsen Museum

Comic slave mask, to front: peaked speira, raised brows, wide trumpet

Ref. Fossing no.295, pl.IV. Cf. *A.G.*, 26/60 (which is *not* like) 'Roman Republic'

UJ 43   Gem   Leningrad Hermitage

Three-quarter mask of slave with fat face and wide twisted trumpet; bored eyes, uneven brows, very smooth hair

Ref. *A.G.*, pl.26/60

iii) Leading slaves with flat-edged trumpet

UJ 44   Gem, red jasper   London, B.M. 2219

Fat-faced slave with striated hair, semicircular twisted trumpet with narrow edge and bored eyes which squint: inscr. ΕΛΔΗΝ

Ref. Walters pl.27

UJ 45   Gem   Leningrad, Hermitage

Three-quarter mask of fat-faced wreathed slave with striated hair and side locks, striated flat edge to deepish twisted trumpet.   Signed ALEXANDER

Ref. *A.G.*, pl.26/65

UJ 46   Gem   Berlin 5279

Three-quarter mask of wreathed slave: fat face and semicircular twisted trumpet with striated edge

Ref. *A.G.*, 41/8

UJ 47   Gem   Rome, Mus. Naz. 78697

Fat slave with smooth twisted trumpet

Ref. R. Righetti, *Rendiconti Pont. Acc.*, 30-31 (1959), 219, fig.50

iv) Bald slaves

UJ 48   Gem, amethyst   London, B.M. 3003

Three-quarter mask of bald slave with fat cheeks and twisted trumpet (25)

Ref. Walters pl.30.   Carlisle collection.   Cf. *A.G.*, 41/10 and 14 (which are wreathed) and Lippold, pl.61/7

v) Wavy-haired slaves

UJ 49   Gem   Berlin 1123

Three-quarter mask of wavy-haired slave with speira and deep trumpet, pointed (27)

Ref. *A.G.* 33/46

e) Women

UJ 50   Gem   ?

Frontal female mask with pseudo-onkos, long hair in corkscrew locks, sloping brows (33)

Ref. *A.G.*, 41/16

UJ 51   Gem

Fat hetaira with wreath and melon hair (perhaps 38)

Ref. Lippold, pl.61/3; *A.G.*, 26/61

Note Probably 1st cent. B.C.

UJ 52   Gem, carnelian   New York, Metropolitan Museum 81.6.131

Profile hetaira with melon hair and corkscrew locks, roll of hair over forehead (39)

Ref. Richter, no.581.   Cf. *A.G.*, 26/63

UJ 53   Gem, sard   London, B.M. 2205

Three-quarter mask of hetaira with ivy wreath (39)

Ref. Walters pl.27

UJ 54   Gem   Berlin 1952

Young hetaira mask with ivy wreath and corkscrew curls (39)

Ref. *A.G.*, 26/64, cf. 41/45

UJ 55   Gem   Berlin 1950

Mask of hetaira with mitra, hair coming to a peak in front and corkscrew curls (41).   Signed APOLLONIDES

Ref. *A.G.*, 26/57.   Cf. 58 (without corkscrew curls), 59 do.

L amp

UL 6   Bronze lamp   Milan

          Slave (22) bending right forward, enormous trumpet
          Ref. Sambon pl.16, no.333

Stone sculpture

US 1   Marble frieze   Oxford 211   3rd cent. A.D.
          H. 0,53 m.
          Mask of soldier (15), slave (27), woman (fragmentary).   Slave with peaked
          speira, youth with pseudo-onkos
          Ref. Michaelis, *Ancient Marbles*, 571, no.122; Rumpf, in *Mimus u. Logos*,
                165, pl.VI
          Note Cf. the soldier on IM 9 and the slave on IL 8

US 2   Marble herm   Lost
          Mask 17
          Ref. Simon 182 n.30c; Ficoroni pl.XVII

US 3   Limestone   Dresden
          H. 0,17 m.
          Mask 17
          Ref. Simon 182 n.33

US 4   Marble mask   ?
          Maison (25)
          Ref. Simon 188 n.8; Smith, *Parthenon*, pl.29

Terracottas

UT 107-123   107-115, *Statuettes*.   107-111 and probably 112-3 have the new slave
              mask.   In particular 108-111 may be compared with AT 31.   107 seems
              to have the new long chiton and 112 the cross-barred stockings.   114
              is not unlike JT 5.
                115 should perhaps be excluded because of its shut mouth

     1. Statuettes

UT 107   Terracotta statuette   Munich 6928
          H. 0,12 m.
          Maison marketing (25): himation over left shoulder, basket in left hand.
          High base
          Ref. *B.H.T.*[2], fig.382
          Note Cf. DT 19, but probably later.   Not before 1st cent. A.D.

UT 108   Terracotta statuette   Munich 6930

H. 0,105 m.

Slave seated on altar (27): arms folded, legs crossed; double-girded chiton seems to come below knee; striated speira, wide twisted trumpet with flat edge. High pedestal

Note Like Munich 6928 (UT 107)

UT 109   Terracotta statuette   London, B.M., Towneley 61   ?Italy

Wavy-haired slave (27).   Dark red clay: flame hair, long locks, uneven brows, petal eyes with depressed pupils; broken off below shoulders

Note Probably dates with AT 31 etc. to 3rd cent. A.D.

UT 110   Terracotta head   New York 10.210.68

H. 0,038 m.

Slave head with striated onkos hair and uneven brows; trumpet with flat edge

Ref. H. McClees, *Daily Life* 18

Note Cf. UT 109

UT 111   Terracotta statuette   Rio de Janeiro, Museu Nacional 1551

H. 0,064 m.

Slave (27) with flame hair, raised brows, right hand up to left shoulder, cloak over left shoulder

Ref. Cf. UT 109

UT 112   Terracotta group on two   Cambridge, Fogg Museum
         step base   1932.56.60

Seven comic actors in himatia with cross-barred stockings.   All with trumpet mouths; three with wavy hair

Note Perhaps 3rd cent. A.D.

UT 113   Terracotta relief   Coll. Gréau

Relief with five comic actors

Ref. Winter, *T.K.*, 426/8; Froehner, pl.81

Note Cf. UT 112

UT 114   Terracotta statuette   London, B.M., M.L. 1904.2-4.424

H. 0,14 m.

?Wife (31): whitish-grey clay.   Trumpet mouth; hands clasped.   Apparently long hair and veil

Note Not unlike JT 5

UT 115   Terracotta head   Rio de Janeiro, Museu Nacional 1714

H. 0,055 m.

Female head with pseudo-onkos, melon hair, earrings, closed lips. (Probably *not* dramatic)

Note Perhaps 3rd cent. A.D.

2. Masks

116-123.   116 is in an extraordinary hard style not unlike AT 52.   117 is probably Italian and not later than first century B.C./A.D.   Cf. NT 13.

118 is probably from Egypt but the clay is not so distinctive as ET 63.   It is probably Early Roman.

120, 121 belong to the general class represented by ZT 59 and therefore are not before first century A.D.

123 is a very fine example of the fat-faced slave and should not be later than first century A.D.

UT 116   Terracotta mask   Munich 7054

H. 0,12 m.

Old man: barley sugar hair; petal eyes with bored pupils

Note The head appears *not* to be a satyr.   Perhaps cf. AT 52.   Perhaps 3rd
cent. A.D.

UT 117   Terracotta mask (roof tile)   Vienna 2991

H. 0,128 m.

Youth (12)

Note Late Hellenistic or very early Roman

UT 118   Terracotta mask   University College London   ?Egypt

Youth with smooth brows, black; black lids with pink above and below, blue
on eyes; bored pupils; elaborate wreath with rosette flowers and vineleaves:
mask 13

Note Perhaps 1st century A.D.

UT 119   Terracotta mask   Leyden (Case 8)

Delicate youth (13)

UT 120   Terracotta mask   Milan, Museo Teatrale

H. 0,17 m.

Wreathed youth (?16) (note mouth not open): bored pupils and iris

Ref. Sambon, no.282, pl.10

UT 121   Terracotta mask (fragment)   Cambridge, Fitzwilliam Museum

H. 0,113 m.

Probably slave: iris and pupil cut out; nose with holes on either side.
Hard orange clay

UT 122   Terracotta mask   Leyden (Case 8)

Leading slave (22)

UT 123   Terracotta relief   Vienna 1832

Wreathed slave (27): fat face; very careful treatment of hair and locks

Note For style compare ZT 50

MASK CATALOGUE

OLD MEN

(i) Hellenistic

Mainland

AJ 1, 3, 4, 6

AL 1

AS 5

AT 1, 2, 3, 19

AV 1, 3, 11, 12, 15, 16-18, 19, 26-8, 29

BT 9

CL 1

CT 3, 4

XT 1, 7

Islands

DM 1

KT 1

YT 8

Asia Minor

MT 8-12

ZA 1

ZL 1

ZS 1, 3

ZT 20, 32, 33, 39

ZV 1

Africa

EI 1

ET 1, 7, 8, 9, 10

FT 1

Sicily and Italy

ST 17

TT 4, 16, 18

NT 20

IT 62

The West

JM 2

Unknown

UJ 1

UL 1

UT 2, 4, 5, 106

241

OLD MEN (cont.)

(ii) Roman

Mainland

AJ   10
AS   6, 7, 8
AT   38, 48, 52
XL   3

Africa

EB   3
EG   1, 3, 4
EL   32, 34

Sicily and Italy

SM   1
NB   5, 7
NM   3, 4, 5
NP   1, 3, 5, 7, 9, 14, 17, 19, 24, 27, 31, 39, 47
NS   1, 3, 7, 8, 9, 17, 22, 24, 25, 26, 28
NT   29, 30, 31-4
IL   4, 6, 7, 9, 10, 20, 24, 25, 37, 38, 44, 52
IM   5
IP   2
IS   3, 5, 10, 12, 13, 14, 16, 18, 31, 45, 49, 50, 53
IT   65, 66

The West

JS   1, 3

Unknown

UB   17
UJ   2, 7, 8, 9, 10, 20, 21, 26, 27, 28, 29, 30, 31
UL   1
UT   116

YOUNG MEN

(i) Hellenistic

Mainland

AJ 1, 2, 5, 6
AS 3
AT 4, 11, 12, 13, 18, 25
AV 15, 25, 30
BT 1, 3, 4, 5, 10, 11, 12, 13, 18
XT 1, 4, 10, 14, 21

Islands

DM 1
DT 3, 4, 5, 17, 18
KT 2
YT 9, 11

Asia Minor

MT 1, 3, 15, 16, 17, 18, 19, 20, 21, 22, 23, 24
ZS 2
ZT 1, 2, 3, 4, 5, 21, 27, 43
ZV 3

Africa

EI 2
EL 28
ET 11, 12, 13, 14, 15, 16, 17, 18, 19, 20, 21, 22
EV 14
FB 1

Sicily and Italy

ST 1, 3, 4, 6, 13, 16, 18, 19, 20, 21, 24, 25, 28
TJ 1, 3, 4
TT 5, 6, 7, 20, 23
GV 1
PT 1, 2
NB 1
NT 1, 2, 3, 4, 5, 6, 13, 17
IT 2, 6, 7, 8, 9, 10, 11, 12, 32, 33, 34, 37, 38, 39, 40, 41, 42

The West

JT 1

Unknown

UB 6
UT 6, 7, 7a, 8, 9, 10, 11, 12, 13, 15, 16, 17, 18, 19, 20, 23, 25, 27, 28, 104

YOUNG MEN   (cont.)

(ii) Roman

Mainland

AJ 7, 12

AS 6, 10

AT 26, 49, 50

CJ 2

CL 4, 5

XL 3

XM 1

Islands

DT 29

KT 7, 8

YT 13

Asia Minor

ZM 2, 3

ZS 4, 5, 6

ZT 53, 54, 61

Africa

EG 2, 9

EI 5

ET 65

EV 16, 17

FM 1, 2, 4

FP 1

FS 1, 2, 3

Sicily and Italy

SM 1

SS 1

NB 4, 8, 9

NJ 1, 2

NM 2, 4, 5, 6

NP 2, 4, 5, 6, 7, 8, 10, 11, 12, 16, 20, 22, 23, 29, 30, 33, 34, 36, 37, 40, 41, 42, 44, 46, 50, 52, 53, 54, 55

NS 3, 4, 5, 10, 11, 12, 16, 17, 18, 22, 25, 27, 28, 29, 30

NT 26, 27, 35, 36, 37, 38, 40

IL 18, 33, 34, 42, 43, 50, 52

IM 2, 4, 5, 7, 9

Sicily and Italy (cont.)

IP 1

IS 4, 5, 10, 13, 14, 15, 18, 19, 20, 24, 27, 29, 32, 33, 39, 42, 44, 47, 49, 53, 56, 58, 59

IT 67, 68, 69, 70, 78, 79, 80

IV 11, 12

The West

JB 1

JS 2, 3, 4

Unknown

UB 24, 25, 26, 27, 28

UG 2

UJ 3, 4, 5, 20, 22, 23, 32, 33, 34, 35

US 1, 2, 3

UT 117, 118, 119, 120

SLAVES

(i) Hellenistic

Mainland

AJ 1, 2, 6

AS 1, 2, 3, 4

AT 5, 17, 20, 23, 24

AV 4, 5, 6, 7, 8, 9, 10, 11, 13, 14, 15, 20, 21, 22, 23, 24, 31, 32, 34, 35, 36

BT 2, 8, 15, 16, 17

CJ 1

CT 2

XT 1, 2, 3, 8, 9, 12, 13, 15, 16, 17, 18, 19, 23

Islands

DL 1, 2, 3, 4

DM 1, 2

DT 6, 8, 9, 10, 11, 12, 14, 15, 19, 20, 22, 23

KL 1

KT 3, 4, 5

YA 1

YT 3, 4, 5, 6, 10

YV 2, 3, 4

Asia Minor

MT 2, 4, 5, 6, 13, 25, 26, 27, 28, 29, 30, 32, 34, 35, 36, 37, 38, 39, 40, 41, 42, 43, 44

ZL 1, 2, 3, 5, 6

ZS 2

ZT 8, 9, 12, 14, 15, 16, 18, 19, 22, 23, 26, 29, 30, 31, 34, 35, 36, 40, 41, 44, 45, 46, 47, 48, 49

ZV 2, 4, 5

Africa

EB 1, 2

EL 1, 2, 3, 4, 5, 6, 7, 8, 9, 10, 11, 12, 13, 14, 15, 16, 17, 18, 19, 20, 21, 22, 23, 24, 25, 26, 27, 29

ET 2, 6, 23, 24, 25, 26, 27, 28, 29, 30, 31, 32, 33, 34, 35, 36, 37, 38, 39, 40, 41, 42, 43, 44, 45, 51, 52, 53, 54, 55, 59, 60, 61

EV 1, 2, 3, 4, 5, 6, 7, 8, 9, 10, 11, 12, 13, 15

FT 3

SLAVES (cont.)

(i) Hellenistic (cont.)

Sicily and Italy

ST 2, 7, 8, 9, 10, 14, 22, 23, 26, 27

TG 1, 2

TJ 1, 2

TT 1, 2, 3, 8, 9, 11, 12, 15, 17, 21, 22, 24, 25, 26, 27, 28, 29, 30

TV 1

PT 3

NB 2, 3

NT 7, 8, 9, 10, 14, 15, 18, 19, 21

NV 1

IC 1

IL 1, 2

IS 1

IT 1, 3, 5, 13, 14, 15, 16, 17, 18, 19, 20, 21, 22, 23, 24, 25, 35, 36, 44, 45, 46, 47, 48, 49, 50, 51, 52, 53, 54, 55, 56, 57, 58

IV 1, 2, 3, 4, 5, 6

The West

JM 2

JT 2

Unknown

UB 1, 2, 3, 4, 8, 9

UL 3, 4, 4a

UT 1, 29, 30, 31, 32, 33, 34, 35, 36, 37, 38, 39, 40, 41, 42, 43, 44, 45, 46, 47, 48, 49, 50, 51, 52, 53, 54, 55, 56, 57, 58, 59, 60, 61, 62, 63, 64, 65, 67, 68, 69, 70, 71, 72, 73, 74, 75, 76, 95, 96, 100, 101, 102, 103

(ii) Roman

Mainland

AJ 7, 9, 13

AL 2, 3, 4, 5

AS 8, 9, 11, 13

AT 27, 28, 29, 30, 31, 32, 33, 34, 35, 37, 39, 40, 41, 42, 43, 46, 47, 51

CL 2, 4, 6

XL 1, 2, 3, 4

XS 1

SLAVES (cont.)

(ii) Roman (cont.)

Islands

KT 9, 10

YS 1, 2

Asia Minor

ZG 1

ZL 7, 8, 9, 10

ZM 2, 3, 4, 5

ZS 5, 6, 7

ZT 50, 51, 52, 55, 56, 57, 58, 59, 60

ZV 6

Africa

EG 2, 5, 10, 11

EI 3

EL 31, 35, 36, 37

ET 62

EV 16, 17

FL 1, 2, 3

FM 4

Sicily and Italy

SM 1

TS 1

TT 31, 32, 33

NB 6

NM 3, 4, 5, 6

NP 4, 5, 6, 8, 13, 14, 21, 22, 23, 24, 25, 27, 38, 43, 44, 45, 46, 50, 51

NS 2, 3, 8, 17, 19, 22, 23, 25, 31

NT 22, 23, 24, 25, 40, 41, 42

NV 2, 3

IB 1, 2, 3, 4

IL 3, 5, 8, 11, 12, 13, 14, 16, 17, 19, 21, 22, 23, 26, 27, 28, 29, 30, 31, 32, 39,
    [41, 45, 46, 47, 48, 49, 50, 51, 52

IM 3, 6, 8, 9

IP 1

IS 4, 8, 9, 14, 17, 19, 21, 22, 25, 27, 30, 31, 34, 37, 38, 41, 43, 46, 47, 48, 50,
    [52, 53, 55

IT 65, 71, 72, 73, 74, 75, 76, 77, 80, 81

IV 8, 9, 10, 13

The West

JS 3

JT 27

Unknown

UB 10, 11, 12, 13, 14, 15, 16, 18, 19, 20, 21,
    22, 23, 29, 30, 31, 32, 33, 34

UG 1

UJ 3, 6, 9, 11-14, 16, 17-19, 23-4, 25, 37-47,
    48, 49

UL 6

US 1, 4

UT 107, 108, 109, 110, 111, 112, 113, 122, 123

WOMEN

(i) Helleni stic

Mainland

AJ 1, 4, 6

AS 3

AT 8, 9, 10, 14, 15, 16, 21, 22

AV 12, 13, 14, 15, 25, 33

BT 6, 7

CT 1

XT 1, 5, 6, 20, 22, 24

Islands

DM 1

DT 1, 2, 13, 25, 26, 27, 28

KT 6

YT 1

YV 1

Asia Minor

MT 45, 46, 47, 48, 49

ZL 3

ZM 1

ZT 6, 7, 10, 11, 13, 24, 25, 28, 37, 38, 42

Africa

ES 1

ET 3, 4, 5, 6, 56, 57

FB 2

FT 2

Sicily and Italy

ST 11, 12, 15, 17

TJ 1

TT 13

GV 1, 2, 3, 4, 5, 6

PT 4

NT 1, 11, 12, 16

IT 1, 26, 27, 28, 29, 30, 31, 59, 60, 61, 62

IV 7

The West   *Unknown*

JM 2   UB 5

JT 3   UT 77, 78, 80, 81, 82, 83, 84, 85, 86, 87, 88,
                                    89, 90, 91, 92, 93, 94, 98

WOMEN (cont.)

(ii) Roman

Mainland

AJ 7, 8, 11

AS 6, 12

AT 37

CL 4

XM 1

XS 2

XT 25

Asia Minor

ZM 2, 3, 4, 5

ZT 62

Africa

EG 6, 7, 8

EI 4

EL 33

ET 63

FM 2, 3

Sicily and Italy

SM 1

SS 2

ST 29

TS 1

NB 8

NM 1, 2, 4, 5, 6

NP 2, 4, 5, 6, 7, 11, 14, 15, 18, 21, 25, 26, 32, 33, 35, 38, 41, 44, 45, 46, 48, 50, 54

NS 6, 7, 8, 13, 14, 15, 20, 27

NT 28, 43, 44, 45, 46, 47, 48

IL 35, 36, 43, 50

IM 4, 5, 6, 7, 9

IS 2, 3, 6, 7, 8, 9, 10, 11, 18, 23, 26, 28, 35, 36, 40, 50, 60

IT 70, 78, 80, 81

IV 14, 15, 16, 17

The West

JM 4

JS 3

JT 5, 6

Unknown

UB 35, 36, 37, 38

UJ 21-3, 25, 50, 51, 52-4, 55

UT 114, 115

SUMMARY INDEX OF KNOWN PROVENANCES

Abdera	AJ	Centocelle	IM
Achmoun	EL	Centuripe	ST
Acholla	FM	Chatby	ET, EV
Agen	IL	Chersonese	IL
Aix-en-Provence	JM	Chiusi	IT
Akmim	EV	Cirencester	IV
Alexandria	EG, EI, EL, ET, EV	Civitavecchia	IL
Alontion	ST	Cologne	IL
Amisos	ZT	Conimbriga	IL
Amphipolis	XT	Corinth	AV, CJ, CL, CS, CT
Antioch	ZM	Corneto	IT
Arezzo	IV	Crete	YV
Arles	JT	Cumae	NT, NV
Athens	AJ, AL, AS, AT, AV,	Cyprus	KL, KT
	EV, IV, XT	Cyrenaica	FT
Banasa	FB		
Begram	ET	Delos	AV, DL, DM, DT
Bône	FM	Delphi	XL, XT
Boscoreale	NJ, NP		
Boscotrecase	NP	Elatea	BT
Boutria	FM, FP	Ephesus	ZL, ZS, ZT
Bovillae	ES	Epidaurus	XT
Breccia	IS	Eretria	YT
Brundisium	TS	Este	IS
Bulgaria	IL		
Butera	ST	Fayum	EL, ET, EV
		Francavilla Fontana	GV
Calvi	JT		
Canino	IT	Galjub	FB
Canopus	EI, EL, EV	Girenti	ST
Canosa	TJ, TV		
Capua	NS, NT	Hadra	AV, ET, EV
		Halai	BT
Carthage	FS		

Haliartos	AV	Oescus	XM
Halicarnassos	ZT	Olbia	AT
Hawara	ET	Ostia	IL, IS, IT
Heraclea Minoa	ST	Oxyrhynchos	ET
Heraklion	YT		
Herculaneum	NB, NP, NS	Paestum	IT, PT
Hildesheim	UJ	Palermo	SM
Holland	JT	Patras	AS
Homs	ZG	Pergamon	EL, ZM, ZS, ZT
		Pettau	IL
Imola	IB, IM	Pompeii	NB, NJ, NM, NP, NS, NT, NV
		Ponticelli	NT
Kalymnos	YT	Pozarevac	XB
Karanis	EL	Pozzuoli	IL
Kertch	XT	Priene	AV, ZL, ZT, ZV
Knidos	ZL	Priolo Bagnoli	SS
Kom-el-Sciugefa	ET	Privernum	IM
Kos	YA, YS		
Kremna	ZS	Rheneia	DT
		Rhodes	YT, YV
Larisa	ZT	Roccavecchia	GV
Lebanon	ZT	Rome	AS, IL, IC, IM, IP, IS
Lipari	ST	Ruvo	TT
London	IL		
		Sabrata	FS
Malta	JM, JS	Sa-el-Hagar	ET
Marzi	IT	St. Rémy	JS
Megara	XT	Sakkara	EL
Mekyberna	XT	Salerno	NP
Melos	YT	Samsun	ZT
Memphis	ET	Seleucia	ZT
Messembria	XT	Selymbria	XT
Misenum	NT	Serra Orlando	ST
Myrina	MT	Side	ZS
Mytilene	YV	Sigéan	IV
		Sinope	ZA
Naples	NP, NT	Smyrna	ZL, ZT, ZV
Naukratis	ET	Southampton	IV
Naxos	ST	South Russia	AJ, AT
Nemi	IS	Stabiae	NP
Nijmegen	IL	Stratonikeia	XS
Nola	NT	Syracuse	IL, ST
		Syria	EG

Tanagra	BT, XT
Tarentum	TJ, TT
Tarquinia	IT
Tarragona	JS
Tarsus	ZL, ZT, ZV
Thebes	BT
Thera	YT
Thessaly	AJ
Thrace	XT
Tipasa	FL
Tivoli	IM, IS, IV
Torre Annunziata	NM
Torre del Palma	JM
Tralles	ZS
Troy	ZT
Tusculum	IM, IS
Tyndaris	ST
Ued Bliboen	FM
Vaison	IL
Vari	AT
Viterbo	IV
Volubilis	FB
Vulci	IT
Wiesbaden	JB

SUMMARY MUSEUM INDEX

(Hellenistic objects precede Roman in each entry)

Acholla		FM
Adana		*Hell.* ZL; ZT; ZV *Roman* ZL; ZT
Adolphseck, Schloss Fasanerie		MT
Agen		IL
Aix-en-Provence		JM
Alexandria Museum		*Hell;* AV; EI; EL; ET; EV *Roman* EI; EV
Amsterdam, Allard Pierson Stichting		*Hell.* ZV; EL; ET; TV; *Roman* EG, ET
Ann Arbor, Kelsey Museum		*Hell.* EL; GV *Roman* ZL; ZT; NV
Aquileja		IT
Arezzo		IV
Athens:	Acropolis Museum	AS
	Agora Museum	*Hell.* AL; AT; AV *Roman* AJ; AL; AS; AT; IV
	French School	MT
	National Museum	*Hell.* AS; AT; AV; BT; CT; XT; YT; MT; ZT; UT
		Roman AJ; AL; AS; AT; ZT

Baltimore		UB
Bammeville Collection		MT
Basel Market		UJ
Basel, private collection		UT
Beirut Museum		ZT
Beirut University		ZT
Belgrade		XB; XT
Benachi Collection		EL; ET; EV
Berlin: State Museum		*Hell.* AJ; AV; BT; CT; XT; DT; YT; MT; ZL; ZM;
		ZS; ZT; ZV; ET; NT; IT; UT
		Roman AS; EB; IS; UJ; UT
Berlin: private collection		UB
Besançon		IL
Bieber Collection		NT
Bircher Collection		ET
Biscari		ST; IL
Bologna		IS
Bône		FM

Bonn	AT; BT; NP
Borelli Collection	EI
Boston	*Hell.* MT; ZT, IV; UB; UT *Roman* ZG; ZV; TT; NP; UB
Bowdoin College	KT
Breccia	IS
Brindisi	TS
Brussels	YV; UT
Bryn Mawr College	IL
Cairo Museum	EV
Calvert Collection	ZV
Cambridge: Fitzwilliam Museum	*Hell.* AV; XT; MT; NT; IT; UT *Roman* XS; IL; UT
Cambridge (Mass.), Fogg Museum	BT; UT
Canosa	TJ
Capua	NT
Carlsruhe	ST; UB; UT
Carthage, Musée Lavigerie	IL
Cassel	IS; UB
Catania	ST
Civitavecchia	IL
Cleveland	ZT; GV
Clieveden	IS
Cobham Hall	IS
Coimbra	IL
Cologne	IS
Compiègne	IL; UT
Constantinople	MT; ZS
Copenhagen: National Museum	*Hell.* AT; BT; XT; YT; ST; IT; UT *Roman* NT
Ny Carlsberg Glyptotek	*Hell.* BT; TT *Roman* IS
Thorwaldsen Museum	*Hell.* UT *Roman* UB; UG; UJ
Corinth	*Hell.* AV; CL; CS; CT *Roman* CJ; CL
Delos	*Hell.* AV; DL; DM; DT *Roman* DT
Delphi	XL; XT
Dresden	*Hell.* EL; ET; IT; UT *Roman* EL; NS; UB; US
Dunedin, Otago Museum	IL
Ephesus	AS
Epidaurus	XT
Este	IS
Evans Collection	TJ

Florence		UB; UT	
Fouquet Collection	*Hell.* EL; ET; EV	*Roman* EL; ET	
Francavilla Fontana		GV	
Frankfurt	*Hell.* EL; ET; EV; UT	*Roman* EL	
Froehner Collection		MT	
Gela		ST	
Geneva		IT	
Grace Collection		ET	
Gréau Collection		UT	
Hamburg		AJ	
Hartwig Collection		NT	
Harvard University	*Hell.* ST; TT; UT	*Roman* IL	
Heidelberg		AT; ZT; EV	
Helbing Collection		ZT	
Heraclea Minoa		ST	
Heraklion		YT	
Herculaneum		NP; NS	
Hildesheim		FB	
Humann Collection		ZT	
Imola		IB; IM	
Ince Blundell Hall		AS; IS	
Kabul		ET	
Kavalla		XT	
Kephisia		AS	
Kos		YS	
Lecce		GV	
Lecuyer Collection		MT; UT	
Leeds		IT	
Lehmann Collection		UB	
Leiden	*Hell.* BT; ZL; ZT; IT; UT	*Roman* FL; UB; UT	
Leipzig	*Hell.* MT; UT	*Roman* UT	
Leningrad, Hermitage	*Hell.* AJ; AT; IT	*Roman* ZL; EL; NT; IL; UJ	
Lipari		ST	

London: British Museum   *Hell.* AS; BT; CJ; XT; KT; YT; YV; MT; ZL; ZT; ES; ET; FT; ST; TT; NT; IC; IL; IT; IV; UB; UT
Roman AS; AT; XL; XS; ZL; EL; TT; NT; IL; IS; IT; UJ; UT

            University College *Hell.* ET; UT   *Roman* ET; UT

            Victoria H Albert Museum XT

Lyon	MT

Machado de Castro	IL	
Madrid	*Hell.* AV; UT	*Roman* NT; UB
Mainz	EL; IL	
Malta	JM; JS	
Manchester	GV	
Mantua	IS	
Mariémont	NP	
Marseille	ET; JT	
Milan	*Hell.* ST; TT; NT; IT; JT; UB; UJ; UL; UT	
	Roman NS; IL; IS; IT; UB; UL; UT	
Miseno	NT	
Montpelier	MT	
Munich: Antiken Sammlungen	*Hell.* AT; XT; ZT; TT; NT; IT; UT	*Roman* IL; UT
Market	UB	
Private Collection	UT	
Mustaki Collection	EI; EL; ET; EV	
Mykonos	AV; DT	
Naples	*Hell.* TG; TJ; NB; NT; IT; JT	
	Roman NB; NJ; NM; NP; NS; NT; IB; IM	
Nauplia	XT	
Nessebur	XT	
New York, Metropolitan Museum	*Hell.* IV; UB; UT	*Roman* NP; UB; UJ; UT
Nicosia, Cyprus Museum	KL; KT	
Nijmegen	IL	
Oescus	XM	
Ostia	IL; IS; IT	
Oxford, Ashmolean Museum	*Hell.* ZT; EL; ET; NV; IL; UL; UT	
	Roman ZT; TT; IV; US	
Paestum	PT; IT	
Palermo	*Hell.* ST; IT	*Roman* SM; NP; UB
Paris: Cab. Med.	*Hell.* IT; UT	*Roman* IT; UB
Louvre	*Hell.* AS; BT; XT; MT; EV; FT. NT; IT; UT	
	Roman FS; NJ; NP; IS	
Petit Palais	UB	
Pettau	IL	
Pompeii	NB; NM; NP; NS; NT; NV	
Ponticelli	NT	
Princeton	*Hell.* EB; ST; UL; UT	
	Roman AS; ZM; EG	
Priverno	IM	

Reggio	TT		
Reus	JS		
Rhodes	ZA		
Rio de Janeiro	UT		
Robinson Collection	IS; XT		
Rome: Capitoline	IM; IS		
Lateran	IM; IS; IT		
Terme	IB; IL; IM; IP; IT		
Torlonia	IT		
Vatican	*Hell.* AS; ET; IV	*Roman* IM; IP; IS	
Villa Albani	IS		
Villa Doria Pamfili	IS		
Wollmann Collection	IL		
Market	IT		
Rubensohn Collection	ET		
Ruvo	TT		
Sabouroff Collection	UT		
Sabrata	FS		
St. Rémy	JS		
Salerno	NP		
Sarajevo	XT		
Sarti Collection	EG		
Schiller Collection	EG; UG		
Schreiber Collection	EL; ET; EV		
Sfax	FM; FP		
Side	ZS		
Sigéan	IV		
Smith, Ray Winfield, Collection	EG		
Sousse	FM		
Stabiae	NP		
Stuttgart	ET		
Syracuse	*Hell.* AV; ST	*Roman* SS; ST; IL	
Taranto	TT; GV		
Tarquinia	IT		
Thebes	BT		
Thera	YT		
Tipasa	FL		
Tivoli	IV		
Toledo	ZT		
Toronto	IS		
Toulouse	JS		
Trieste	TT		

Utrecht	JT; UT	
Vercelli	GV	
Verona	AS	
Vescovali	UJ	
Vienna: Kunsthistorisches Museum	*Hell.*	BT; XT; YV; MT; ZT; EB; ET; ST; NT; UT
	Roman	ZS; IL; IS; IT; UB; UT
University	ZS	
Warsaw	IL	
Weimar	UJ	
Wiesbaden	JB	
Würzburg	IT	
Yale Art Museum	AV; EG	

CONCORDANCE

I. HELLENISTIC

NO.	TK	B.D.	B.H.T.[1]	B.H.T.[2]	G.T.P.	P.C.F.	Robert
AJ 1					C 4		
AJ 2-6							
AL 1							
AS 1							
AS 2		168	265				
AS 3-5							
AT 1-11							
AT 12					C 1		
AT 13-14							
AT 15			276	350	C 2		
AT 16					C 3		
AT 17-25							
AV 1-24							
AV 25					C 5		
AV 26-36							
BT 1							
BT 2					C 52	91	
BT 3					C 55		
BT 4-7							
BT 8	423/9	89b		152		121	
BT 9							38
BT 10-14							
BT 15	243/1						
BT 16-18							
CJ 1					C 53		

NO.	TK	B.D.	B.H.T.[1]	B.H.T.[2]	G.T.P.	P.C.F.	Robert
CL 1							
CS 1							
CT 1-2							
CT 3	420/4						43
CT 4							
XT 1-7							
XT 8	415/3	86	98	156	C 56	81	24
XT 9	415/1	88		398			
XT 10-17							
XT 18							16
XT 19, 20							
XT 21		67		340	C 67a	55a	
XT 22		67		363	C 67b	55b	
XT 23, 24							
DL 1-4							
DM 1					C 61a		
DM 2					C 61b		
DT 1-16							
DT 17		57	207	293	C 62	50	
DT 18-24							
DT 25							77
DT 26-28							
KL 1							
KT 1					C 58		
KT 2-6							
YA 1							
YT 1							
YT 2	429/2						
YT 3	419/4					134	
YT 4						136	
YT 5		169	267	390			
YT 6-12							
YV 1-4							

NO.	TK	B.D.	B.H.T.[1]	B.H.T.[2]	G.T.P.	P.C.F.	Robert
MT 1	426/6	142	241	341		114	87
MT 2	427/6	85	96	154		110	17
MT 3	430/3						
MT 4	425/3				C 70		34
MT 5	425/4						
MT 6	425/5						
MT 7							
MT 8	426/1						
MT 9	426/2	146		386	C 65	106	33
MT 10-13							
MT 14		162	252			107	37
MT 15	426/5	155	140	342			
MT 16	430/2						
MT 17	429/5	56	204-5	291-2	C 68	49	
MT 18							
MT 19		144	249	372	69	120	51-52
MT 20		141	230	338	66		98
MT 21							
MT 22			257	345			
MT 23-24							
MT 25	425/1						
MT 26	425/2		214	298			89
MT 27	427/7	153	234	396			90
MT 28	427/4	150	236	399	71		22, 23
MT 29	425/6		213	297			
MT 30	427/5	154	235	397		129	27
MT 31							
MT 32	426/4	143	248	379		124	26
MT 33							
MT 34	425/7			405			91
MT 35	423/2						
MT 36							
MT 37	425/8					1 04	40

NO.	TK	B.D.	B.H.T.[1]	B.H.T.[2]	G.T.P.	P.C.F.	Robert
MT 38				409			
MT 39	427/3		271			125	21
MT 40-42							
MT 43	188/4						
MT 44							
MT 45	428/5	157	246	360	75	149	64-5
MT 46	428/4						79
MT 47			285	364			
MT 48-49							
ZA 1							
ZL 1-6							
ZM 1							
ZS 1							
ZS 2		166	273	380	72	53c	28
ZS 3							
ZT 1							
ZT 2		164	255	343		115	
ZT 3-4							
ZT 5			256	344			
ZT 6			287	366			
ZT 7-9							
ZT 10	428/6		278	352		147	83-4
ZT 11							
ZT 12					63		
ZT 13-15							
ZT 16							92
ZT 17							
ZT 18			269	389			
ZT 19							
ZT 20				387			30
ZT 21-28							
ZT 29	427/8		215	299			

NO.	TK	B.D.	B.H.T.[1]	B.H.T.[2]	G.T.P.	P.C.F.	Robert
ZT 30-31							
ZT 32							31
ZT 33							32
ZT 34-37							
ZT 38					74	157	
ZT 39-48							
ZT 49							100
ZV 1-3							
ZV 4	427/1						
ZV 5							
EB 1				410			
EB 2							
EI 1-2							
EL 1-29							
ES 1					(A 78)	194	
ET 1					64		
ET 2-5							
ET 6			416	547			104-5
ET 7-61							
EV 1-15							
FB 1-2							
FT 1							
FT 2					73		
FT 3	419/3						
ST 1-6							
ST 7	424/7						
ST 8-28							
TG 1-2							
TJ 1					8		
TJ 2-4							
TT 1		87	97	155	9		
TT 2		89c		400	10		

NO.	TK	B.D.	B.H.T.[1]	B.H.T.[2]	G.T.P.	P.C.F.	Robert
TT 3							
TT 4			212	296			
TT 5							
TT 6			408	549			
TT 7							
TT 8	423/6						
TT 9-12							
TT 13		178	288a	367			
TT 14			288b	367			
TT 15	467/6			354		144	
TT 16-18							
TT 19							60
TT 20-30							
TV 1							
GV 1-2							
GV 3				7			
GV 4							
GV 5				6			
GV 6							
PT 1					14		
PT 2					17		
PT 3					16		
PT 4					15		
NB 1-3							
NT 1							
NT 2	430/5						
NT 3-5							
NT 6	430/6	145	250	374	12	119	
NT 7-10							
NT 11			107				
NT 12	428/2	156	244	353	11		
NT 13							

NO.	TK	B.D.	B.H.T.[1]	B.H.T.[2]	G.T.P.	P.C.F.	Robert
NT 14							35
NT 15			268	391			
NT 16-19							
NT 20	399/9						
NT 21	424/1						
NV 1							
IC 1							
IJ 1-8							
IL 1-2							
IS 1			253	335			
IT 1-12							
IT 13	424/12	289	408			126	20
IT 14-28							
IT 29		173	282	358	13	148	99
IT 30-31							
IT 32			412	553			
IT 33	431/5		410	551			
IT 34	431/3						
IT 35			411	552			
IT 36	423/8						
IT 37-49							
IT 50			261	375			
IT 51-55							
IT 56							56
IT 57-62							
IT 63		140	226	325			
IT 64	430/7		227	326			
IV 1-3							
IV 4				411		130	
IV 5-7							
JM 1-2							
JT 1-3							

NO.	TK	B.D.	B.H.T.[1]	B.H.T.[2]	G.T.P.	P.C.F.	Robert
UB 1-2							
UB 3			415				
UB 4			211	295			
UB 5-6							
UB 7			210	406			
UB 8				403			
UB 9			413	554a			
UJ 1							
UL 1-5							
UT 1-4							
UT 5							19
UT 6-8							
UT 9						150	68
UT 10-13							
UT 14				385			
UT 15					54		
UT 16-30							
UT 31							93
UT 32			274	381		92	29
UT 33-53							
UT 54	425/10						25
UT 55-61							
UT 62		149	233	402			
UT 63-64							
UT 65		147	247a	368			
UT 66		148	247b	368			
UT 67-71							
UT 72			209	407			
UT 73-78							
UT 79		171	275	348		146	82
UT 80-83							
UT 84		172	277	351			

NO.	TK	B.D.	B.H.T.[1]	B.H.T.[2]	G.T.P.	P.C.F.	Robert
UT 85-94							
UT 95	424/10						
UT 96-99							
UT 100	424/2						
UT 101				394			57
UT 102							94
UT 103-106							

II. ROMAN PERIOD

NO.	TK	B.D.	B.H.T.[1]	B.H.T.[2]	G.T.P.	P.C.F.	Robert
AJ 7						206/4	
AJ 8						206/2	
AJ 9							
AJ 10						206/3	
AJ 11-13							
AL 2-5							
AS 6				316			
AS 7-8							
AS 9			266	810		137	
AS 10						116	
AS 11-13							
AT 26-31							
AT 32						135	
AT 33-36							
AT 37				796			
AT 38-52							
CJ 2							

NO.	B.D.	B.H.T.[1]	B.H.T.[2]	G.T.P.	P.C.F.	Robert
CL 2-6						
XB 1						
XL 1-4						
XM 1			315	C 57		
XS 1-2						
XT 25						
DT 29						
KT 7						
KT 8				C 59		
KT 9						
KT 10				C 60		
YS 1-2						
YT 13						
ZG 1						
ZL 7-10						
ZM 2-3						
ZM 4			321			
ZM 5						
ZS 4				C 78		
ZS 5-6						
ZS 7		420	584			
ZT 50-62						
ZV 6						
EB 3			413	C 76		103
EG 1-11						
EI 3-4						
EI 5			320			
EL 30-37						
ET 62-65						
EV 16-17						
FL 1-3						
FM 1-4						

NO.	B.D.	B.H.T.[1]	B.H.T.[2]	G.T.P.	P.C.F.	Robert
FP 1						
FS 1		537		C 77		
FS 2-3						
SM 1				C 21		
SS 1-2						
ST 29						
TS 1						
TT 31		263	388			
TT 32-33						
NB 4-9						
NJ 1						
NJ 2				C 24		
NM 1	136	242	347	C 19	95	
NM 2	135	239	346	C 20		
NM 3						
NM 4			565			
NM 5				C 21		
NM 6				C 21		
NP 1-3						
NP 4				C 44a	151	69
NP 5				C 44b		18,70,97
NP 6		524		C 41		
NP 7				C 40		
NP 8				C 43		
NP 9				C 42		
NP 10-12						
NP 13	134	237	371	C 25	98	9
NP 14		229	327	C 28	101	
NP 15-20						
NP 21			771	C 34		39
NP 22			770	C 33	100	54
NP 23		519	765	C 35		

NO.	B.D.	B.H.T.[1]	B.H.T.[2]	G.T.P.	P.C.F.	Robert
NP 24				C 36		86
NP 25				C 37		88
NP 26				C 38		
NP 27				C 39	99	53
NP 28-34						
NP 35		447a	762			
NP 36		447b	761			
NP 37						
NP 38	131	243	383	C 29	96	
NP 39			334			
NP 40-44						
NP 45	133	228	328	C 26		
NP 46	132	238	395	C 30	97	72
NP 47		448	763			
NP 48			760			
NP 49		345/6	472/3	C 23		
NP 50-55						
NS 1						
NS 2				C 45a		
NS 3				C 45b		
NS 4				C 46a		
NS 5				C 46b		
NS 6				C 46c		
NS 7				C 47a		
NS 8				C 47b		
NS 9		254	330			
NS 10-12						
NS 13	175	281	356		152	63
NS 14						
NS 15	176	286	362		154	
NS 16					59	
NS 17	138	259	563		159	

NO.	B.D.	B.H.T.[1]	B.H.T.[2]	G.T.P.	P.C.F.	Robert
NS 18-19						
NS 20	174	280	361		153	
NS 21						
NS 22			562			102
NS 23			566			
NS 24						
NS 25	130	225	324	C 48	94	85
NS 26-27						
NS 28				C 32		
NS 29-31						
NT 22-26						
NT 27			548	C 27		
NT 28		409	548	C 27		
NT 29-30						
NT 31				C 18		101
NT 32-48						
NV 2-3						
IB 1-4						
IL 3-42						
IL 43	53	518	797			
IL 44-49						
IL 50		424	582			
IL 51-52						
IM 1-2						
IM 3		262	401			
IM 4						
IM 5			808			
IM 6	137	270	329		158	
IM 7-8						
IM 9		542	802			
IP 1		427				
IP 2		525-8	559-61			10,107-121

NO.	B.D.	B.H.T.[1]	B.H.T.[2]	G.T.P.	P.C.F.	Robert
IS 2-9						
IS 10	129	223	317	C 49	93	96
IS 11-12						
IS 13						15,73
IS 14	139	258	564		160	14
IS 15-29						
IS 30	152	232	558			
IS 31		539	805			
IS 32-34						
IS 35				C 50		
IS 36						
IS 37	167	264	393			
IS 38						2
IS 39						3
IS 40	177	284	365	C 51	156	P1.1
IS 41	151	231	556-7			
IS 42		541	809			
IS 43-46						
IS 47						4
IS 48-52						
IS 53						1
IS 54-58						
IS 59	55	532	788			
IS 60						
IT 65		425	587	C 22		
IT 66-79						
IT 80	52	515	793		65	
IT 81		516-7	794-5			
IV 8-17						
JB 1						
JM 3-4						
JS 1-4						

NO.	TK	B.D.	B.H.T.[1]	B.H.T.[2]	G.T.P.	P.C.F.	Robert
JT 4-7							
JV 1							
UB 10				555			
UB 11			418	580			
UB 12-15							
UB 16			202	581			
UB 17			414	554b			
UB 18-35							
UB 36						155	
UB 37-38							
UG 1-2							
UJ 2							36
UJ 3-55							
UL 6							
US 1-4							
UT 107				382			
UT 108-112							
UT 113	426/8						
UT 114-123							

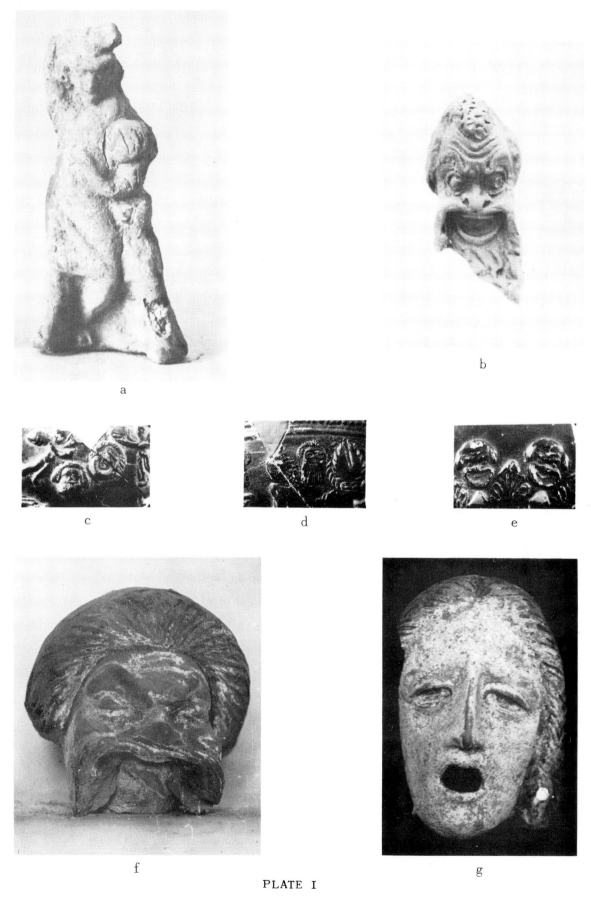

PLATE I

a) Thebes, from Halai (BT 1)   b) Agora T 213 (AT 2)

c) Agora P 22191 (AV 15)   d) Agora P 18666 (AV 16)   e) Agora P 17085 (AV 23)

f) Alexandria 24129 (ET 2)   g) Alexandria 24130 (ET 3)

a

b

c

PLATE II

a   Mykonos Museum (AV 25)
b & c Cleveland Museum of Art (GV 1)

a

PLATE III

b   c

a) Verona, Museo Archeologico (AS 8)

b) Athens (AS 4)   c) Malta, Roman Villa Museum (JS 1)

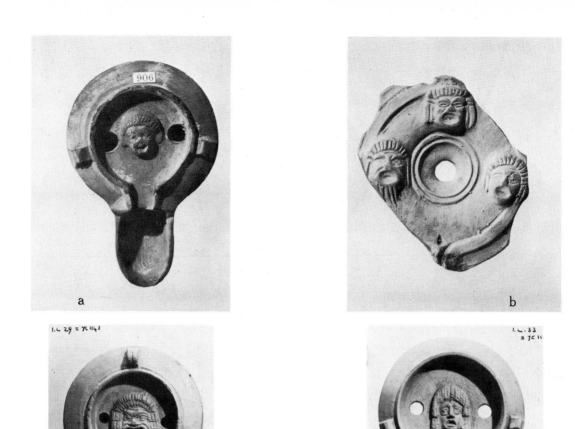

PLATE IV

a) British Museum 906 (IL 28)   b) British Museum 1231 (XL 3)

c) British Museum 898 (IL 29)   d) British Museum 905 (IL 33)

e) British Museum 986 (IL 37)

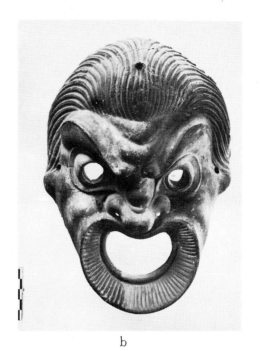

PLATE V

a) Agora T 3635 (AT 31)   b) Agora T 478 (AT 32)

c) Agora T 2404 (AT 37)   d) British Museum E 70 (IT 81)

a

b

c

PLATE VI

a   Princeton University Art Museum 40.435 (ZM 4)
b   Rome, Lateran Museum (IM 9)
c   Ince Blundell Hall 232 (IS 50)